# THE BALLAD OF AMERICA:

The history of the United
States in Song and Story

# THE BALLAD OF AMERICA:

## The History of the United States in Song and Story

## BY JOHN ANTHONY SCOTT

GROSSET & DUNLAP
PUBLISHERS    NEW YORK

For John

THE BALLAD OF AMERICA:
THE HISTORY OF THE UNITED STATES IN SONG AND STORY

Grosset & Dunlap Edition, 1967
Published by arrangement with Bantam Books, Inc.

PUBLISHED SIMULTANEOUSLY IN THE UNITED STATES AND CANADA

PRINTED IN THE UNITED STATES OF AMERICA

# Contents

# Immigrants 284

# The Negro People 301

## VII  BETWEEN TWO WORLD WARS 324

## VIII  SINCE THE WAR 362

# Introduction

During the past ten years, there has been a great revival of interest in traditional music in America. Sales of folk song records run into the millions. Guitars today are as numerous on college campuses as bicycles, sometimes more so. The Newport Folk Festival of 1964 impressed its organizers with attendance of seventy thousand enthusiasts, mostly young, at its sessions. Magazines dealing with folk songs and their performers have burgeoned. *Sing Out* alone, which appears five times a year, has a circulation of approximately forty thousand. Itinerant singers find large and receptive audiences on college campuses, in high school and elementary school assemblies, and in summer camps. The coffee house has both reflected and promoted the folk song revival. College students, playing to packed audiences, have begun to stage their own folk festivals and "hoots." "Folk" is invading the academic curriculum: Several major universities now offer courses and degrees in folklore.

The passion for folk music is manifested primarily among young people, but it would be wrong to dismiss it as merely a youthful craze, a new fad, or as a form of youthful protest. In fact, the revival is a search for roots, for a sense of identity, for a concept of the world we live in, for a vision of the future. The meaning of American nationality, of American ideals, of dedication to America, are all involved.

This book is an attempt to show how the story of the American people is revealed in their song; to provide an introduction to this national song heritage, and to indicate its extent, variety, and beauty; to make some little-known singing materials easily and cheaply available; and, in response to many requests, to provide historical songs for use at various levels of the educational system.

The book had its origins in a course given by Bill Bonyun and the author at the 16th Annual Seminars on American Culture under the sponsorship of the New York State Historical Association, Cooperstown 1963. It represents an expansion of the thoughts presented at Cooperstown, together with a transcription of a number of the songs used by way of illustration.

The songs in this book, chosen from literally thousands, had to pass rather rigid selection tests. I sought songs that conveyed most clearly, most *typically,* a given national mood or experience; that were examples of the finest melodies and lyrics available; and that had proved their effectiveness and their popularity with modern audiences and modern singers, both student and adult.

A person is, ethically and nationally speaking, cultivated, when he learns to love and cherish the songs of his people; such a person may lack formal education, but he will yet be, in a human sense, an educated being. This fact struck Cecil J. Sharp, the great English musician and teacher, with great force when he visited the Southern Appalachians during the years 1916–1918. Sharp found the mountain people largely illiterate and lacking in formal education; but they were deeply versed in their own musical tradition and deeply attached to it. "I have no doubt," he wrote, "but that this delightful habit of making beautiful music at all times and in all places largely compensates for any deficiencies in the matter of reading and writing."*

As a people, we have, most of us, lost this precious ability "to make music at all times and in all places." Many Americans possess a fund of songs, but can only be induced to sing them on rare occasions; and the number of traditional songs known to and sung by all of us without exception is astonishingly small. Like Sharp's mountaineers, we Americans have a remarkable song heritage *available* to all of us, but we do not *utilize* it fully; we do not learn it, cherish it, teach it to our children, and sing it in our daily lives. But perhaps the folk song revival will help to change this situation; perhaps the day will come when every child will learn, as he grows up, hundreds of songs that tell the American story with fullness, feeling, and depth, and that constitute the essence of the national song heritage.

It was with the thought that it might help, just a little, to bring that day nearer, that this book was prepared. It is only a very small beginning in the musical approach to our national story. It can only suggest tentatively the wonders of this musical heritage and help arouse a curiosity to explore it further.

My indebtedness to singers, scholars, and musical collections is indicated throughout this book and in the bibliography. Beyond this, my chief debt is to Bill Bonyun. Few insights in this field are as rich as his, and I have benefited from his friendship more than I can say. Thanks also go to Dr. Louis Jones, President of the New York State Historical Association, and to the members of the Cooperstown seminar for the collective enthusiasm and wisdom which they contributed to the shap-

*English Folk Songs from the Southern Appalachians, Cecil J. Sharp. (London and New York: Oxford, 1960), xxv.

ing of this project; and to my own students, who have sung many of the songs reproduced here, and have taught me much about them.

JOHN ANTHONY SCOTT
HOLLAND, MASSACHUSETTS

# Note on the Music

The songs included in this book are pitched in keys suitable for the ordinary voice and are easy for the average guitarist to play. For most of them, simple chord progressions have been given. But there are some songs to which any kind of conventional musical accompaniment is a hindrance rather than a help. In the case of laments, instrumentation may often be a barrier between the singer's utterance of sorrow and the listener. Work songs and "shouts," for example, often need either no accompaniment, or only an elementary rhythmic one, such as hand-clapping. A few songs included in this collection, mostly work songs and laments, have no accompaniment. Marked in the index with an asterisk (*), they are, hopefully, an introduction to the beauties of unaccompanied singing.

# I

# THE

# COLONIAL

# PERIOD

---

WHAT KIND OF SONGS did the people of this country sing during the colonial period? The majority of the settlers who arrived here during the seventeenth and eighteenth centuries came from the British Isles—from England, Scotland, Wales, and Ireland. They brought with them a vast heritage of British and Irish melodies and lyrics, dance tunes, marches, and sacred songs. This store constituted the starting point for the development of American national music. It would be transformed and modified, as time went on, both by the contributions of other immigrant peoples and by the nature of American experience itself; but it would remain an influence of major proportions in shaping American musical expression. Americans, throughout their history, would draw upon this British heritage as they strove to develop and create a unique, American national song and music.

What was the nature of this heritage? British song itself had been evolving for centuries. A rich and many-sided expression of the life of an island people, it included courting songs, love songs, and laments; pipe and fiddle tunes for dancing

1

and marching; songs of work and songs of the sea; psalms and carols; and ballads relating great events in the life of the people, and their struggles, triumphs, and disasters. All of this material united melody of extraordinary simplicity and beauty to lyrics of vivid imagery and imaginative power.

Accordingly, the first section of the chapter that follows is devoted to "the British Heritage." It contains a small selection of British songs chosen to give some idea of the variety of musical material brought by the colonists from their native land. All of the songs reproduced here were actually sung on the colonial seaboard during the seventeenth and eighteenth centuries. Dance and bagpipe tunes are not included here, since they fall beyond the scope of this book; and some of the sea songs will be found further on when we come to discuss seafaring (see pp. 126-147 below). Only one Irish song, "The Bonny Boy," is included; even this is only half-Irish, since it represents the wedding of an English lyric to an Irish melody. Irish songs will receive fuller attention as we go on. Irish immigrants who came here during the colonial period were Gaelic rather than English in language and culture; Irish song was the product of a proud and independent civiliation, and it possessed marvelous poetic and melodic qualities all its own. It has been, as much as English song, an influence of first-rate importance in the shaping of the American musical tradition —an aspect not given separate treatment, but woven into our story throughout.

When these British songs arrived at our shores, a process of change and transformation set in. This process, from the start of our history, reflected and gave expression to the emergence of a separate American identity. The colonists had crossed three thousand miles of ocean; they had severed the living, day-to-day bond with the motherland. They had come to a new country in which entirely new problems were to occupy their full attention. From the very beginning, therefore, they were developing a new style of living, and with it new and appropriate forms of expression. So it is not surprising that the colonists began to sing the old songs in a new way, with various changes of plot, lyric, and music. Since thousands of Americans, scattered throughout a huge area along the colonial seaboard, were singing the same songs, hundreds of *variants*, or new ways of singing the old songs, arose. In other words, the old songs began to be Americanized; but not, at first, through radical or far-reaching changes, but through endless minor shifts in expression, emphasis, rhythm, melody, and vocabulary.

That Americans took their traditional songs wherever they went provides a partial answer to another question: What kind of songs did pioneers and frontier people sing? The answer is rooted in the colonial period, but takes us far beyond it. The pioneers sang the traditional songs wherever the frontier went, from New England to the plains of Texas, to the wilds of Michigan, to the coast of California. These songs have been traced and recorded throughout the Union; they bear witness to the fantastic extent of the diffusion of the original British heritage and of its enduring appeal to the pioneers, loggers, cowboys, farmers, Indian fighters, trappers, rivermen and canaleeers who opened up the continent. The traditional songs have been sung continuously on this side of the Atlantic in an ever-expanding area from the time of the first settlements in Massachusetts to the final elimination of the frontier two and one-half centuries later.

For this reason, too, it is not surprising that British enthusiasts studying their own song heritage have found a trail leading them to Canada and to the United States; for this heritage has been preserved in North America more fully than in Britain itself. The Industrial Revolution hit Great Britain with full force at the opening of the nineteenth century, and swept the rural population rapidly and completely off the land and into the industrial centers. Traditional singing was severely affected, and survived mainly in remote and outlying rural districts. But in America, at this very same time, the Revolution had just been won and the West was being opened up in an era of unprecedented expansion. Thus, the vitality of rural singing in America was retained well into the twentieth century—time enough for song enthusiasts, both British and American, to collect, record, and transcribe the heritage, one of the major achievements of modern scholarship.

The traditional songs were an important element in the creation of the American nation, for they provided Americans with knowledge of a common tradition, a common literature, and a common morality. They gave a scattered and struggling people a sense of unity and common destiny amidst new and difficult problems. To provide unity and spiritual bonds between people of the same nationality has been, immemorially, one of the central functions of song. Because this is so, we use throughout this book the term "national song" to denote

3

music that deals with our common past, our common destiny, our common experience, and our common values. This, in my opinion, is preferable to the much-abused term "folk song"; the latter has vague and even mystical overtones that we ought to try to avoid in a precise discussion of the subject. It is helpful to think of national song as a spectrum of musical expression ranging from hymns and sacred song to, for example, rock 'n' roll. This spectrum is vast in extent precisely because it reflects all aspects and varieties of our people's thought, life, and common experience.

As time went by, a second kind of variation crept into American singing; new lyrics were written and set to traditional tunes—a more fundamental variation than the first. Americans now began to produce songs that were not merely variants of the old ones, but that were actually new, that reflected and gave expression to the radically new issues and conflicts of colonial life. As this began to happen, a native, distinctively American song music took its first giant step forward.

Accordingly, the second section of the chapter that follows, entitled "Colonial Songs and Ballads," is devoted to a selection of these first national songs. Some of these followed the English models closely, but added new verses born of the experience of frontier life. "The Old Man Who Lived in the Woods," and "Sweet William" are good examples. Others, such as "The Death of General Wolfe," "Springfield Mountain," or "The Young Man Who Wouldn't Hoe Corn," were altogether new, and the lyrics were native American products from start to finish. All of these songs illustrate a principle of continuity and of differentiation in the making of national music; they exemplify the art of mastering a tradition and at the same time adding to it and making it over. This process has been fundamental in the creation of American national song, and its roots lie deep in the colonial era. We shall find it repeated over and over and illustrated many times in the pages of this book.

We talk of "songs and ballads." How, precisely, are these terms to be differentiated? There are no precise lines dividing songs and ballads, and we need not worry about an exact definition. The ballad is often thought of as telling a story, and in this it is contrasted with songs that are more lyrical, more personal in their expression of human emotion. Ballads recount a calamity, a feat of heroism, the fighting of a battle, the sink-ing of a ship, a natural disaster, an act of violence or treachery,

4

and they convey their message somewhat as a movie does, by linking a succession of brilliant and evocative images that the mind sees with a musical dialogue that the ear hears. Many ballads, furthermore, include highly personal and lyrical elements, as when they give ecstatic utterance to delight in the beauty of nature, or when they comment on the tragedy which they unfold. "Song and ballad" must not, therefore, be contrasted or differentiated too mechanically or rigidly. It is helpful to think of national song, in this connection, as a spectrum of human expression ranging from a stark, impersonal narration of calamitous events to the profoundly personal, lyrical utterance found in the blues or in the traditional Irish lament, the *chaoine*.

The first colonists sang the traditional ballads and songs from memory and transmitted them to their children by word of mouth. New ballads, by contrast, whether indigenously American or imported from the motherland, were in most cases written down; it was natural and inevitable that the printing press should become a powerful instrument for the diffusion of such material. Such printed ballads—broadside ballads, as they are called—provide the raw material for the study of many of our historical songs. These broadsides, providing news in verse form and appropriate editorial comment, were in effect singing newspapers. The classic example of such a ballad given in this chapter is "The Death of General Wolfe" (see p. 36).

Some people have argued that there is a distinction between the "pure" art of the traditional ballads of the type of "Bawbee Allen" or "Sir Patrick Spens" and the "vulgar" outpourings of the topical or broadside ballads. Both historically and artistically, the distinction appears to us invalid. We are not concerned with all the broadside ballads, but only with the best of them, those that most clearly and fully convey to us the meaning of a past age. The best of these songs have extraordinary literary qualities, of which the pages of this book will provide eloquent proof. These broadside ballads are indispensable to an understanding of our national history, and our song heritage would be vastly poorer without them.

How did the colonists sing their songs? For the most part they sang unaccompanied, using no instruments at all; and this, not because they did not prize musical accompaniment, but simply because the conditions under which they sang did not permit the use of instrumentation. People in colonial days and throughout the greater part of American history, sang under every conceivable kind of circumstance and on every occa-

5

sion. They had songs for work, washing dishes, seafaring, logging, hunting, war, mourning, and love. There was a time for everything, and there was a song for everything. The very omnipresence of song in people's lives guaranteed that the human voice itself and the human voice alone should be the supreme vehicle for musical expression. You cannot play a guitar, nor even a mouth organ, while you are plowing a field, washing dishes, changing a baby's diaper, or cutting a tree down. Out of necessity, therefore, the people relied upon the unaided power of the voice; they came to cherish it as the most marvelous instrument of all. The imagery of the traditional songs, their melodic power, their sheer humanity, these more than compensated for a lack of accompaniment.

Thus, we do the past wrong if, when we sing its songs today, we overlard them with instrumental accompaniment so emphatic that it stands between the song itself and the audience. Accompaniment must be used, if at all, with subtlety and great discrimination—to accent rhythm, provide harmonic color, and connect verses while the singer catches his breath. And nothing more. For the rest, the style of traditional singers from rural areas both in the United States and Canada has been abundantly recorded; we can study it from the life. In singing traditional songs, we must be guided not only by a grasp of traditional style, but, finally, by our own understanding of the meaning of the songs we sing, by our own sense of integrity in conveying meaning. The important thing is not to strive for a fake "authenticity" but to grasp and convey by singing the essence of the mood, experience, and event, about which we are singing. In this way, the past is recreated imaginatively and emotionally in our singing, and comes to life.

We have said that traditionally the American people sang their songs without accompaniment. But this does not mean that they did not possess instruments, and did not use them skilfully and effectively. On the crew of a square-rigger, there would likely be a fiddler or harmonica player; Negro slaves developed the fretless banjo, the banjo, and the washtub bass; Scottish highlanders brought the skirl of the bagpipe to North Carolina and New York; colonial militia paraded and marched away to war to the sound of fife and drum; country people created a variety of "folk" instruments, including the incomparable dulcimer. But there was always an appointed time for the playing of instruments, and it was usually when men and women were at leisure, or marching to war, or dancing. Such times, in the life of a hard-working people, were relatively few.

6

# The British Heritage

## Bawbee Allen

"Barbara Allen" is a ballad that has been sung for three centuries, at the very least, in all parts of the British Isles and Eire. Its wide diffusion throughout the United States, and the endless variety of melody and lyric found, are evidence that it was brought to the colonies in the earliest days.

The version reproduced here comes from Scotland, and is given to us from the family tradition of the great Scottish folk singer, Ewan MacColl. It has been included here, from the hundreds of American and British versions that might have been chosen, for a number of reasons. Sir John Graeme, in the first place, is shown as a flesh-and-blood man who fought a duel and died for love. This is much truer to life than the common and generally accepted version of "a spineless lover who gave up the ghost without a struggle." In the second place, MacColl's melody is, in this editor's judgment, among the most perfect that we inherit. And finally, melody and lyric combined provide a classic example of the great and passionate art of the ballad at its best.

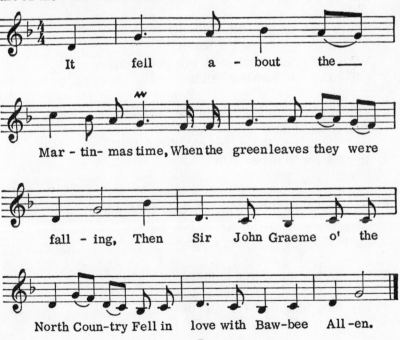

It fell a - bout the ___ Mar - tin - mas time, When the green leaves they were fall - ing, Then Sir John Graeme o' the North Coun - try Fell in love with Baw - bee All - en.

2. He's sent his man all through the town,
   To the place where she was dwelling,
   "Come down, come down to my master dear,
   If your name be Bawbee Allen."

3. O slowly slowly rose she up,
   And slowly she went to him;
   And when she came to his bedside:
   "Young man, I think you're dying."

4. " 'Tis I am sick and very sick,
   And it's a' for Bawbee Allen."
   "It's better for me ye'll never be,
   For bonnie Bawbee Allen.

5. "When ye were in the tavern, sir,
   And at the wine was swilling,
   Ye made the toasts go round and round,
   But slighted Bawbee Allen."

6. He's turned his face unto the wall,
   And death was with him dealing,
   "Then fare ye well my kind friends all,
   But be kind to Bawbee Allen.

7. "Then put your hand unto the wall,
   And there you'll find a token,
   With my gold watch and my gold ring,
   Give that to Bawbee Allen.

8. "Then put your hand unto my  side,
   And there you'll find a warrant;
   And there you'll get my blood-red shirt,
   It bled for Bawbee Allen."

9. She had not gone a step, a step,
   When she heard the death bell knelling,
   And every clap the death bell gave,
   Said "Woe to Bawbee Allen."

10. "O mother dear, you'll make my bed,
    You'll make it soft and narrow;
    My love has died for me this day,
    I'll die for him tomorrow."

# I Will Give My Love an Apple

This song illustrates well the extraordinary lyrical qualities so often to be found in the old ballads. The version given here has been collected in both England and Nova Scotia with practically identical words and melody. Other versions have been popular in the United States, but none of these, in the opinion of the editor, compare with the Nova Scotian version given here, and which deserves to be more widely known.

2. How can there be an apple without e'er a core?
   How can there be a dwelling without e'er a door?
   How can there be a palace wherein she may be,
   That she may unlock it without e'er a key?

3. My head is an apple without e'er a core,
   My mind is a dwelling without e'er a door,
   My heart is the palace wherein she may be,
   And she may unlock it without e'er a key.

4. I will give my love a cherry without e'er a stone,
   I will give my love a chicken without e'er a bone,
   I will give my love a ring, not a rent to be seen,
   I will give my love a baby and no crying.

5. How can there be a cherry without e'er a stone?
   How can there be a chicken without e'er a bone?
   How can there be a ring, not a rent to be seen?
   How can there be a baby and no crying?

6. When the cherry's in blossom it has no stone,
   When the chicken's in the egg it has no bone,
   When the ring's a-running, there's not a rent to be seen
   When the baby's a-getting, there's no crying.

# The Keys of Canterbury

The old songs were often cast in dialogue form, as a conversation between lovers, or between father and daughter, mother and son, etc. The dramatic possibilities of the song, the sense of reality conveyed by it, were in this way vastly enhanced.

"The Keys of Canterbury," a classic example of a courting song in dialogue, is found in practically identical form on both sides of the Atlantic and is also widely known in a number of parodies. In the Southern version given here, the dialogue form is emphasized by an alternation of major and minor keys, and also by a change of beat. English versions of the song are uniformly in minor key and 6/8 time.

"Mad - am I will give to you the
keys of Can - ter - bur - y, And
all the bells of Lon - don Town shall
ring and make you mer - ry; If
you will be my dar - ling, my

joy— and my dear, If you will go a-walk-ing with me an - y - where."

"Sir, I'll not ac - cept of you the keys of Can - ter - bur - y, Though all the bells of Lon - don Town should ring and make me mer - ry, And I'll not be your bride, your joy, and your dear, And I'll not take a walk with you an - y - where."

"Madam, I will give to you a little ivory comb,
To fasten up your golden locks when I am not at home;
If you will be my darling, my joy, and my dear,
If you will go a-walking with me anywhere."

"Sir, I'll not accept from you a little ivory comb
To fasten up my golden locks when I am not at home;
And I'll not be your bride, your joy, and your dear,
And I'll not take a walk with you anywhere."

"Madam, I will give to you a pair of boots of cork,
One was made in London, the other made in York;
If you will be my darling, my joy, and my dear,
If you will go a-walking with me anywhere."

"Sir, I'll not accept of you a pair of boots of cork,
Though one was made in London, the other made in
York;
And I'll not be your bride, your joy, and your dear,
And I'll not take a walk with you anywhere."

"Madam, I will give to you the keys to my heart,
And all my sacred promises that we shall never part;
If you will be my darling, my joy, and my dear,
If you will go a-walking with me anywhere."

"Sir, I will accept of you the keys to your heart,
To lock it up for ever that we never more may part,
And I will be your bride, your joy, and your dear,
And I will take a walk with you anywhere."

# The Sycamore Tree

Over the centuries, this song has achieved an extraordinary popularity on both sides of the Atlantic, particularly among children. During slavery days, Negro people in the South appropriated it as their own (see pp. 207-8). Pioneers carried it throughout the length and breadth of the United States. The version given here, chosen for its delightful vitality and the lilting beauty of the melody, comes from Florida.

"Oh, hang - man, hang - man, slack-en your rope, And wait a lit - tle while;_ I think I see my fa - ther com - ing, A - rid - ing from man - y a mile." "Oh, have you come with sil - ver and gold_ And mon - ey to buy me free,_ Or

have you come to see me hung Up -
on the syc - a - more tree?"__ "No
gold nor sil - ver have__ I here, Nor
mon - ey to buy__ you free;__ But
I have come to see__ you hang Up -
on the syc - a - more tree."__

*Repeat with mother, brother, sister, and finally lover, who replies:*

"Yes gold and silver have I here,
And money to buy you free;
But I've not come to see you hang
Nor hung you shall not be."

From *Folk Songs of Florida,* by Alton C. Morris. Published by the University of Florida Press, 1950. Used by permission.

# The Trees They Grow So High

This ballad exercises an almost uncanny influence over the singer: it communicates a seemingly inexhaustible sense of the mystery of life, its joy and its sadness. Many versions have been collected in the British Isles, and the number of fine melodies to which the lyric has been set is altogether remarkable. Robert Burns tried his hand at "improving" this song, with indifferent success. Irish variants were brought by immigrants to Canada and the United States to provide the basis for two unique and indigenous American songs, "The Jam on Gerry's Rock," and "Peter Emberley" (see pp. 175 and 270).

To understand this song it is only necessary to know that child marriages in Europe, either for the consolidation of family estates or for the alliance of royal dynasties, were not at all uncommon during the feudal period and until quite recently. Scottish tradition links the ballad to the marriage arranged in 1634 between Elizabeth Innes of Craigston and the boy heir to the Urquhart estates. The child husband died while still at school.

We reproduce two beautiful versions from widely separated parts of the British Isles: from Somerset and Devon, in the west of England; and from Eire, where the version given is entitled "The Bonny Boy."

*(West of England)*

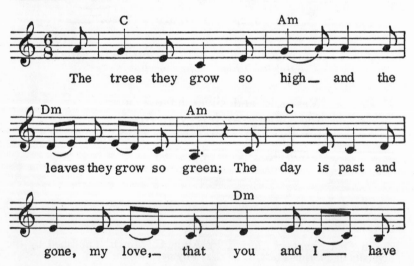

The trees they grow so high— and the leaves they grow so green; The day is past and gone, my love,— that you and I— have

16

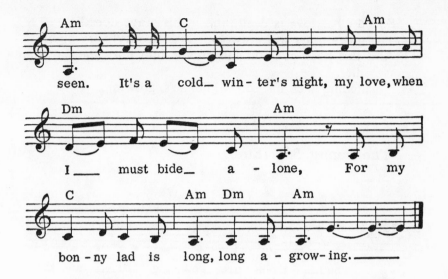

seen. It's a cold— win- ter's night, my love, when
I ___ must bide ___ a - lone, For my
bon - ny lad is long, long a - grow- ing. _____

2. "Oh father, dearest father, you've done to me much wrong;
   You've tied me to a boy when you know he is too young;
   For he is but sixteen, and I am twenty-one,
   And my bonny lad is long, long a-growing."

3. "Oh daughter, dearest daughter, I've done to you no wrong,
   For I have wedded you to a noble lord's son.
   And he shall be the lord, and you shall wait upon,
   And your bonny lad is young, but he's growing.

4. "We'll send your love to college all for a year or two,
   And then perhaps in time the boy will do for you;
   I'l buy you white ribbons to tie about his waist,
   To let the ladies know that he's married."

5. As she went a-walking by yonder churchyard wall,
   She saw four and twenty young men a-playing at the ball;
   She called for her own true love, but they would not let
       him come,
   They said the lad was young, but a-growing.

6. And at the age of sixteen he was a married man,
   And at the age of seventeen the father to a son;
   And at the age of eighteen, on his grave the grass grew
       green,
   For death had put an end to his growing.

7. So now her love is dead, and in his grave does lie,
   The green grass will grow over him so very, very high;
   And this poor girl will mourn for him until the day she
       dies,
   A-watching o'er his son while he's growing.


*The Bonny Boy (Eire)*

The___ trees are grow-ing tall___ and the

leaves are grow-ing green; And man-y a day_ and

night have___ gone since_ you and I have

seen: The win-ter nights are com

ing, and_ I must bide a - lone, For my

bon - ny boy is long, long a - grow - ing.

2. "O father, dear father, you've done what's very wrong,
   To marry me to this bonny boy and he so very young,
   He being sixteen years and I being twenty-one,
   He's my bonny boy, he's young, but he's growing."

3. "O daughter, dear daughter, don't mind what people say,
   He will be a man to you when you are old and gray,
   He will be a man to you when I am dead and gone,
   He's your bonny boy, he's young, but he's growing."

4. At the age of sixteen he was a married man,
   And at the age of seventeen the father of a son,
   And at the age of eighteen on his grave the grass grew
         green,
   Cruel death had put an end to his growing.

5. "I will buy my love a shroud of the ornamental brown,
   And while they are weaving it the tears they will run down;
   For once I had a true love and now he's dead and gone
   And I lost this bonny boy while he was growing."

6. Come all you pretty fair maids, a warning take from me,
   And never build your nest on the top of any tree,
   For the green leaves they will wither, and the roots they
         will decay,
   And the blushes of your bonny boy will soon fade away.

# The Bonnie Lass o' Fyvie

This ballad with its passionate and lyrical overtones has been sung in Scotland since the eighteenth century. English versions, possibly of greater age, are also known, though the relationship of these to the Scottish song is far from clear. The "Bonnie Lass o' Fyvie" was most probably brought to the New World by Scottish immigrants who settled in North Carolina during colonial times; the song has been found primarily in the South. In the American versions, "Fyvie" becomes "'Ivory" or "Ireo," and Ned, the captain's name, becomes "Wade." He is buried not "in the lowlands of Fyvie," but in "the lowlands of Louisiana." The lyrics reproduced here were published in Buchan, Scotland in 1906 by Gavin Greig, the great Scots song collector. The melody is traditional.

2. "O come down the stairs, pretty Peggy," he said,
   "O come down the stairs pretty Peggy, O,
   O come down the stairs, comb aside your yellow hair,
   Take the last farewell of your daddy, O.

3. "It's I'll give ye ribbons, love, I'll give ye rings,
   And I'll give ye necklaces of lammer, O,
   And I'll give ye silken gowns flounced to your knees,
   If ye would come down to my chamber, O."

4. "I thank you for your ribbons, love, I thank you for your
        rings,
   I thank you for your necklace of lammer, O.
   I do not want gowns to suit my degree,
   I would scorn to be seen in your chamber, O.

5. "A soldier's wife I never shall be,
   A soldier shall never enjoy me, O;
   For I never do intend to go to a foreign land,
   So I never shall marry a soldier, O."

6. The colonel cries "Mount boys, mount boys, mount,"
   But the captain he cries "Tarry, O,
   O tarry, O tarry another day or two,
   Till we see if this bonnie lass will marry, O.

7. "There is many a bonnie lass into bonnie Auchterless,
   And many a bonnie lass in the Carioch, O,
   There's many a bonnie Jean in the town of Aberdeen,
   But the flower of them all lies in Fyvie, O."

8. "I'll drink no more of your claret wine,
   I'll break no more of your glasses, O;
   But tomorrow is the day that I must go away,
   So farewell to Fyvie's lasses, O."

9. Early next morning we all marched away,
   And O, but the captain he was sorry, O,
   For the drums they did beat, o'er the bonnie bogs of Gight,
   And the band played the Lowlands of Fyvie, O.

10. Long, long ere they came to old Meldrum town
    Their captain they had to carry, O,

And long long ere they came to bonnie Aberdeen,
They had their captain to bury, O.

11. Green grow the birches on bonnie Ythanside,
    And low lie the Lowlands of Fyvie, O;
    Our captain's name was Ned, and he died for the maid,
    He died for the chambermaid of Fyvie, O.

# Lord Ronald

A brooding sense of the world's evil and a passionate cry of pain and weariness are embodied in "Lord Ronald," one of the starkest and loveliest of the classic ballads. Long a favorite in the British Isles, the United States, and Canada, the story is unfolded by a dramatic use of the dialogue form. Many of us get our first introduction to this song when as children we sing a parody of it, "Billy Boy." The version chosen for reproduction here was selected for the special beauty of its melody, which is Scottish.

"Where hae you been a' day, Lord Ron - ald, my son? Where hae you been a' day, my hand - some young one?" "I've been in the wood hunt - ing; moth - er, make my bed soon, For I'm wea - ry, wea-ry hunt - ing, and fain would lie down."

23

2. "O where did you dine, Lord Ronald my son?
O where did you dine, my handsome young one?"
"I dined with my sweetheart; mother, make my bed soon,
For I am weary, weary hunting, and fain would lie down."

3. "What got you to dine on, Lord Ronald my son?
What got you to dine on, my handsome young one?"
"I got eels boiled in water that in heather doth run,
And I am weary, weary hunting, and fain would lie down."

4. "What did she wi' the brew o' them, Lord Ronald my son?
What did she wi' the brew o' them, my handsome young
one?"
"She gave it to my hounds for to live upon,
And I am weary, weary hunting, and fain would lie down."

5. "Where are your hounds now, Lord Ronald my son?
Where are your hounds now, my handsome young one?"
"They are all swelled and bursted, and so will I soon,
And I am weary, weary hunting, and fain would lie down."

6. "What will you leave your father, Lord Ronald my son?
What will you leave your father, my handsome young
one?"
"I'll leave him my lands for to live upon,
And I am weary, weary hunting, and fain would lie down."

7. "What will you leave your mother, Lord Ronald my son?
What will you leave your mother, my handsome young
one?"
"I'll leave her my Bible for to read upon,
And I'm weary, weary hunting, and fain would lie down."

8. "What will you leave your sweetheart, Lord Ronald my
son?
What will you leave your sweetheart, my handsome young
one?"
"I'll leave her the gallows-tree for to hang upon,
And I'm weary, weary hunting, and fain would lie down."

## Sir Patrick Spens

This ballad is included here as an example of folk poetry and the ballad art at its very greatest. The lyric is reproduced, with minor changes in spelling, from the first published version of the song that appeared in 1765. This is rounded out by the addition of verses 8–10 which appear in one form or another in other published versions and are necessary for the dramatic continuity of the story. The age of this ballad, the extent and nature of any factual basis for it, are unknown; there is certainly no record of Sir Patrick Spens as a great Scottish mariner. Though we may be reasonably certain that the ballad came to Virginia and North Carolina with Scottish settlers in colonial times, it has evidently been little sung in the United States. The majestic melody with which the lyric is here linked comes to us through the singing of Ewan MacColl.

The king sits in Dum - fer - line — town, Drink - ing the blood - red — wine: "O where will I get a — good sail - or To sail this ship of — mine?"

2. Up and spoke an eldern knight,
  Sat at the king's right knee:
"Sir Patrick Spens is the best sailor
  That sails upon the sea."

3. The king has written a broad letter,
   And signed it with his hand,
   And sent it to Sir Patrick Spens
   Was walking on Leith sand.

4. The first line that Sir Patrick read,
   A loud laugh laughed he;
   The next line that Sir Patrick read,
   The tear blinded his eye.

5. "O who has done this ill deed,
   This ill deed done to me,
   To send me out this time of the year,
   To sail upon the sea?

6. "Make haste, make haste, my merry men all,
   Our good ship sails the morn:"
   "O say not so my master dear,
   For I fear a deadly storm.

7. "Late, late yester e'en I saw the new moon,
   With the old moon in her arm,
   And I fear, I fear, my dear master,
   That we will come to harm."

8. They had not sailed a league, a league,
   A league but barely three,
   When the sky grew dark and the wind blew loud,
   And angry grew the sea.

9. "O where will I get a good sailor,
   To take my helm in hand,
   Till I get up to the tall topmast,
   To see if I can spy land?"

10. He had not gone a step, a step,
    A step but barely one,
    When the bows of our goodly ship did break,
    And the salt sea it came in.

11. O our Scots nobles were right loath
    To wet their cork-heeled shoon;
    But long e'er all the play was played
    Their hats they swam aboon.

12. O long, long may their ladies sit
     With their fans into their hands,
Or ere they see Sir Patrick Spens
     Come sailing to the land.

13. And long, long may their ladies stand,
     With their gold combs in their hair,
Waiting for their own dear lords,
     For they'll see them no more.

14. Half o'er, half o'er to Aberdour,
     It's fifty fathoms deep;
And there lies good Sir Patrick Spens
     With the Scots lords at his feet.

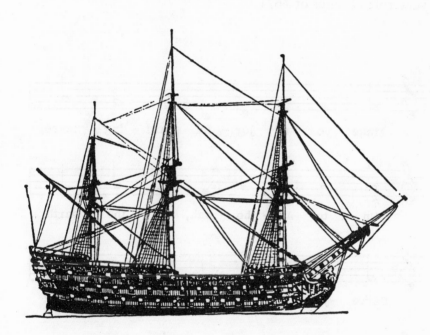

# Psalm 100
## (A Psalm of Praise)

From the beginning of American history there has been an intimate connection between "spiritual" or sacred song, and popular song. The first thing that the Puritans did, musically speaking, was to translate the Psalms from the original Hebrew and set them to folk melodies, or, as they put it, to "the graver sort of tunes of our own country songs." The psalms so set were put to many uses; for worship on the Sabbath, private devotionals, work in the field, marching into battle, and other time of trial. "Old Hundred," or "Psalm 100," was one of the best known and most sung of the old devotional songs. We reproduce the lyric as given in the Bay Psalm Book of 1640, together with the melodic line as given in Ravenscroft's Psalter of 1621.

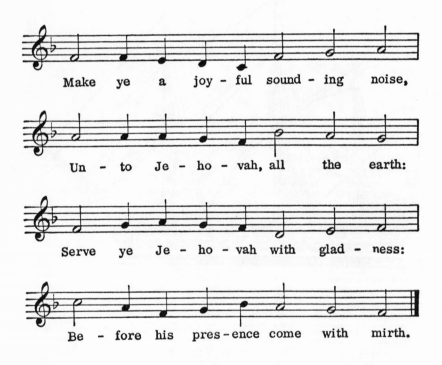

Make ye a joy - ful sound - ing noise,

Un - to Je - ho - vah, all the earth:

Serve ye Je - ho - vah with glad - ness:

Be - fore his pres - ence come with mirth.

Know that Jehovah he is God,
Who hath us formed it is he,
And not ourselves: his own people
And sheep of his pasture are we.

Enter into his gates with praise,
Into his courts with thankfulness:
Make ye confession unto him,
And his name reverently bless.

Because Jehovah he is good
For evermore is his mercy:
And unto generations all
Continue doth his verity.

# Colonial Songs and Ballads

## Soldier, Soldier, Won't You Marry Me?

This charming dialogue song is undoubtedly of English origin, but its widespread popularity in the United States and the variety of forms in which it has been sung entitle it to be considered as a traditional American song. The dialogue is amusing to act out, and furthermore it makes a sharp point. Colonial militiamen were responsible for their own outfitting with clothes, guns, and boots. The government in those days, in sharp contrast to our own times, assumed no responsibility in such matters. Militiamen often went ragged and when on active duty picked up what they could where they could. They had a reputation, evidently, as a down-at-heel, thieving lot.

The variant of the song as reproduced here was transcribed by Cecil J. Sharp from the singing of Mrs. Carrie Ford in North Carolina. The melody is sung on the five-tone, or pentatonic scale.

"Sol - dier, sol - dier, won't you mar - ry me?" It's_ O a fife and drum: "How can I mar - ry such a pret - ty girl as you, When I've

30

got no hat to put on, When I've

got no hat to put on?"

Off to the tailor she did go,
As hard as she could run,
Brought him back the finest that was there,
"Now soldier, put it on."

"Soldier, soldier, won't you marry me?"
It's O a fife and drum:
"How can I marry such a pretty girl as you
When I've got no coat to put on?"

Off to the tailor she did go,
As hard as she could run,
Brought him back the finest that was there,
"Now soldier, put it on."

"Soldier, soldier, won't you marry me?"
It's O a fife and drum:
"How can I marry such a pretty girl as you
When I've got no shoes to put on?"

Off to the shoe shop she did go,
As hard as she could run,
Brought him back the finest that was there,
"Now soldier, put them on."

"Soldier, soldier, won't you marry me?"
It's O a fife and drum:
"How can I marry such a pretty girl as you
With a wife and two babies at home?"

Reprinted by permission of Oxford University Press from *English Folk Songs from the Southern Appalachians*, collected by Cecil J. Sharp and edited by Maud Karpeles. Copyright © by Oxford University Press, London and New York, 1932.

# Siubhail a Gradh

This song is a fine example of a lament that has been sung continuously on both sides of the Atlantic since the late seventeenth century, and that has also developed in the United States in a distinctively American form.

"Siubhail a Gradh" arose out of the agonies of Irish struggle against British rule. In 1688, rebellion broke out and was crushed by the English king, William of Orange. The Treaty of Limerick, which terminated hostilities in 1691, provided honorable terms for the Irish warriors: they might take the oath of allegiance to England, or they might leave their native land for exile and for military service on the continent. The majority of Eire's leaders, the flower of her aristocracy, chose exile. There remained to them hope that they might one day come home, sword in hand, under the leadership of a "King's son from across the sea," to deliver their country from the hated British rule.

"Siubhail a Gradh" records a nation's desolation and the glimmering spark of its hope, still lingering in defeat. Irish immigrants to the New World brought this song with them. In time, it rooted itself in American soil, and became a lament for militiamen departed to fight the French or the British. The Gaelic refrain dropped away, or survived only as a nonsense rhyme; the melody became Americanized. We reproduce here the Irish lyric and one of the beautiful melodies to which it was set; and an American version found originally among Irish settlers in the Hudson Valley, and transmitted to us through the family tradition of the New York song collector, John Allison.

### Come, My Love (Eire)

I wish I were on yon green hill, 'Tis there I'd sit and cry my fill, And__

I'll sell my rack, I'll sell my reel,
I'll sell my only spinning wheel,
To buy my love a sword of steel,
My darling and my life, I love you so.

*Refrain*

But now my love has gone to France,
To try his fortune to advance,
If he come back, 'tis but a chance,
My darling and my life, I love you so.

The refrain is translated from the Gaelic by Samuel Preston Bayard and John Anthony Scott.

I'll dye my petticoat, I'll dye it red,
And round the world I'll beg my bread,
For the lad that I love from me is fled,
My darling and my life, I love you so.

*Refrain*

\*     \*     \*

*The Gaelic refrain, often still sung by Irish singers along
with the English verses, goes as follows:*

Siubhail, siubhail, siubhail a gradh,
Ní leigheas le fagháil acht leigheas an bháis.
Ó d'fhág tu mise, is bocht mo chás,
Is go dteidhidh tu a mhúirnin slán.

## Johnny Has Gone for a Soldier (Hudson Valley)

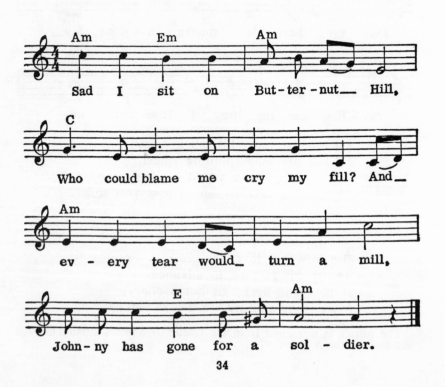

Me oh my, I loved him so,
Broke my heart to see him go,
And only time can heal my woe,
Johnny has gone for a soldier.

I'll sell my clock, I'll sell my reel,
Likewise I'll sell my spinning wheel,
To buy my love a sword of steel,
Johnny has gone for a soldier.

Sad I sit on Butternut Hill,
Who can blame me cry my fill?
And every tear would turn a mill,
Johnny has gone for a soldier.

# The Death of General Wolfe

The ballad of the death of General Wolfe is a historical song of unusual importance, and also one of the first American broadside ballads of which we have a record.

In the colonial period, British settlers were moving slowly and painfully westward from their coastal beach heads between the Appalachian barrier and the sea. In the race for empire and for the interior of the American continent, they had been outflanked by the French. From the days of Champlain to those of Montcalm, a series of brilliant explorations had brought the entire Mississippi valley under French control. Britain's mainland colonies thus grew up in the shadow of French power and with an acute awareness of French rivalry. In colonial days, the military conflict between Britain and France erupted time and again—all along the frontier, in New Brunswick and New Scotia, in the valleys of the Hudson and the St. Lawrence.

The climax of the battle for North American dominion came with the French and Indian Wars which began in 1754 in the Ohio valley, and culminated with the siege of Quebec in 1759. British victory in this struggle obliterated French power in the New World and opened a new chapter in the history of the North American continent.

The hero of the siege of Quebec and the victor of September 13, 1759 was the young British commander General James Wolfe, who died in the hour of triumph. It was understandable that he should become an American national hero whose great exploit in storming the Heights of Abraham should find enduring expression in song.

The version of the great ballad in celebration of Wolfe that is reproduced here is a composite of two broadsides in the Harris Collection of the University of Rhode Island, and one in the Isaiah Thomas Collection of the American Antiquarian Society. Other versions printed in early American songbooks testify to the widespread popularity of this song. It was, of course, also well known in Canada. The wonderful Dorian melody to which the words are here set was collected from Canadian singers in Newfoundland.

Come all ye young men all, let this de-light you; Cheer up, ye young men all, let noth-ing fright you. Nev-er let your cour-age fail when you're brought to tri-al, Nor let your fan-cy move at the first de-ni-al.

2. Bad news is come to town, bad news is carried,
Bad news is whispered round, my love is married.
Bad news is come to town, I fell a-weeping,
They stole my love from me while I lay sleeping.

3. "Love, here's a diamond ring, if you'll accept it,
'Tis for your sake alone, long time I've kept it;
When you this posy read think on the giver,
Madam, remember me, or I'm undone for ever."

4. So then this gallant youth did cross the ocean,
To free America from her invasion;
He landed at Quebec with all his party,
The city to attack, being brave and hearty.

37

5.  Brave Wolfe drew up his men, in a line so pretty,
    On the plains of Abraham before the city;
    A distance from the town the French did meet him,
    With a double number they resolved to beat him.

6.  The French drew up their men, for death prepared;
    In one another's face the armies stared,
    While Wolfe and Montcalm together walked
    Between their armies they like brothers talked.

7.  Each man then took his post at their retire,
    So then these numerous hosts began to fire—
    The cannon on each side did roar like thunder,
    And youths in all their pride were torn asunder.

8.  The drums did loudly beat, colors were flying,
    The purple gore did stream, and men lay dying,
    When shot off from his horse fell this brave hero,
    And we lament his loss in weeds of sorrow.

9.  The French began to break, their ranks were flying,
    Wolfe seemed to revive while he lay dying.
    He lifted up his head while guns did rattle,
    And to his army said, "How goes the battle?"

10. His aide-de-camp replied, " 'Tis in our favor;
    Quebec with all her pride, nothing can save her;
    She falls into our hands with all her treasure,"
    "O then," brave Wolfe replied, "I die with pleasure."

11. Bad news is come to town, bad news is carried,
    Some say my love is dead, some say he's married.
    As I was a pondering on this, I feel a-weeping,
    They stole my love from me while I lay sleeping.

Melody from Elisabeth B. Greenleaf and Grace Y. Mansfield *Ballads and Sea Songs of Newfoundland,* Harvard University Press. Copyright 1933 by the President and Fellows of Harvard College, 1961 by Elisabeth Bristol Greenleaf and Grace Yarrow Mansfield.

# Sweet William

This song came to America from Britain in colonial days. Taken by pioneers all the way from the east coast to California, it underwent many changes of lyric, and was used as a commentary on all kinds of tragic experiences in American life. In wartime, it became a lament over a fate that robbed young women of their lovers. On the frontier and in the logging camps, under the title "The Pinery Boy," it bewailed the hard, dangerous life of the lumberman. During the gold rush, it became a commentary on the craze for quick riches that snatched men from their sweethearts and lured them to death in Panamanian swamps or on desert trails. The uniquely American melody given here is from North Carolina; the mode is Aeolian (A to A on the white keys of the piano). The lyric is a composite, put together from dozens of partial and corrupted texts that have been left to us.

It was ear-ly, ear-ly all in_ the spring, That my boy Wil-lie went to serve the King; The_ night was dark and the wind blew_ high, It was then that I lost my dear sol-dier boy.

2. The night is long and I can find no rest,
   The thought of Willie runs in my breast;
   I'll search the green woods and village wide
   Still hoping my true love for to find.

3. A soldier's life is a cruel life,
   It robs young ladies of their heart's delight,
   Causes them to weep and causes them to mourn
   The loss of their true love never to return.

4. "Father, father build me a boat,
   That on the ocean I may float,
   I'll hail every vessel that passes by,
   There to inquire for my sweet soldier boy."

5. She had not been sailing far on the main,
   When she spied a ship coming in from Spain:
   "Captain, oh captain, tell me true,
   If my sweet William is with your crew."

6. "What was the color of your true love's hair?
   What kind of rig did your true love wear?"
   "His eyes were blue, his lips like wine,
   Ten thousand thousand times they've met with mine."

7. "Lady, lady, he is not here;
   He was killed in battle, my dear.
   At the head of Rocky Island, as we passed by,
   There we left your sweet soldier boy."

8. She wrung her hands, she tore her hair,
   She sobbed and sighed in her despair,
   She run her boat against a rock,
   I thought, in my soul, her heart it would break.

9. "Go dig my grave both wide and deep,
   Put a marble stone at my head and feet;
   And above my breast carve a turtle dove
   To let the world know I died for love."

Melody reproduced by permission of Oxford University Press from *English Folk Songs from the Southern Appalachians,* collected by Cecil J. Sharp and edited by Maud Karpeles. Copyright © by Oxford University Press, London and New York, 1932.

# The Old Man Who Lived in the Woods

The story of the man who competed with his wife to see which of them could do more work came from the Old World. Evidently, it was a favorite of the American settlers, for it has been found everywhere—in the North, South, and Midwest. During its travels, the song picked up unique and original American lyrics, loading upon the wretched husband's shoulders as many chores as there were in a woman's day. Such versions are of great length, but they give a vivid impression of the endless toil that fell to a woman's lot on the average pioneer farm: washing the dirty laundry, churning the cream, milking the cow, feeding the animals, spinning and winding the yarn. The melody given here is taken from the singing of the New England folklorist Bill Bonyun.

There was an old man who lived in the woods, As you shall plain-ly see, Who said he could do more work in a day, Than his wife could do in three. "With all my heart!" the old wom-an said, "But

then you must al - low, That you must do my

work for a day, And I'll go fol -low the plow."

3. "You must milk the tiny cow,
    Lest she should go quite dry,
    And you must feed the little pigs
    That live in yonder sty.

4. "You must watch the speckled hen,
    For fear she lays astray,
    And not forget the spool of yarn
    That I spin every day."

5. The old woman took the staff in her hand,
    And went to follow the plow;
    And the old man took the pail on his head
    And went to milk the cow.

6. But Tiny she winked and Tiny she blinked,
    And Tiny she tossed her nose,
    And Tiny she gave him a kick on the shins
    Till the blood ran down to his toes.

7. Then "Whoa, Tiny!" and "So, Tiny!
    My pretty little cow, stand still!
    If ever I milk you again," he said,
    "It will be against my will."

8. And then he went to feed the pigs
    That lived within the sty;
    The old sow ran against his legs
    And threw him in the mire.

9. And then he watched the speckled hen
    Lest she might lay astray;
    But he quite forgot the spool of yarn
    That his wife spun every day.

10. Then the old man swore by the sun and the moon,
    And the green leaves on the trees,
That his wife could do more work in a day
    Than he could do in three.

11. And when he saw how well she plowed,
    And ran the furrows even,
He swore she could do more work in a day
    Than he could do in seven.

# Springfield Mountain

The life of a frontier farmer in colonial days was a harsh, dangerous, and precarious one. Death might strike without warning in many different ways: disease or epidemic, forest accident, Indian raid, the attack of a wild animal, or the bite of a poisonous snake. These perils gave an urgent significance to the theme of religious revivalism that kept pace with westward-moving settlement. Repent now, and give your soul to God, while there is time: tomorrow may be too late.

"Springfield Mountain" is a classic example of this revivalist message and its expression in song. The version given here is traditional in New England, and tells the story of an accidental death that actually occurred at Wilbraham, Massachusetts, in the middle of the eighteenth century. This song has been found in one form or another throughout the Union, which attests to the universality of the experience with which it deals. The simple yet beautiful melody is sung on five notes of the scale and is of mixed modality, that is, it has no dominant emphasis in either major or minor key. It is harmonized with two chords, a major chord and its relative minor.

"Springfield Mountain" has been called the first truly American folk song. This statement really does not have very much meaning, since the Americanization of British song was so gradual and continuous a process. It is a good example of traditional ballad form, and the melody slightly resembles Psalm 100. For "The Pesky Sarpent," a comic version of "Springfield Mountain," and its significance in New England history, see page 156.

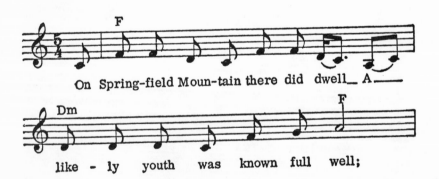

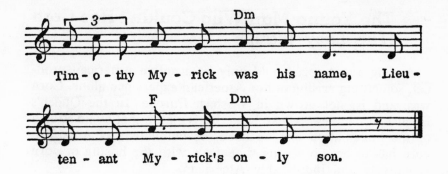

Tim-o-thy My-rick was his name, Lieu-ten-ant My-rick's on-ly son.

2. On Friday morning he did go
   Down to the meadow for to mow;
   He mowed and mowed around the field
   Till a poisonous serpent bit his heel.

3. When he received his deathly wound
   He laid his scythe down on the ground;
   For to return was his intent
   Crying out loud long as he went.

4. His cries were heard both near and far,
   But no friend to him did appear;
   They thought he did some workman call,
   And so poor boy alone did fall.

5. Day being done, now, and night coming on,
   The father went to seek his son,
   And soon his only son he found
   Cold as a stone, dead on the ground.

6. He took him up and bore him home,
   And all the time did cry and mourn,
   Saying "I heard, but did not come,
   And now I'm left alone to mourn."

7. 'Twas the seventh of August in seventeen sixty-one,
   That this sad accident was done;
   Let this a warning be to all,
   To be prepared when God doth call.

Transcribed from the singing of Bill Bonyun, by permission.

# The Young Man Who Couldn't Hoe Corn
## (The Lazy Man)

A song about corn could only be a native American product, something arising out of American experience alone. Corn was, and is, not grown in Western Europe. In the Queen's English, it denotes "wheat," and this is a crop that by no stretch of the imagination can be hoed, or cultivated, as American corn has to be. So a song that deals with the hoeing of corn is natively and indubitably American.

The wide distribution of this song in all the Atlantic seaboard states, both North and South, indicates its age and colonial origins. In its own way it makes the same point as "Springfield Mountain" and "The Old Man Who Lived in the Woods"—that colonial life was an unending battle with nature, and that a man who couldn't or wouldn't work in the fields was no man at all.

As one would expect, this song went westward with the pioneers. Versions of it have been found in Iowa and Nebraska.

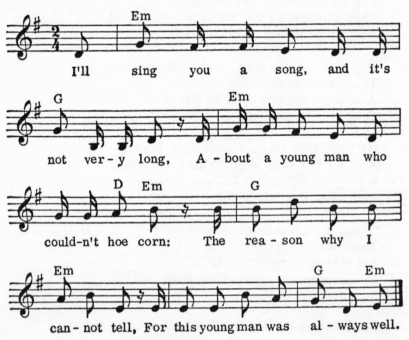

I'll sing you a song, and it's not ver-y long, A-bout a young man who could-n't hoe corn: The rea-son why I can-not tell, For this young man was al-ways well.

46

2. He planted by the moon in the month of June,
   And in July it was knee high;
   But in September there came a frost,
   And all this young man's corn was lost.

3. He went to the corn field and peeped in,
   The careless weeds had grown to his chin,
   The careless weeds had grown so high,
   They caused this young man for to cry.

4. He went to his nearest neighbor's door,
   Where ofttimes he had been before;
   And when his courtship he'd begun,
   She asked him if he'd hoed his corn?

5. He hung his head and drew a sigh,
   "Oh no, dear madam, no not I;
   I've tried and tried but all in vain,
   I fear I shall not raise a grain."

6. "Then why do you ask me for to wed,
   When you can't even raise your own cornbread?
   Single I am and single I'll remain,
   For a lazy man I won't maintain."

# Jenny Jenkins

"Jenny Jenkins" is a courting song that in colonial days enjoyed a widespread popularity. It has none of the stateliness of "The Keys of Canterbury," but exhibits instead a typical American bounce. It is based upon traditional color symbolism: red stands for sin, blue for faithfulness, white for purity, and so on; by asking the girl what dress she intends to wear, the young man hopes to learn something of her attitude toward him. But some of the colors used are merely an excuse for a nonsense rhyme, which makes it immediately appealing to children. Bill Bonyun and I have sung this song for years at Old Sturbridge Village: it is a continuing favorite of young and old alike.

"Will you wear red, oh my dear, oh my dear, Will you wear red, Jen-ny Jen-kins?" "No I won't wear red, it's a col-or I dread, I'll buy me a fol-de-rol-de, til-de-tol-de,

seek - a  dou - ble,  us - a - caus - a

roll,____  Jen-ny  Jen-kins  roll".____

2. "Will you wear green, oh my dear, oh my dear,
   Will you wear green, Jenny Jenkins?"
   "No I won't wear green, it's a shame to be seen,"
   I'll buy me a fol-de-rol-de, etc.

3. "Will you wear white, oh my dear, oh my dear,
   Will you wear white, Jenny Jenkins?"
   "No I won't wear white, 'cause the color's too bright,"
   I'll buy me a fol-de-rol-de, etc.

4. "Will you wear yellow, oh my dear, oh my dear,
   Will you wear yellow, Jenny Jenkins?"
   "No I won't wear yellow, might be chased by a fellow,"
   I'll buy me a fol-de-rol-de, etc.

5. "Will you wear pink, oh my dear, oh my dear,
   Will you wear pink, Jenny Jenkins?"
   "Well, I might wear pink, but I'd still have to think,"
   I'll buy me a fol-de-rol-de, etc.

6. "Now will you wear blue, oh my dear, oh my dear,
   Will you wear blue, Jenny Jenkins?"
   "No, I won't wear blue 'cause the color's too true,"
   I'll buy me a fol-de-rol-de, etc.

7. "Then *what* will you wear, oh my dear, oh my dear,
   What will you wear, Jenny Jenkins?"
   "Now what do you care, so I don't go bare?"
   I'll buy me a fol-de-rol-de, etc.

# Katie Cruel

"Katie Cruel" originated in New England in colonial times, and has been sung there continuously from the eighteenth century until today. Colonial militiamen used it as a marching song; children sang it as a jingle and speeded the tempo to a skipping pace; for women it was either a lullaby or a lament that captured well the dreaming loneliness and pain of love. Peggy Seeger sings a children's version which is reproduced in the *Young Folk Song Book* (New York: Simon and Schuster, 1963) as one of her most requested songs. Bill Bonyun and I have been singing the more serious version to audiences at Old Sturbridge Village for a number of years; it seems to have an instant and universal appeal.

When I first came to town, They called me the rov - ing jew - el; Now they've changed their tune, And call me Ka - ty Cru - el, O lit - tle lol - ly - day, O the lit - tle li - o day. O that I were where I

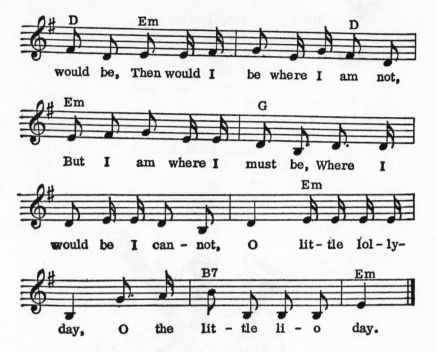

would be, Then would I be where I am not,

But I am where I must be, Where I

would be I can-not, O lit-tle lol-ly-

day, O the lit-tle li-o day.

I know who I love,
And I know who does love me;
I know where I'll go,
And I know who'll go with me,
    O little lolly day,
    O the little lioday.

O that I were where I would be,
Then would I be where I am not,
But I am where I must be,
Where I would be I cannot,
    O little lolly day,
    O the little lioday.

Through the woods I'll go,
And through the bogs and mire,
Straightway down the road,
Till I come to my heart's desire,
    O little lolly day,
    O the little lioday.

O that I were where I would be,
Then would I be where I am not,

But I am where I must be,
Where I would be I cannot,
O little lolly day,
O the little lioday.

Eyes as bright as coal,
Lips as red as cherry,
And 'tis her delight
To make the young folks merry,
   O little lolly day,
   O the little lioday.

# II
# THE
# AMERICAN
# REVOLUTION

---

THE UNITED STATES grew up in an age of empires—a whole epoch of European history stretching from the fifteenth to the end of the nineteenth century. During this period, Europeans explored and mapped the entire globe and erected great overseas empires. The theory underlying such empire-building was called the mercantile theory and was, with appropriate variations, common to all the colonizing powers. In general terms, the theory stated that colonies existed and should be exploited principally for the military, naval, and commercial advancement of the "mother country" and her citizens; that colonies must be held subordinate in every way; and that their main purpose was to provide raw materials, shipping, markets, manpower, and bullion necessary to the European nations in their race for supremacy.

The hard facts of American life soon conflicted with British rule in both theory and practice, for from the very first days of settlement the colonists were slowly but surely developing as an independent nation with objectives and interests all of their own. A nation is a group of people bound over a long period of time by powerful and permanent ties: a common land, common traditions, common beliefs, a common culture, a common system of law, and self-rule. All of these Americans either inherited or created during the colonial periods. They cleared, settled, and made their own the great and beautiful land lying between the Atlantic Ocean and the Appalachians; brought all the people, by means of the great "awakenings" or revivals of the late seventeenth and eighteenth centuries, into the fold of a common Protestant religion; inherited a common English culture which they adapted to their own uses; underwent common trials and experiences in the struggle to settle a new land and create a new society; and developed institutions and laws to regulate local affairs.

By the middle of the eighteenth century, the growing initiative and independence of the colonies became clear to the English; the elimination of French power from the Western Hemisphere by the French and Indian Wars and the Treaty of Paris of 1763 brought into the open the divergence of British and colonial interests. England, if she wished to use to her advantage the French Empire she had just won, could not hesitate to impose her authority on the refractory colonies. The colonies, too, had ideas about the development of the continent, and they differed not a little from those of England.

From 1763 to 1774 the struggle by the colonies against complete submission to British imperial control was fought openly. The story is familiar. As we know, the Revolution came because it was clear to the colonials that Britain sought to impose upon them a sweeping political and military control; they could either fight for their freedom or submit to vassalage.

But the Revolution that broke out in 1775 had world significance. It was the first occasion in the modern age a colony challenged a mother country's claim to absolute sovereignty over it and succeeded in absolutely extinguishing that claim. Of all the pioneering that Americans have ever done, this is perhaps the most notable. From that day to this, over the course of nearly two centuries, colonial nations have continued to press this challenge to colonizing powers. America took the first great step in an ongoing battle to rid the world of nations that rule and nations that are ruled, to create an international community of free, equal, and independent peoples.

Song played an important role in the struggles of the American Revolution. As we have seen, broadside ballads were brought to America from England during colonial times, and in the eighteenth century American writers began to create and publish broadsides of their own. But it was not until the Revolution that broadside balladry came of age in this country. The revolutionary crisis witnessed an extraordinary outpouring of topical songs, many of which first appeared either as broadsides or in newspaper columns. They satisfied a number of needs arising from the war itself: to convey news of battles and naval engagements, to celebrate triumphs, to poke fun at the enemy, to promote an understanding of war aims, and to arouse the courage of men and women.

Many of the songs of the Revolution have vanished from popular tradition, and have been preserved only in written form. Our chief sources are the files of contemporary newspapers, broadside ballad collections such as the Isaiah Thomas Collection of the American Antiquarian Society, and song books published for the most part after the fighting was over.

The songs of the American Revolution are of great value to us today. The story of that struggle may be told vividly and accurately through its songs; from the considerable material left us, it is possible to select a group that will provide a stirring and eloquent narrative of almost epic dimension. Moreover, these songs provide us with insight into both the mood of the revolutionary era and the meaning of the revolutionary struggle, seen from the viewpoint of those individuals who were actually engaged in it. Their songs help us discover our own historical roots and traditions in the American Revolution, and to identify with those people whose sacrifices made the existence of America possible. Finally, these songs have an international significance. To the extent that we understand our own Revolution we can understand the liberation movements currently taking place in Africa, Asia, India, Latin America, and Indonesia.*

*Part of the commentary accompanying the songs in this chapter first appeared in *The American Revolution through Its Songs and Ballads*, by Bill Bonyun and John Anthony Scott: and is reproduced here by permission of Heirloom Records, Brookhaven, N. Y.

# Young Ladies in Town

In 1763, with the end of the war against France, the British took swift steps to make certain the colonists interfered in no way with the empire won from the French, confined their activities to the Atlantic seaboard, and maintained the subordinate political position from which they were so obviously threatening to break away. A standing army was established in America with its commander, General Thomas Gage, as imperial viceroy. Colonial movement into the Mississippi Valley was prohibited by royal proclamation. Plans were made for a stricter enforcement of the Navigation Laws and for the raising of a colonial revenue that would flow directly into the imperial treasury.

Colonial resistance to this "new imperial policy," as it was called, was so widespread that it may be termed national. It took the form of mass demonstrations against measures like the Stamp Act, the evasion of import duties by smuggling, the boycott of British goods, and the refusal to vote supplies for the use of the British occupation troops.

The new spirit of militant opposition to Great Britain is excellently illustrated by "Young Ladies in Town." This song came into being as a result of the Townshend Acts of 1767 which decreed that Americans must pay duties on imported British lead, paint, glass, and tea. The American reaction was to boycott all British imported goods, with the hope that the loss of the American market would bring the British authorities to their senses.

This boycott was in effect for two years and inflicted staggering losses upon British trade. The song, which first appeared in the *Boston Newsletter* in 1769, appealed to American women to foreswear the use of British textiles and British tea, and to make homespun a symbol of dedication to the national cause; the song is noteworthy for its impassioned appeal to women to place love of country above love of finery. Mahatma Gandhi was to make a similar appeal to the people of India a century and a half later; he too, made the village spinning wheel a symbol of national independence.

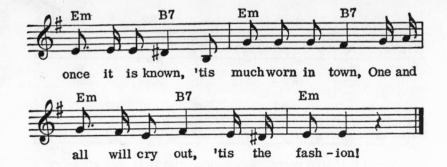

once it is known, 'tis much worn in town, One and
all will cry out, 'tis the fash-ion!

And as one all agree that you'll not married be
    To such as will wear London factory;
But at first sight refuse, tell 'em you will choose
    As encourage our own manufactory.
No more ribbons wear, nor in rich silks appear,
    Love your country much better than fine things;
Begin without passion, 'twill soon be the fashion
    To grace your smooth locks with a twine string.

Throw away your bohea, and your green hyson tea
    And all things of a new-fashioned duty;
Get in a good store of the choice Labrador
    There'll soon be enough here to suit ye.
These do without fear, and to all you'll appear
    Fair, charming, true, lovely, and clever;
Though the times remain darkish, young men will be sparkish,
    And love you much stronger than ever.

# The Rich Lady over the Sea

As everyone knows, the tea tax was the spark that set off the revolutionary explosion. In 1770, Britain withdrew all of the obnoxious Townshend duties except the tax on tea. Three years later, British interests moved to dump quantities of Indian tea on the American market at prices which would have destroyed the colonists' own trade and established a British monopoly of the market. This threat led to the famous Boston act of defiance of December 16, 1773.

Britain reacted to the Boston Tea Party in the spring of 1774 by suspending Boston's town meeting, closing its port to commerce, and establishing direct military rule under General Gage himself. Three British generals, Henry Clinton, John Burgoyne, and William Howe, were dispatched across the Atlantic with reinforcements to put down the rebellion.

These measures led to the Revolution because it was clear to all the colonists what was intended for them, as well as for Boston, should they be rash enough to incur the royal displeasure. Thus, Boston's cause became the national cause, the Continental Congress was convened in Philadelphia in September 1774, and measures to organize resistance were initiated. The war began in earnest the following year with the skirmishes at Lexington and Concord. By May 1775, all of New England was in arms, and the British found themselves besieged in Boston.

"The Rich Lady over the Sea" is perhaps the best of many songs about the tea party; its message is expressed in vivid terms that even a child can understand. The little girl has grown up. She is going to assume a position of equality and independence in relation to her mother.

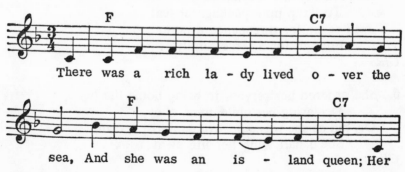

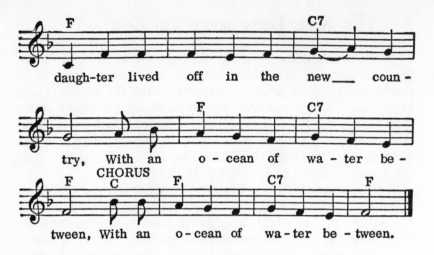

daugh-ter lived off in the new___ coun -

try, With an o - cean of wa - ter be -

**CHORUS**

tween, With an o - cean of wa - ter be - tween.

2. The old lady's pockets were fillèd with gold,
     Yet never contented was she;
   So she ordered her daughter to pay her a tax
     Of thruppence a pound on the tea.
*Chorus: repeat the last line of each verse.*

3. "O mother, dear mother," the daughter replied,
     "I'll not do the thing that you ask;
   I'm willing to pay a fair price on the tea,
     But never the thruppeny tax."
*Chorus*

4. "You shall!" cried the mother, and reddened with rage,
     "For you're my own daughter, you see;
   And it's only proper that daughter should pay
     Her mother a tax on the tea."
*Chorus*

5. She ordered her servant to be called up
     To wrap up a package of tea;
   And eager for threepence a pound, she put in
     Enough for a large family.
*Chorus*

6. She ordered her servant to bring home the tax,
     Declaring her child must obey,
   Or, old as she was, and woman most grown,
     She'd half whip her life away.
*Chorus*

7. The tea was conveyed to her daughter's own door,
        All down by the oceanside;
    But the bouncing girl poured out every pound
        On the dark and boiling tide.
*Chorus*

8. And then she called out to the island queen,
        "O mother, dear mother," called she,
    "Your tea you may have when 'tis stepped enough,
        But never a tax from me."
*Chorus*

# The Folks on t'Other Side the Wave

Having first appeared in England in 1776, this little song was published the following year as a broadside. A warning to His Majesty's government of the consequences of undertaking a war to suppress the colonial revolt, it is marked by an almost uncanny sense of the realities of life. It foreshadows clearly the grim nature of the struggle that Britain would encounter in the effort to put down a rebellion three thousand miles from her own shores. America, the song hints, is not a second Ireland—a tiny country that may be overridden with impunity by British military might: it is a vast continent, whose permanent occupation in the face of American resistance will be impossible. The patriotic ferver of the Americans, plus the vast spaces and natural wealth of the country, will make conquest impossible. Clearly embodied in the song is the concept of a people's war against a foreign invader, and, beyond that, a whole new era of colonial struggle against foreign domination and exploitation.

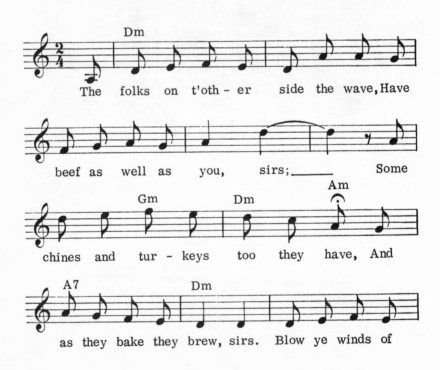

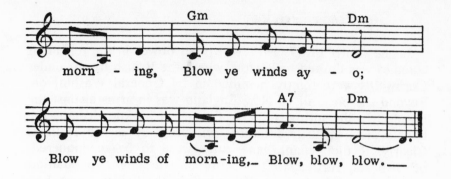

morn - ing, Blow ye winds ay - o;

Blow ye winds of morn-ing,_ Blow, blow, blow.__

What though your cannon raze their towns,
 And tumble down their houses;
They'll fight like devils, blood and bones,
 For children and for spouses.
*Chorus*

Another truth, nay, 'tis no boast,
 Nor yet the lie o' the day, sirs;
The saints on Massachusetts' coast
 Gain if they run away, sirs.
*Chorus*

For further than your bullets fly
 A common man may run, sirs;
And wheat will grow beneath a sky
 Where cannot reach a gun, sirs.
*Chorus*

# Sir Peter Parker

In the winter of 1775–1776, British power in the rebellious colonies was limited to Boston, where the British troops under Cornwallis were tightly hemmed in by General Washington. Beyond the port, all of New England was in arms against the invader. In the spring of 1776, the British, acknowledging the hopelessness of their situation, withdrew by sea to Halifax. Clearly, if the defiant Americans were to be reconquered, other bases, further to the south and among a population some portion of which was friendlier to the British cause, had to be sought. Accordingly, the plan of campaign for 1776 called for the invasion and occupation of the port of New York. In addition, an expedition was dispatched in June, under the joint command of Sir Henry Clinton and Admiral Sir Peter Parker, with instructions to occupy Charleston, South Carolina.

The approach to Charleston harbor was dominated by Fort Moultrie, on Sullivan's Island. The British plan of attack provided that Sir Henry Clinton and his marines would land on Sullivan's Island and attack the fort from the north, while Sir Peter Parker used his naval artillery to pound the American installation from the sea.

Matters did not work out as the British had planned. Clinton landed on Long Island, just adjacent to Sullivan's Island, but failed to take his troops across the narrow inlet dividing the two; Parker had to attack Fort Moultrie unaided. The American defenders gave a good acount of themselves, and on June 28, 1776, drove off the British nine ship flotilla with heavy losses. Sir Peter's temper, already frayed by Clinton's failure, was not improved when, as he stood on the quarter-deck of his flagship, the *Bristol,* an American shot blew off his pants.

An observer with the British fleet gave the following account of the American defense:

Our ships, lying nine hours before the battery, were obliged to retire with great loss. The provincials reserved their fire until the shipping were advanced within point blank shot. Their artillery was surprisingly well served, it is said under the command of a Mr. Masson and De Brahm. It was slow, but decisive indeed. They were very cool, and took great care not to fire except their guns were exceedingly well directed: but there was a time when the battery appeared to be silenced for more than an hour. The navy say, had the troops been ready to land at this time, they could have taken possession; how that is, I will not pretend to say. I will rather suppose it; but the fire became exceedingly severe when it was renewed again, and did amazing execution, after the battery had been supposed to have been silenced. This will not be believed when it is first reported in England. I can scarcely believe what I saw on that day; a day to me one of the most distressing of my life.

Sir Peter Parker and Sir Henry Clinton were obliged to sail away again for New York, arguing bitterly over who was to blame for this fiasco. The American victory occasioned the appearance of the sparkling propaganda piece printed below, which put the tale of woe into Sir Peter's own mouth. This song set the whole country laughing. Beneath the witty thrusts lay an exhilarating thought: How do the British expect to take an entire continent when they cannot even capture a small island?

My lords, with your leave, An account I will give that de-serves to be
writ-ten in me-tre; For the
reb-els and I have been pret-ty nigh, Faith
al-most too nigh for Sir Pe-ter! Ti-mi-
al-der-ry O, ti-mi - al-der-ry ay, Faith,

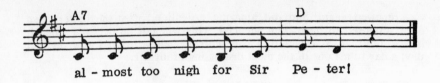

al - most too nigh for Sir Pe - ter!

2. With much labor and toil
   Unto Sullivan's Isle,
   I came firm as Falstaff or Pistol;
   But the Yankees, God rot 'em,
   I could not get at 'em;
   They most terribly mauled my poor *Bristol.*
*Chorus*

3. Bold Clinton by land
   Did quietly stand,
   While I made a thundering clatter.
   But the channel was deep,
   So he only could peep
   And not venture over the water.
*Chorus*

4. Devil take 'em, their shot
   Came so swift and so hot,
   And the cowardly dogs stood so stiff, sirs!
   That I put ship about
   And was glad to get out
   Or they would not have left me a skiff, sirs!
*Chorus*

5. Now, bold as a Turk,
   I proceed to New York,
   Where with Clinton and Howe you may find me.
   I've the wind in my tail, and am hoisting sail,
   To leave Sullivan's Island behind me.
*Chorus*

6. But, my lords, do not fear,
   For before the next year,
   Although a small island could fret us,
   The continent whole,
   We shall take, by my soul,
   If the cowardly Yankees will let us.
*Chorus*

# Nathan Hale

The Yankees might laugh at Sir Peter Parker, but the New York campaign was no laughing matter. In July, 1776, Howe's fleet sailed up the East River and landed British troops in Brooklyn, where they came within a hair's breadth of destroying Washington's forces. Washington slipped away to Manhattan and retreated helter-skelter up the island and into Westchester, with the British in hot pursuit.

Nathan Hale gave his life for his country on September 22, 1776, during the retreat of the American forces from New York City. Descended from an old, established New England family, Hale was born in Coventry, Connecticut, and graduated from Yale College in 1773 with distinction. When the war broke out, he took a commission in the Continental army and was sent on a mission by General Washington behind the British lines. Attempting to regain his own command via the King's Bridge connecting Manhattan with the Bronx, he was arrested and hanged as a spy. According to the *Freeman's Journal,* Hale, when at the gallows, ". . . made a sensible and spirited speech, among other things told them they were shedding the blood of the innocent, and that if he had ten thousand lives, he would lay them all down, if called to it, in defence of this injured, bleeding country."

The lyric for "Nathan Hale" was printed by Frank Moore in *Songs and Ballads of the American Revolution,* but he gives no information as to its origins. It is probably of earlier date than the melody to which it is here set, which was composed after the end of the Revolution. The melody, as given here, is transcribed from the singing of Bill Bonyun.

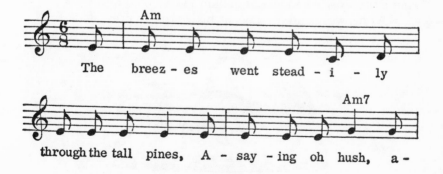

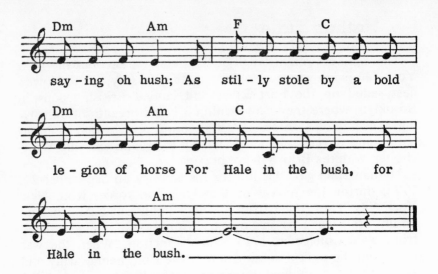

say – ing oh hush; As stil – ly stole by a bold

le – gion of horse For Hale in the bush, for

Hale in the bush.

Cooling shades of the night were a-coming apace,
    The tattoo had beat, the tattoo had beat;
The noble one sprang from his dark lurking place,
    To make his retreat, to make his retreat.

The guard of the camp on that dark dreary night
    Had a murderous will, had a murderous will;
They took him and bore him afar from the shore
    To a hut on the hill, to a hut on the hill.

They took him and bound him and bore him away
    Down the hill's grassy side, down the hill's grassy side;
'Twas there the base hirelings in royal array
    His cause did deride, his cause did deride.

The fate of a martyr the tragedy showed,
    As he trod the last stage, as he trod the last stage;
And Briton's will shudder at gallant Hale's blood,
    As his words do presage, as his words do presage.

# The Dying Redcoat

This is a song of extraordinary significance in the study of the American Revolution. A broadside ballad of unknown authorship, it relates the experience of a British soldier from his embarkation from England in December 1773 until his death in the New York campaign in September 1776.

The ballad is said to have been written by a British sergeant fatally wounded in the fierce conflict resulting from the British landing on Manhattan on September 16; but whether this is true or not, the song was evidently popular with Americans, and it enables us to see how those actually involved in the revolutionary struggle viewed themselves: Patriots rise up "like grasshoppers" to defend their country; the land is a garden place full of "bitter weeds," that is, men who spread death and destruction from their rifles and are not afraid to die for their freedom. The British soldier finds that he has met his end as the result of a campaign far different from the type for which he was trained, or which he might have expected to fight in Europe. His antagonists are a people in arms. The song, further, is as remarkable for its insistence on the righteousness of the American cause as for the compassion which it expresses for the British soldier wrongly torn from his home to die a futile death in an alien land.

The lyric reproduced here is a composite of several broadsides that have survived in the collections of the University of Rhode Island and the American Antiquarian Society. The song has remained in oral tradition until recent times. Helen Hartness Flanders collected a version from Mrs. Ellen Nye Lawrence of Vermont in 1931.

'Twas on De - cem-ber's fif-teenth day, When we set_ sail_ for A - mer - i - ca; 'Twas

on that dark and dis-mal day, When
we set_ sail_ for A - mer - i - ca. 'Twas
on that dark and___ dis-mal time,_ When
we set sail for the North-ern clime, Where
drums do beat and trum-pets sound, And
un - to_ Bos - ton_ we_ were bound.

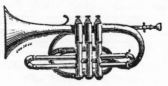

And when to Boston we did come,
We thought by the aid of our British guns,
To drive the rebels from that place,

70

To fill their hearts with sore disgrace.
But to our sorrow and surprise,
We saw men like grasshoppers rise;
They fought like heroes much enraged,
Which did affright old General Gage.

Like lions roaring for their prey,
They feared no danger or dismay;
Bold British blood runs through their veins,
And still with courage they sustain.
We saw those bold Columbia's sons
Spread death and slaughter from their guns:
Freedom or death! these heroes cry,
They did not seem afraid to die.

We sailed to York, as you've been told,
With the loss of many a Briton bold,
For to make those rebels own our King,
And daily tribute to him bring.
They said it was a garden place,
And that our armies could, with ease,
Pull down their town, lay waste their lands,
In spite of all their boasted bands.

A garden place it was indeed,
And in it grew many a bitter weed,
Which will pull down our highest hopes
And sorely wound our British troops.
'Tis now September the seventeenth day,
I wish I'd never come to America;
Full fifteen thousand has been slain,
Bold British heroes every one.

Now I've received my mortal wound,
I bid farewell to Old England's ground;
My wife and children will mourn for me,
Whilst I lie cold in America.
Fight on America's noble sons,
Fear not Britannia's thundering guns;
Maintain your cause from year to year,
God's on your side, you need not fear.

The melody given here was learned by Frank Warner from the singing of John Galusha of Minerva, N. Y., and is transcribed by permission.

# The Battle of Trenton

Britain's major thrust against the colonists was centered upon New York in 1776. As we have seen, the experience proved to be a disastrous one for the Americans. In the summer and fall of this year, Sir William Howe occupied New York and New Jersey with only token opposition. And, as the British armies advanced, the American forces melted away. By the end of 1776, Washington retained command of only a few hundred men; he had withdrawn far to the south, beyond the Delaware.

But on Christmas Day, amid ice and freezing sleet and snow, the American commander-in-chief staged a justly famous and totally unexpected counterattack. Crossing the Delaware, he drove out the Hessian mercenaries occupying the outposts of Trenton and Princeton, regained control of New Jersey, and immensely boosted the morale of the colonists and their will to continue resistance. "The Battle of Trenton," a song of uncertain date and composition, is a stirring march song that successfully captures the mood of a great turning point in the national struggle.

A contemporary account, from the *Freeman's Journal* of January 21, 1777, provides the following information about the action of Christmas Day:

General Washington, finding it absolutely necessary to rouse the spirits of the army, which have been sorely depressed by the long series of disasters which have attended us for almost the whole of this month, resolved to attempt surprising a considerable body of Hessians, quartered at Trenton, consisting of about nineteen hundred, and a detachment of British light horse. The plan was as spiritedly executed as it was judiciously concerted, and terminated in fully answering the warmest expectations of its projectors. December 25, orders were given for a large part of the army to have three days provisions ready cooked, and forty rounds a man, and to be ready to march by three o'clock in the afternoon; accordingly the farthest brigades marched by two oclock. About eleven o'clock at night it began snowing, and continued so until daybreak, when a most violent northeast storm came on, of snow, rain, and hail together. Early the American army, which did not exceed twenty-four hundred men, crossed the Delaware with several companies of artillery, and thirteen field pieces, and formed in two divisions; one commanded by General Greene, the other by General Sullivan, and the whole by General Washington. The attack began about seven o'clock by the vanguard of Sullivan's division, who attacked the Hessians' advance guard, about a mile from the town. These they soon drove off, when the whole pushed with the utmost vigor for the town, which they immediately entered. General Greene's division attacked the town on the other side at the same time. The Hessians did as much as could be expected from people so surprised, but the impetuosity of our men was irresistible; fifteen minutes decided the action, and the enemy threw down their arms and surrendered as prisoners of war.

On Christ - mas day in sev - en - ty - six, Our

rag - ged troops with bay - o - nets fixed For

Tren - ton marched a - way. The Del - a - ware see! the

boats be - low! The light ob - scured _ by

hail and snow: But no signs of dis - may.

2. Our object was the Hessian band,
   That dared invade fair freedom's land,
   And quarter in that place.
   Great Washington he led us on,
   Whose streaming flag in storm or sun,
   Had never known disgrace.

3. In silent march we passed the night,
   Each soldier panting for the fight,
   Though quite benumbed with frost.
   Greene, on the left, at six began,
   The right was led by Sullivan,
   Who never a moment lost.

4. Their pickets stormed, the alarm was spread,
   That rebels risen from the dead,
   Were marching into town.
   Some scampered here, some scampered there,
   And some for action did prepare,
   But soon their arms laid down.

5. Now, brothers of the patriot bands,
   Let's sing deliverance from the hands
   Of arbitrary sway.
   And as our life is but a span,
   Let's touch the tankard while we can,
   In memory of that day.

# The Fate of John Burgoyne

Spring, 1777. Two years had passed since Lexington and Concord. Yet the British could boast only the occupation of Manhattan—a hollow boast, since they dared not venture far from the port. Supply lines were cut, foraging parties ambushed. Out of reach, elusive, Washington held his forces in the New Jersey hills, watching, waiting.

The British Government, rubbing its face in surprise, prepared for a decisive campaign against the rebels in the summer of 1777. Burgoyne, one of the trio of generals sent to Boston in 1775, the dandy who carried wine, women, and song with him on his campaigns, Gentleman Johnny, was ordered to push down the Hudson Valley and to cut off New England from the rest of the colonies. Sir William Howe's role, this year, was to occupy Philadelphia, a second important base.

Everything went wrong for Gentleman Johnny on his invasion from Canada via the familiar Lake Champlain-Hudson route. Guerrillas in his rear cut off his supplies. Gates, Arnold, and Morgan blocked his advance. By October 1777, his own mistakes and his enemy's valor had brought Burgoyne to surrender at Saratoga, for the British one of the most colossal disasters of the war. But all was not lost, for they still controlled New York; and, while Burgoyne was fighting his last battles, Howe had slipped off by sea, invaded Philadelphia, and settled down comfortably in the colonists' capital.

This delightful song, "The Fate of John Burgoyne," tells of the general's humiliation. With appropriately satiric humor, it is here set to the tune of "The Girl I Left Behind Me."

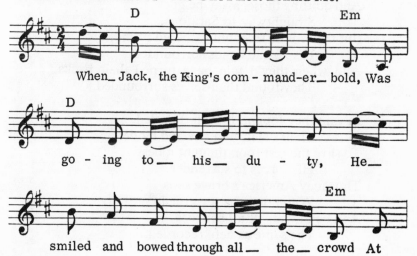

ev - ery bloom - ing beau - ty. The
Low - er House sat mute as mouse To
hear his grand o - ra - tion, And__
all the peers with loud - est cheers, Pro -
claimed him to the na - tion.

Then off he went to Canada,
　　　Next to Ticonderoga,
And quitting those, away he goes
　　　Straightway to Saratoga.
But the sons of freedom gathered round,
　　　His hostile bands surrounded,
And when they'd fain have turned their backs
　　　They found themselves surrounded.

In vain they fought, in vain they fled,
　　　Their chief, humane and tender,
To save the rest soon thought it best
　　　His forces to surrender.
Thus may America's brave sons
　　　With honor be rewarded,
And be the fate of all her foes
　　　The same as here recorded.

# The Battle of the Kegs

In October 1778, the British occupied Philadelphia, and Washington went into winter quarters close by, at Valley Forge. The sufferings of that winter are well known. Not so familiar is the fact that the Americans then began to experiment with floating mines (floating kegs, primed to explode on contact) to harass British shipping on the Delaware. The British, understandably, took steps to neutralize these weapons; on January 5, 1778, they fired at and exploded a number of these kegs as they floated down river.

These circumstances gave rise to the following delightful ballad by the American poet Francis Hopkinson. It is one of the wittiest and most telling satires in the entire American literary heritage. The events which occasioned the poet's mockery were related in the *New Jersey Gazette,* January 21, 1778, with a certain amount of pardonable exaggeration:

Philadelphia has been entertained with the most astonishing instance of the activity, bravery, and military skill of the royal navy of Great Britain. The affair is somewhat particular, and deserves notice. Some time last week, two boys observed a keg of singular construction, floating in the river opposite the city; they got into a small boat, and attempted to take up the keg, it burst with a great explosion, and blew up the unfortunate boys.

Yesterday, January 5, several kegs of a like construction made their appearance. An alarm was immediately spread through the city; various reports prevailed, filling the city and the royal troops with consternation. Some reported that the kegs were filled with armed rebels, who were to issue forth in the dead of night, as the Grecians did of old from their wooden horse at the siege of Troy, and take the city by surprise; asserting that they had seen the points of their bayonets through the bungholes of the kegs.

Others said they were charged with the most inveterate combustibles, to be kindled by secret machinery, and, setting the whole Delaware in flames, were to consume all the shipping in the harbor; whilst others asserted that they were constructed by magic art, would of themselves ascend the wharves in the night time, and roll all flaming through the streets of the city, destroying everything in their way.

Be this as it may, certain it is that the shipping in the harbor, and all the wharves in the city, were fully manned, the battle began, and it was surprising to behold the incessant blaze that was kept up against the enemy, the kegs. Both officers and men exhibited the most unparalleled skill and bravery on the occasion; whilst the citizens stood gazing as solemn witnesses of their prowess. From the *Roebuck* and other ships of war, whole broadsides were poured into the Delaware. In short, not a wandering ship, stick or drift log but felt the vigor of the British arms.

The action began about sunrise, and would have been completed with great success by noon, had not an old market woman coming down the river with provisions, let a small keg of butter fall overboard, which (as it was then ebb) floated down to the scene of action. At sight of this unexpected reinforcement of the enemy, the battle was renewed with fresh fury, and the firing was incessant till the evening closed the affair. The kegs were totally demolished or obliged to fly, as none of them have shown their *heads* since.

It is said his Excellency, Lord Howe, has despatched a swift sailing packet with an account of this victory, to the court of London. In a word, Monday, the fifth of January, 1778, must ever be distinguished in history for the memorable *Battle of the Kegs.*

Gal - lants at - tend, and hear a friend, Trill forth har - mo - nious dit - ty: Strange things I'll tell, which late be - fell In Phil - a - del - phia cit - y. 'Twas ear - ly day, as po - ets say, Just when the sun was ris - ing, A sol - dier stood on a log of wood, And saw a sight sur - pris - ing.—

2. As in a maze, he stood to gaze,
   The truth can't be denied, sir,
 He spied a score—of kegs, or more,
   Come floating down the tide, sir.

A sailor too, in jerkin blue,
    The strange appearance viewing,
First damned his eyes, in great surprise,
    Then said, "Some mischief's brewing.

3.  "These kegs now hold the rebels bold,
    Pack'd up like pickled herring:
And they're come down to attack the town,
    In this new way of ferrying."
The soldier flew, the sailor too,
    And, scared almost to death, sir,
Wore out their shoes, to spread the news,
    And ran till out of breath, sir.

4.  Now up and down throughout the town,
    Most frantic scenes were acted:
And some ran here, and some ran there
    Like men almost distracted,
Some fire cried, which some denied,
    But said the earth had quaked:
And girls and boys, with hideous noise,
    Ran through the town half naked.

5.  Sir William he, snug as a flea,
    Lay all this time a-snoring,
Nor dreamed of harm, as he lay warm
    In bed with Mrs. Loring.
Now in a fright he starts upright,
    Awaked by such a clatter;
He rubs his eyes, and boldly cries,
    "For God's sake what's the matter?"

6.  At his bedside, he then espied
    Sir Erskine in command, sir,
Upon one foot he had one boot,
    And t' other in his hand, sir.
"Arise! Arise!" Sir Erskine cries;
    "The rebels—more's the pity—
Without a boat, are all on float,
    And ranged before the city.

7.  "The motley crew, in vessels new,
    With Satan for their guide, sir,

Packed up in bags or wooden kegs,
    Come driving down the tide, sir.
Therefore prepare for bloody war;
    These kegs must all be routed;
Or surely we despised shall be,
    And British courage doubted."

8. The royal band now ready stand,
    All ranged in dread array, sir,
With stomach stout to see it out,
    And make a bloody day, sir.
The cannons roar, from shore to shore,
    The small arms make a rattle:
Since wars began I'm sure no man
    E'er saw so strange a battle.

9. The fish below swam to and fro,
    Attacked from every quarter;
Why sure, thought they, the devil's to pay,
    'Mongst folk above the water.
These kegs 'tis said, tho' strongly made,
    Of rebel staves and hoops, sir,
Could not oppose their powerful foes,
    The conquering British troops, sir.

10. From morn to night, these men of might
    Displayed amazing courage;
And when the sun was fairly down,
    Retired to sup their porridge:
An hundred men with each a pen,
    Or more upon my word, sir,
It is most true, would be too few,
    Their valor to record, sir.

11. Such feats did they perform that day
    Upon these wicked kegs, sir,
That years to come, if they get home,
    They'll make their boasts and brags, sir.

# Paul Jones's Victory
## (Poor Richard and the Serapis and Alliance)

In April 1778, good news arrived from France. A French-American alliance that promised aid to the revolutionary cause in men, money, and arms had been signed. It was a black day for the British. Sir Henry Clinton, now commander-in-chief, fearing the intervention of the French fleet, abandoned Philadelphia and drew his forces back to New York. A line of troops wound across the Jersey flats, harassed and pursued by the patriot forces. Then the British set to work to fortify Manhattan, still their only refuge in the colonies.

But the bright promise which the French alliance seemed to hold for the Americans was, for various reasons, not immediately realized, and in the years 1778–1779 a stalemate set in. The British forces were too small to conquer so huge a country whose hostile population was so scattered; and the colonists lacked the naval power that held the key to victory.

Lacking the strength to build a navy, the colonists resorted to harassing tactics. Privateers were authorized by government commission to scour the seas and to capture British merchantmen. After the conclusion of the treaty with France, these privateers fitted out in French ports and sailed brazenly about in British waters; they became a menace to British commerce.

John Paul Jones, an American sea captain, commanded a small squadron of fourth- or fifth-rate frigates provided by the French. A dramatic duel took place off Flamborough Head on September 23, 1779 when Jones encountered the *Serapis* and the *Scarborough,* English men o' war, commanded by Captain Pearson, which were convoying the Baltic merchant fleet home to London. After a fierce battle between the *Serapis* and Jones' leaky tub, the *Bonhomme Richard,* Pearson surrendered and his ship sank. Paul Jones was obliged to abandon his ship too, but he had established a new tradition.

This naval epic found expression in one of the most famous broadside ballads of the times. Often reprinted, it has remained in oral tradition until our own days.

An A-mer-i-can frig-ate, a frig-ate of fame, With guns mount-ed for-ty, the Rich-ard by name,— For to cruise in the chan-nel of old Eng - land, And a val-iant com-mand-er, Paul Jones is the man.

We had not sailed long before we did spy
A large forty-four, and a twenty so nigh,
With fifty bold seamen well laid in with store,
In consort pursued us from the old English shore.

About twelve at noon Percy came alongside,
With a speaking trumpet; "Whence came you?" he cried,
"It's now give an answer, I hail'd you before,
Or this moment a broadside into you I will pour."

Paul Jones then he says to his men every one,
"Let every bold seaman stand true to his gun;
We'll receive a broadside from these bold Englishmen,
And like true Yankee heroes return it again."

The melody given here was learned by Frank Warner from the singing
of C. K. Tillett of Wanchese, North Carolina. Transcribed by permission.

The contest was bloody, both decks ran with gore,
The sea seemed to blaze when the cannon did roar;
"Fight on my brave boys," then Paul Jones he cried,
"We will soon humble this bold Englishman's pride."

We fought them eight glasses, eight glasses  so hot,
Till seventy bold seamen lay dead on the spot,
And ninety bold seamen lay bleeding in gore,
While the pieces of cannon most wretched did roar.

Our gunner in a fright to Paul Jones he came;
"We make water quite fast, and our side's in a flame;"
Then brave Jones he said in the height of his pride
"If we can't do no better boys, sink alongside."

The *Alliance* bore down while the *Richard* did rake,
Which caused the heart of poor Percy to ache;
Our shot flew so hot they could not stand us long,
And the flag of proud Britain was forced to come down.

So now my brave boys, you have taken a prize,
A large forty-four and a twenty likewise;
Both noble vessels well laden with store,
We'll bend on all canvas for New England once more.

God bless the widows who shortly must weep
For the loss of their husbands now sunk in the deep;
Here's a health to Paul Jones, a sword in his hand,
Who led us to battle and gave the command!

# The Ballad of Major André

Paul Jones' exploit was one bright flash in the long winter of stalemate, the winter of 1779–1780—a time to test a man's soul. Washington and his rebel band was encamped in New Jersey and the New York highland, watching Clinton, waiting in the snow that lay feet deep upon the frozen ground in a winter that seemed eternal.

General Benedict Arnold spent these winter months in Philadelphia, as Commandant of the American forces in the capital. One of the most heroic of Washington's officers, he had acquitted himself brilliantly in the grim winter invasion of Canada (1775–1776) and in the Saratoga campaign. He had gained a reputation second to none as a brave and patriotic soldier. Assigned to the Philadelphia post when the British withdrew in 1778, he gave himself over to luxury and entered into relations with loyalists. He was reprimanded by Washington, passed over for promotion, and became disgruntled. Worse than this, he fell simultaneously into debt and into doubt. Was it really possible for a few bickering and ragged colonials to win a war against the mightiest Empire in the world?

A desperate need for money did the rest. Arnold entered into communication with Sir Henry Clinton, British commander-in-chief. The latter instructed him to obtain from Washington the command of West Point. Construction of the fort on the west bank of the Hudson River had just been completed. It commanded the approach to the New York highlands from the south, was the key to Washington's defensive position, and assured contact between New England and the rest of the colonies.

Washington reluctantly yielded to Arnold's request (he felt that a good field commander was wasted in such a post). Arnold assumed his new command in the spring of 1780.

The man whom Sir Henry Clinton had assigned to maintain connection with the commander of West Point and to perfect the plot for the surrender of the fort was his adjutant, young Major John André. On September 20, 1780, a British man o' war, the *Vulture,* sailed up the Hudson and dropped anchor off Croton Point. John André rowed ashore and met with Arnold among the trees foresting the west bank of the river. The general had the plans of the fort with him. The discussion was prolonged by some tedious bartering over the price of treason.

The *Vulture* came under the fire of American shore batteries, and dropped back down river without André. The young adjutant had no alternative but to make his way back to the British lines by land. In West Haverstraw, an accomplice provided him with civilian clothes and a horse. Armed with a pass from Arnold "to go to the lines of White Plains or lower if he thought proper, he being on public business," André set out for Manhattan. He crossed the Hudson at King's Ferry, headed east to Yorktown, and then south through the no-man's-land of Westchester county. Traveling all night, he reached Tarrytown by mid morning, September 23. There he was arrested by a group of American militiamen headed by John Paulding. A search discovered the plans of West Point concealed in his boot.

Arnold got wind of the arrest and fled to New York City on the *Vulture* which, providentially, had returned. André went on trial on September 29 at Washington's headquarters in Tappan, N. Y., was found guilty of espionage, and sentenced to die. On October 2, he was hanged on the hill that bears his name in the presence of a sad and troubled crowd of American soldiers and civilians.

The magnificent Hudson Valley ballad that is reproduced below immortalizes the soldier who was hung and pillories the traitor who fled. This uniquely American ballad comes down to us through the family tradition and the singing of John Allison, noted New York song collector.

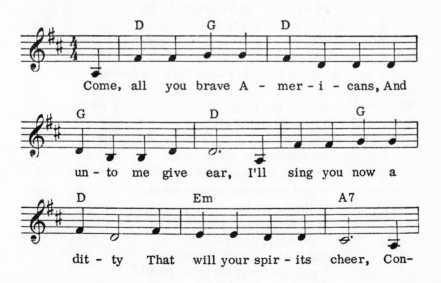

Come, all you brave A - mer - i - cans, And un - to me give ear, I'll sing you now a dit - ty That will your spir - its cheer, Con-

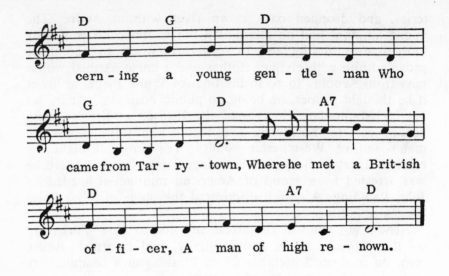

cern - ing a young gen - tle - man Who came from Tar - ry - town, Where he met a Brit-ish of - fi - cer, A man of high re - nown.

2. Then up spoke this young hero,
   Young Paulding was his name;
   "O tell us where you're going, sir,
   And also whence you came."
   "I bear the British flag, sir,"
   Up answered bold André,
   "I have a pass that takes me through,
   I have no time to stay."

3. Then others came around him,
   And bade him to dismount:
   "Come tell us where you're going,
   Give us a strict account;"
   Young Paulding said, "We are resolved
   That you shall ne'er pass by";
   And so the evidence did prove
   The prisoner a spy.

4. He begged for his liberty,
   He pled for his discharge,
   And oftentimes he told them,
   If they'd set him at large,
   "Of all the gold and silver
   I have laid up in store,
   But when I reach the city
   I will send you ten times more."

5. "We scorn this gold and silver
   You have laid up in store,"
   Van Vert and Paulding both did cry,
   "You need not send us more."
   He saw that his conspiracy
   Would soon be brought to light,
   He begged for pen and paper
   And he asked for to write.

6. The story came to Arnold
   Commanding at the Fort:
   He called for the Vulture
   And sailed for New York;
   Now Arnold to New York has gone,
   A-fighting for his King,
   And left poor Major André
   On the gallows for to swing.

7. André was executed,
   He looked both meek and mild,
   His face was fair and handsome,
   And pleasantly he smiled.
   It moved each eye with pity,
   And every heart there bled,
   And everyone wished him released
   And Arnold in his stead.

8. He was a man of honor!
   In Britain he was born,
   To die upon the gallows
   Most highly he did scorn.
   And now his life has reached its end
   So young and blooming still—
   In Tappan's quiet countryside
   He sleeps upon the hill.

# Lord Cornwallis's Surrender

In 1780, the decisive campaign of the war got under way. Lord Charles Cornwallis, sent from England to launch a full scale invasion of the South, planned to drive up through the Southern states, summon the loyalists to his standard, and conquer Georgia, the Carolinas, and Virginia one by one.

England's experience in other parts of the country repeated itself, but on a vaster scale. Southern patriots rose against the invader. Southern forest and swamp fighters under Marion, Sumter, and Davidson ambushed foraging parties and cut off supply trains. Nathanael Greene's army remained in the field, battered but unbeaten. Cornwallis found himself among a hostile people. He could win battles, but he could not win the war. Caught up at Yorktown between Washington and his troops by land and de Grasse and the French fleet by sea, he thus came to the same end as Burgoyne. On October 19, 1881, Cornwallis surrendered with his entire army. This catastrophe in effect ended the war. The British army, about six thousand strong, marched out between two lines of American and French troops, grounded arms, and was placed under guard. An American officer described the scene in the New Jersey *Gazette* (November 7) as follows:

> The British officers in general behaved like boys who had been whipped at school; some bit their lips, some pouted, others cried; their round, broad-brimmed hats were well adapted to the occasion, hiding those faces they were ashamed to show. The foreign regiments made a much more military appearance, and the conduct of their officers was far more becoming men of fortitude.

"Lord Cornwallis's Surrender" is a famous contemporary broadside which gives an accurate picture of the scene and captures the mood of American elation. The melody makes the humiliation of the British more complete: it is "The British Grenadiers," one of the proudest marching songs of the British army.

Come all you brave A - mer-i - cans, the

truth to you I'll tell, 'Tis of a sad mis-
for - tune, to Bri - tain late be -
fell; 'Twas all in the heights of York — town, where
can-nons loud did roar; They sum-moned Lord Corn-
wal - lis to fight or else give o'er.

Come all you brave Americans,
    The truth to you I'll tell,
'Tis of a sad misfortune,
    To Britain late befell;
'Twas all in the heights of Yorktown,
    Where cannons loud did roar;
They summoned Lord Cornwallis
    To fight or else give o'er.

The summons then to be served,
    Was sent unto my Lord,
Which made him feel like poor Burgoyne,
    And quickly draw his sword,
Say, must I give these glittering troops,
    These ships and Hessians too,
And yield to General Washington,
    And his bold rebel crew?

A grand council then was called,
  His Lordship gave command,
Say, what think you now my heroes,
  To yield you may depend—
For don't you see the bombshells fly,
  And cannons loud do roar,
Count de Grasse lies in the harbour,
  And Washington's on shore.

'Twas the nineteenth of October,
  In the year of eighty-one,
Lord Cornwallis he surrendered
  To General Washington.
They marched from their posts, brave boys,
  And quickly grounded arms,
Rejoice you brave Americans,
  With music's sweetest charms.

Six thousand chosen British troops
  To Washington resigned,
Besides some ships and Hessians
  That could not stay behind;
With refugees and blackamores,
  Oh, what a direful crew!
It was then he had some thousands,
  But now he's got but few.

Here's a health to great Washington,
  And his brave army too,
And likewise to our worthy Greene,
  To him much honor's due.
May we subdue those English troops,
  And clear the eastern shore,
That we may live in peace, my boys,
  While wars they are no more.

# III

# THE

# EARLY

# NATIONAL

# PERIOD

THE UNITED STATES, after having achieved independence, did not isolate itself from the European civilization of which it was a product. "Isolation" as a traditional American ideal originally expressed by Washington and Hamilton meant isolation only from the *military* conflicts of Europe. As the young nation matured, its links—spiritual, cultural, economic, and technological—with the parent civilization did not diminish, but increased.

The first years of independence, from 1790 to 1814, have been termed by historians "the early national period." American experience during this time vividly illustrates the country's profound involvement with Europe. The United States was then involved in the crisis in which the whole Western world found itself, and its life and thinking reflected that crisis. Only in the context of the international community within which American nationality was developing can we appreciate the meaning of the songs Americans were then writing and singing.

What was this context? In 1789, George Washington was inaugurated first President of the United States in New York City, and in that year the French Revolution began. In 1793, the Bourbon monarchy, symbol of a cruel and dying feudal order, came crashing down, and thrones throughout Europe began to shake. Throughout the Western World, the peoples had begun to glimpse a vision of republican democracy and of freedom from the tyranny of kings; and everywhere they were marching passionately toward their ideal.

Many of the great national songs of this time reflect this new mood, and the songs of the United States are no exception. A new nation had been born in freedom. Its songs in this period were characterized by an exalted national tone, a sometimes boastful self-assurance, and the confidence of youth. Lyrical, passionate, even flowery, they expressed the new style in literature and politics that we call romanticism.

But in Europe, the early dawn was soon darkened by clouds. The French Revolution fell victim to a new monarchist tyranny when Napoleon became first consul in 1800 and made himself Emperor in 1802. A man of boundless ambition, he sought to build an empire through the enslavement of millions of his fellows; and he brought all of Europe under his control or influence. First, he conquered the Germanys and Italy; then, he advanced into Spain, Poland, and Russia. For 13 years, he engaged Great Britain in a life-and-death struggle.

American reaction to this crisis followed a pattern born of the revolutionary experience in the years 1776-1783. France, traditionally, had been America's friend, and Britain its foe. Britain's involvement, furthermore, in an all-out struggle for survival gave the United States a golden opportunity to wrest from the British Empire advantages which the latter was in no position to withhold; the War of 1812 was undertaken precisely for such objectives. The latter included land acquisitions in Canada and Florida, the destruction of British influence among the Indians of the Old Northwest, and the elimination of British interference with American shipping on the high seas, which was considered to be an intolerable affront to an independent power.

Below we reproduce some of the great songs that arose from this war, in which the United States was fighting on Napoleon's side, though not allied with him. The songs reflect not only the national reaction to incidents in the struggle, but also an unabashed admiration of Napoleon, the military genius who had toppled thrones and twisted the British lion's tail with, one might say, an almost American impudence.

The early national era not only produced songs about war-but also songs of protest against the senseless slaughter of human life, which blasted the hopes of youth and wasted a people's most precious resources. One of the very greatest of such songs was an Irish broadside ballad brought to the New World by immigrants; it provides the last song in our selection for this period. The dream of peace it expressed was to be the keynote of American national policy for nearly half a century. America, in the era of construction that was to come, must isolate herself from the brutal realities of European war; she must pursue a policy of peace that would enable her to devote her mighty resources to the building of a strong and civilized state.

# Caitilín Ní Uallacháin
## (Cathaleen Ni Houlihan)

The American Revolution was an event of international significance, the first successful action by a colonial people in the modern world against a foreign power. The Revolution's world-wide impact was both immediate and continuing.

This fact is vividly illustrated by the almost immediate reaction in Eire. The Irish, a people whose land, religion, and national traditions were distinctly their own, had for centuries suffered under and resisted British occupation. By the eighteenth century, Britain's long struggle to fasten her rule upon the entire country had met with final and complete success. Eire was reduced to a colonial dependency, a land whose wealth and vitality were drained by an absentee aristocracy. The poverty and misery in which the mass of her landless people dwelt were, in 1776, eloquent proof of the disheartening effect of colonial status and despotic rule.

But the Irish, though beaten, nursed a stubborn dream of freedom, of deliverance from tyranny. They remembered when Patrick Sarsfield and his warriors had fought Britain with the aid of the Catholic King, James, and the French. One day, they believed, the King's son, James, would return from France across the sea. Then all of Eire would respond to his call, would rise to battle for freedom.

The shot fired at Bunker Hill in 1775, heard around the world, echoed nowhere more loudly than in Eire. In 1798, it triggered a great uprising led by Wolfe Tone, protestant, patriot, and visionary. This struggle ended in failure, but it produced one of the most famous and beautiful of Eire's national songs—*Caitilín ní Uallacháin*. Once there had been a woman so-named, and a love song for her. *Caitilín* now came to symbolize the country, Eire herself. It is a song noteworthy for its flaming spirit, its exalted vision of freedom, its readiness to accept death rather than shame, its identification of the Catholic Irish with the oppressed of all the world as symbolized by Israel.

The Irish failure of 1798 was closely bound up with the destiny of the United States; thereafter, many Irish would emigrate to the New World with the love of liberty in their hearts. Thus, this song, *Caitilín,* casts its luster over the history of the United States in the early national period. For, more than most songs of this time, it reveals to us the exalted national mood then prevailing, the value and the meaning that people then attached to life, and the cause for which a man might sacrifice it.

Our hopes run high, the time is nigh To make the test of war, Our plans are laid, our weapons made, And soon our guns will roar. Let others sleep! We watch will keep To hail a new day's dawn, When the king's son shall be seen with Cath-a-leen Ni Houl-i-han.

Our hated foes must not suppose
    That we shall fear to die,
Though the clouds are dark we still can mark
    God's rainbow in the sky.
As the Red Sea sand became dry land
    When Moses led Israel on,
May Jesus save thee, Cathaleen
    Ni Houlihan!

# Green Grow the Rushes O

Robert Burns has an extraordinary importance in the history of American song. This Scotsman was one of the world's great song writers, who expressed his love of man and life in a host of incomparable lyrics which he wedded to traditional Scots melodies. Burns' creative work and thought illuminate the struggle for freedom in the modern era. Many of his songs—he wrote more than six hundred—were widely sung in the United States during the nineteenth century; they have left an enduring imprint upon American national music.

Burns was born in 1759, the son of an impoverished Ayrshire farmer. He spent his youth toiling on the farm; there burned in his soul a fierce desire for knowledge and a passion for his people's songs. Years of bleak labor were lightened for this hungry youth by the melodies that chased through his head as he followed the plough.

Rejected in love and living in dire poverty, Burns was, in 1786, at the point of emigrating to the New World. But then his first book of poetry was published, and it took his countrymen by storm. For them, Burns epitomized the most exalted aspects of the national, romantic, revolutionary movement of his day: the deep love of country and of man, the simplicity of life, the lyrical apotheosis of the human condition, the hatred of human bondage, and the sense of human equality.

We reproduce here a song, "Green Grow the Rushes O" which represents, in its perfection, the best that Burns ever wrote. As with most of his songs, the lyrics are his own, and the melody is traditional.

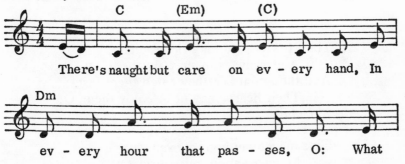

sig - ni - fies the life of man, And
'twere not for the las - ses, O?

REFRAIN

Green__ grow the rush - es, O,
Green__ grow the rush - es, O, The
sweet - est hours__ that e'er are spent, Are
spent a - mong the las - ses, O.

The worldly race may riches chase,
    And riches still may fly them, O;
And though at last they catch them fast,
    Their hearts may ne'er enjoy them, O.
*Refrain*

Give me a quiet hour at even,
    My arms about my dearie, O;
And worldly cares and worldly men,
    May all go topsyturvy, O.
*Refrain*

For you so prim you sneer at this,
    You're naught but senseless asses, O;
The wisest man the world e'er saw,
    He dearly loved the lasses, O.
*Refrain*

Old Nature swears the lovely dears
    Her noblest works she classes, O;
Her prentice hand she tried on man—
    And then she made the lasses, O.
*Refrain*

# Jefferson and Liberty

The Federalist Party, of which George Washington was titular head, made important contributions to American life in the years following the Revolution. The Federalists elaborated the Constitution, secured its ratification, and organized the machinery of the new national government. But in the last decade of the eighteenth century, when they enjoyed uninterrupted control of the presidency and of Congress, the Federalists pursued policies that made them unpopular with large numbers of Americans. Their financial and foreign policies in particular, it was charged, were governed by a narrow and selfishly exclusive class interest.

By 1798, the tide was running strong against the Federalists. In that year, they brought the country to the brink of war with its traditional ally, France; and they passed the Alien and Sedition Acts in order to muzzle opposition to the conflict when it should break out. One of these acts at the very least (the Sedition Act) was unconstitutional and an obvious flouting of the Bill of Rights.

All in all, there was not a little to be said for the charge that Federalist rule had brought down upon the American people those dire evils which Jefferson's followers had predicted would be the consequence of Federalist control of the National government.

"Jefferson and Liberty" is a campaign song that first appeared during the elections of 1800, and it remains one of the most popular campaign songs of American history. It celebrates the simple virtues of Jeffersonian philosophy, elation at the approaching end of Federalist rule, and boundless confidence in the nation's destiny as a free and democratic Republic. This great vision of the American dream is appropriately set to an Irish jig tune with a majestic sweep all its own.

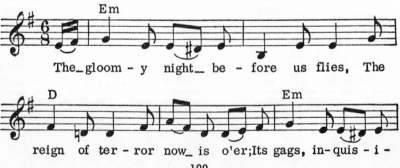

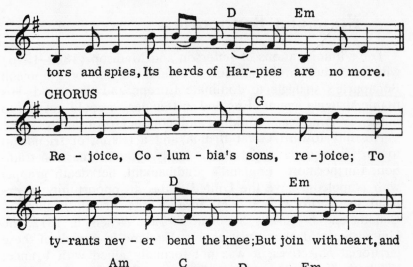

tors and spies, Its herds of Har-pies are no more.

CHORUS

Re - joice, Co - lum - bia's sons, re - joice; To

ty-rants nev - er bend the knee; But join with heart, and

soul and voice, For Jef - fer-son_ and lib - er- ty.

No lordling here with gorging jaws
Shall wring from industry the food,
Nor fiery bigot's holy laws
Lay waste our fields and streets in blood!
*Chorus*

Here strangers from a thousand shores
Compelled by tyranny to roam,
Shall find, amidst abundant stores
A nobler and a happier home.
*Chorus*

Here Art shall lift her laurel'd head,
Wealth, Industry, and Peace divine;
And where dark, pathless forests spread,
Rich fields and lofty cities shine.
*Chorus*

# Napoleon Bonaparte

The administrations of Jefferson and Madison (1800–1816) witnessed the unfolding, and the final climax, of Napoleon Bonaparte's struggle to dominate Europe and the world. His titanic struggle against England in this period could not fail to influence American thinking and conduct profoundly.

Hostility toward Great Britain and a feeling of friendship toward France was, by 1800, a firmly rooted American tradition. Furthermore, England's predicament, her death grapple with Napoleon, gave the United States an opportunity to expand its territory at the expense of the British Empire in Canada and of its ally Spain in Florida. When, in 1812, the United States declared war against England in pursuit of these territorial objectives, it was not formally allied with France; but both Napoleon and the American Republic were simultaneously fighting the same enemy, England, and were thus, in effect, allies. Accordingly, Napoleon became a continuing symbol of America's traditional feeling of friendship for France, a feeling reinforced by the fact that the French dictator had renounced his territorial claims to lands beyond the Mississippi by the Louisiana Purchase agreement of 1803.

In Europe itself, furthermore, Napoleon Bonaparte had been a strangely contradictory force. Wherever his conquering armies marched, tyranny and oppression followed in their wake; but with them had come, almost like an infection, the ideas of the French Revolution. From the safe distance of three thousand miles, Americans might be pardoned if they saw this cruel and dangerous dictator through a romantic haze, if they saw in him no more than the symbol of a revolutionary nation, France, resisting its traditional foe.

It is, therefore, not surprising that the song, "Napoleon Bonaparte," with its sumptuous melody, has been found widespread in North America: in Newfoundland, New England, New York, the South, and the Midwest. It probably originated as a broadside ballad in Eire. Irish admiration for Great Britain's mighty antagonist and the Irish lament for his fallen greatness could not fail, for the reasons given above, to find an echo in the hearts of many Americans.

Now Na - po - leon_ he has done with his
wars and his fight - ing. He has gone to the
land he can take no de - light in. He may
set him down and tell of the bat - tles
he has been in,_ While for - lorn he does
mourn on the isle of St. Hel - e - na.

Louisa does weep for her husband's departing;
She dreams when she sleeps and she wakens broken-hearted.
Not a friend to console or even those who might be with her,
While forlorn she does mourn on the Isle of St. Helena.

The rude rushing waves all around the shores are washing;
Now the high billows roar, on the rough rocks are dashing.
He may look to the moon, to the great mount of Diana,
While forlorn he does mourn on the Isle of St. Helena.

All you that have wealth beware of ambition,
Lest in some degree of health you should change your condition.
Be steadfast in time, for what's to come you know not,
And your days they may end on the Isle of St. Helena.

You Parliaments of war, and your Holy Alliance,
To the prisoner of war you may now bid defiance.
For your base intrigues and your baser misdemeanors,
Have caused him to die on the Isle of St. Helena.

# The Bonny Bunch of Roses O

This song originated as a broadside and is still sung in England, Scotland, and Eire. The fine melody to which it is here set was recorded by Elisabeth B. Greenleaf in Newfoundland in 1929 from the singing of Mrs. Patrick Lahey of Fortune Harbor. That it was highly popular in the United States as well as in Britain is evidenced by its having been reproduced in many songbooks of the early national period, though it apparently has not survived in this country in oral tradition. The lyric reproduced here, a composite of many partial and corrupted texts, illustrates the high quality of poetic feeling and imaginative sweep which the broadside ballad sometimes achieved.

"The Bonny Bunch of Roses O" is cast in the form of a dialogue between Napoleon Bonaparte's son, the Duke of Reichstadt (1811–1832), and his wife, the Empress Marie Louise, after the Emperor's fall from power and exile to St. Helena. The princeling dreams of his future glory, of when he will follow in his father's footsteps and one day take the field against Great Britain, referred to symbolically here as "the bonny bunch of roses." Reichstadt's mother, dreaming wistfully of the glory that was, and will never be again, speaks of the fallen Emperor almost in the same vein that Cleopatra spoke of Mark Anthony:

> In his livery
> Walkt crowns and crownets; realms and islands were
> As plates dropt from his pocket.

By a few swift verses, this song brilliantly condensed the Napoleonic saga, and, for Americans, vividly crystallized the central events of the times in which they lived.

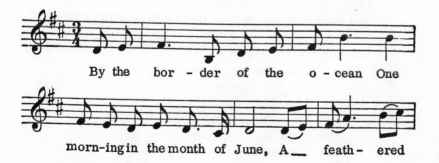

By the bor - der of the o - cean One morn-ing in the month of June, A__ feath - ered

song-ster His cheer-ful notes did sweet-ly tune. There I o-ver-heard a la-dy Who seemed to be in grief and woe, Con-ver-sing with young Bo-na-parte A-bout the Bon-ny Bunch of Ros-es, O.

Then up spoke young Napoleon
    And takes his mother by the hand,
Saying "Mother dear have patience,
    Til I am able to command.
Then I will raise an army
    And through tremendous dangers go,
And I never will return again
    Til I have conquered the Bonny Bunch of Roses O."

"O son, don't be so venturesome,
    For England has a heart of oak:
England, Ireland, Scotland—
    Their unity may not be broke.
Remember your brave father,
    In St. Helena he lies low,
And if you follow after,
    Beware the Bonny Bunch of Roses O."

"When first you saw great Bonaparte,
  You fell upon your bended knee,
You asked your father's blessing,
  He granted it right manfully.
'Dear son,' says he, 'I'll take an army,
  Over the frozen Alps I'll go;
Then I will conquer Moscow
  And return to the Bonny Bunch of Roses O.'

"Your father raised great armies,
  Likewise kings to bear his train,
He was so well provided he
  Could sweep the world for gain.
But when he came to Moscow
  Nigh overpowered by the driving snow,
All Moscow was a-blazing.
  And he lost the Bonny Bunch of Roses O."

"Now do believe me mother,
  For I'm on my dying bed,
If I had lived, I would have been brave,
  Now I droop my youthful head.
But while our bones lie moldering,
  And weeping willows o'er us grow,
The fame of great Napoleon
  Shall shame the Bonny Bunch of Roses O."

Melody from Elisabeth B. Greenleaf and Grace Y. Mansfield, *Ballads and Sea Songs of Newfoundland*, Harvard University Press. Copyright 1933 by the President and Fellows of Harvard College, 1961 by Elisabeth Bristol Greenleaf and Grace Yarrow Mansfield.

# The Constitution and Guerrière

The War of 1812 broke out, ostensibly, over the issue of British interference with American commerce and the need to enforce the fundamental right to freedom of the seas. In permitting this conflict to break out and failing to neutralize United States hostility, British diplomacy committed a serious error; England was, at the time, engaged in a life-and-death struggle with Napoleon and could ill afford another foe. From the American point of view, Madison's declaration of war in July 1812 was equally ill-advised. It rested upon an estimate of the country's preparedness which had no basis in fact; the territorial ambitions of the War Hawks who precipitated the adventure far exceeded their abilities. The inevitable result was two and one-half years of see-saw conflict that humiliated both sides and ended in a stalemate.

The war was indecisive by land, and both sides found solace in the events that occurred at sea. Because the American navy had made considerable progress since the days of Paul Jones, the war at sea was marked by a series of duels between British and American men o' war. These dramatic and colorful engagements, although absolutely indecisive, were diverting, at least to the onlookers. As one commentator has aptly observed:

> The engagements between British and American frigates did little or nothing to settle the final issue of the war. As sporting events, testing the skill and the courage of the combatants and arousing the emotions of the supporters of the ships engaged, they were without equal.*

In early August 1812, Captain Isaac Hull, commanding the U.S. frigate *Constitution,* was cruising in mid-Atlantic, with the general mission of harrying British commerce. When he encountered the English frigate *Guerrière,* commanded by Captain James Dacres, he decided to stand and fight. Dacres unlimbered his guns and fired upon the *Constitution,* but Hull, much to the disgust of his crew, refused to return fire until literally within hailing distance of his antagonist. He then fired a series of broadsides with crushing effect. The *Guerrière* was completely disabled and obliged to surrender. The American vessel was superior to its rival in tonnage and firepower, but news of the victory sent American morale sky high.

*H. F. Beirne, *The War of 1812* (New York: Dutton, 1949), 124.

This was the first time that a British man o' war had struck its colors to an American since the time of Paul Jones.

The Boston broadside commemorating Hull's triumph is one of the best known and remembered of the songs to which the War of 1812 gave rise. Set to the tune of a rousing English drinking song, it expresses to perfection the cocksure Yankee boastfulness of that time.

2. The *Guerrière*, a frigate bold, on the foaming ocean rolled,
   Commanded by Dacres the grandee, O;
   With as proud a British crew as a rammer ever drew,
   They could flog the tars of France so neat and handy, O!

3. Then Dacres loudly cries, "Make this Yankee ship your
         prize,
   You can do it in thirty minutes so neat and handy, O;
   Twenty-five's enough, I'm sure, and if you'll do it in a score,
   I'll treat you to a double tot of brandy, O!"

4. The British shot flew hot, which the Yankees answered not,
   'Til they got within a space they thought was handy, O;
   "Now," Hull says to his crew, "Boys, let's see what you
         can do,
   If we take this boasting Briton we're the dandy, O!"

5. The first broadside we poured swept their mainmast over-
         board,
   Which made this lofty frigate look abandoned, O;
   Then Dacres he did sigh, and to his officers did cry,
   "I did not think these Yankees were so handy, O!"

6. Our second told so well, that their fore and mizzen fell,
   Which doused the royal ensign so neat and handy, O;
   "By George!" says he, "We're done!" and they fired a lee
         gun,
   And the Yankees struck up Yankee Doodle Dandy, O!

7. Now fill your glasses full, let's drink a toast to Captain
         Hull,
   So merrily we'll push around the brandy, O;
   For John Bull may drink his fill, and the world say what
         it will,
   The Yankee tars for fighting are the dandy, O!

# The Chesapeake and the Shannon

Not all these naval engagements turned out so well. In May 1813, Captain Philip Broke, commanding the British frigate *Shannon* then blockading Boston, issued this challenge to Captain James Lawrence, commanding the *Chesapeake:*

As the *Chesapeake* appears now ready for sea, I request you will do me the favor to meet the *Shannon* with her, ship for ship, to try the fortunes of our respective flags.

News of the challenge spread rapidly. On June 1, the day appointed for the contest, crowds thronged the Boston waterfront. By early evening, the two vessels were engaged at point-blank range. Lawrence, mortally wounded, was carried below, and gave his never-forgotten last order, "Don't give up the ship." But the British boarded the *Chesapeake,* struck its colors, and took the prize in tow to Halifax.

Now it was Britain's turn to sing a boastful song, which is reproduced below, to the same tune as "The Constitution and the Guerrière." But the people of Nova Scotia who saw the two vessels coming into port on July 6 did not talk or sing of the engagement. The scenes of mutilation and death which they were obliged to witness had been too frightful.

1.  The Chesapeake so bold, out of Boston as we're told,
    Came to take the British frigate neat and handy, O.
    The people in the port all came out to see the sport
    And the bands played Yankee Doodle Dandy, O.

2   Before this fight begun, the Yankees made such fun,
    Saying "We'll tow her up to Boston so neat and handy, O;
    And after that we'll dine, treat our sweethearts all with
        wine,
    And we'll dance a jig of Yankee Doodle Dandy, O."

3.  Our British frigate's name that for the purpose came
    To cool the Yankees' courage so neat and handy, O
    Was the Shannon—Captain Broke, all his crew had hearts
        of oak
    And in fighting were allowed to be the dandy, O.

4. The action scarce begun when they flinchèd from their
      guns,
   They thought that they had worked us neat and handy, O;
   But Broke he moved his sword saying "Come, my boys,
      we'll board,
   And we'll stop them playing Yankee Doodle Dandy, O."

5. When the Britons heard this word, they quickly sprang on
      board,
   And seized the Yankees' ensign neat and handy, O;
   Notwithstanding all their brags the British raised their
      flags;
   On the Yankees' mizzen-peak they flew so dandy, O.

6. Here's to Broke and all his crew who with courage stout
      and true
   Fought against the Yankee frigate neat and handy, O;
   O may they ever prove, in fighting or in love,
   That the British tars will always be the dandy, O!

# The Hunters of Kentucky

This famous ballad tells the story of the greatest American military triumph of the War of 1812, Andrew Jackson's defeat of the hard-bitten British veterans at the battle of New Orleans on January 8, 1815. Written by Samuel Woodworth shortly after the conclusion of the war, "The Hunters of Kentucky" served as a campaign song during Jackson's first effort to win the presidency in 1824. It became immensely popular during the actual years of Jackson's presidency, 1829–1837. Since this victory was decisive in sending Jackson to the White House, the song also had its share in the making of a President.

Napoleon's defeat in 1814 boded no good for the United States. Britain was now freed from her military commitment in Europe and could therefore give her undivided attention to the American foe. Accordingly, in the summer of 1814, a thrust against Louisiana was planned: to close the mouth of the Mississippi, tie up American commerce, and attempt to re-establish England's territorial power in the heart of the North American continent.

Andrew Jackson, commander of the Seventh Military District, with headquarters at Mobile, was in charge of the military forces in that area. In November, he arrived at New Orleans and personally directed the city's defenses. Fort St. Philip, near the mouth of the Mississippi, was manned; batteries were erected, and a defensive force was assembled. Tennessee and Kentucky riflemen began to arrive shortly before Christmas.

The British, meanwhile, massed at Jamaica for the invasion. A striking force of 10,000 men was stiffened by a corps of hardened veterans from the campaign against Napoleon in Portugal and Spain; Major General Sir Edward Pakenham, a hero of that same Peninsular war, was sent from England to assume command.

The main British thrust toward New Orleans came from the south, up along the bank of the Mississippi between the river and the cypress swamps to the east. Jackson drew up his forces along the Rodriguez Canal, below the city, on a line a little more than half a mile in extent, running east and west, and anchored on one flank by the river and on the other by the swamps. He fortified this line with gun batteries, and awaited the enemy. Jackson's forces were thus disposed squarely across Pakenham's line of march, between the British army and New Orleans.

113

A series of minor skirmishes was climaxed by Pakenham's frontal attack upon the American position at dawn on January 8, 1815. As the morning mists lifted, an unforgettable sight met the eyes of the defenders:

Across the wide plain, in the river haze, moved the British regiments in solid front, their red and white uniforms giving a bold touch of color to the somber lowlands. It was a sight that only a few men in Jackson's army . . . had ever before witnessed. A shout broke from Carroll's troops and was taken up by the Kentuckians. No one could tell whether it was a shout of confidence or one of delight over the spectacle presented by the advancing columns. They came silently, without drumbeat, without firing, into artillery range.*

Armed with Kentucky rifles, the Western marksmen wrought terrible destruction upon these advancing troops. Jackson inflicted over 2,000 casualties upon the British at a cost of only 21 dead to himself. The ballad reproduced here is a masterpiece of understatement which gives little hint of the grimness of the engagement. But as a serious account of the experience from the viewpoint of the victor, it is not very far from the truth. Men who had survived the inconceivable hardships and horrors of Wellington's Peninsular campaign were broken by the small arms fire of the Tennessee and Kentucky militia.

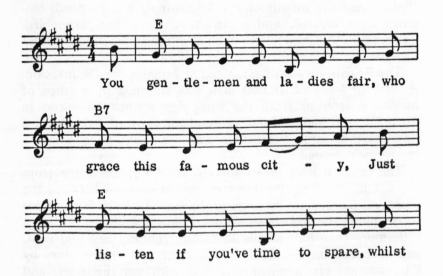

You gen-tle-men and la-dies fair, who grace this fa-mous cit-y, Just lis-ten if you've time to spare, whilst

*Glenn Tucker, *Poltroons and Patriots* (New York: Bobbs, Merrill, 1954), II, 699.

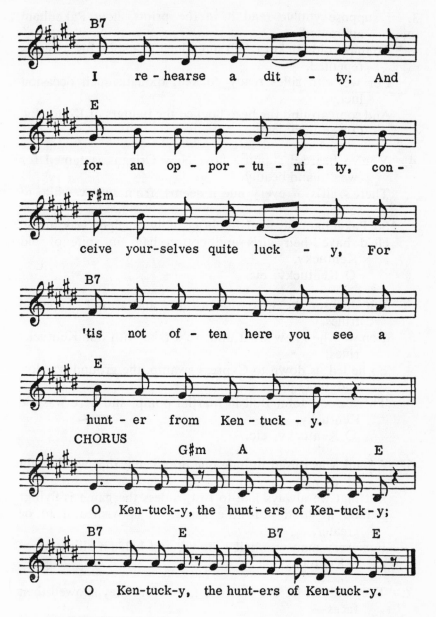

I re-hearse a dit-ty; And for an op-por-tu-ni-ty, con-ceive your-selves quite luck-y, For 'tis not of-ten here you see a hunt-er from Ken-tuck-y.

CHORUS

O Ken-tuck-y, the hunt-ers of Ken-tuck-y; O Ken-tuck-y, the hunt-ers of Ken-tuck-y.

2. We are a hardy freeborn race, each man to fear a stranger,
   Whate'er the game we join the chase, despising toil and
       danger;
   And if a daring foe annoys, whatever his strength and
       forces,
   We'll show him that Kentucky boys are "alligator horses."
       O Kentucky, etc.

3. I suppose you've read it in the prints, how Pakenham attempted
   To make old Hickory Jackson wince, but soon his schemes repented,
   For we with rifles ready cocked, thought such occasion lucky,
   And soon around the hero flocked the hunters of Kentucky,
      O Kentucky, etc.

4. You've heard I suppose how New Orleans is famed for wealth and beauty.
   There's girls of every hue it seems, from snowy white to sooty,
   So Pakenham he mad his brag, if he in fight was lucky,
   He'd have their girls and cotton bags in spite of old Kentucky,
      O Kentucky, etc.

5. But Jackson he was wide awake, and wasn't scared at trifles,
   For well he knew what aim we'd take with our Kentucky rifles;
   So he led us down to Cypress swamp, the ground was low and mucky,
   There stood John Bull in martial pomp, and here was old Kentucky,
      O Kentucky, etc.

6. A bank was raised to hide our breast, not that we thought of dying,
   But that we always like to rest, unless the game is flying:
   Behind it stood our little force: none wished it to be greater,
   For every man was half a horse, and half an alligator,
      O Kentucky, etc.

7. They did not let our patience tire before they showed their faces—
   We did not choose to waste our fire, but snugly kept our places;
   And when so near to see them wink, we thought 'twas time to stop 'em;
   And 'twould have done you good, I think, to see Kentuckians drop 'em.
      O Kentucky, etc.

116

8. They found at last 'twas vain to fight when lead was all
       their booty,
   And so they wisely took to flight, and left us all our beauty,
   And now if danger e'er annoys, remember what our trade
       is,
   Just send for us Kentucky boys, and we'll protect you,
       ladies,
       O Kentucky, etc.

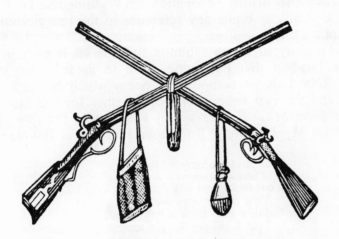

# Johnny Bull, My Jo, John

"Johnny Bull" began life as a broadside ballad shortly after the termination of the War of 1812. That it was reprinted and appeared in a number of collections in succeeding years indicates that the song enjoyed a measure of popularity. We may think of it as a brilliant recapitulation of the war from the American viewpoint; it stresses the American national achievement, puts the best face possible on disgraceful episodes like the British occupation of Washington, D. C., in 1813, and quietly omits any reference to the less glorious aspects of the military effort.

The melody to which "Johnny Bull" is set is perhaps one of the loveliest that has come down to us from the olden days. Robert Burns composed a poem which he set to this tune, and the two were published together for the first time in the *Scots Musical Museum* in 1790 under the title "John Anderson My Jo, John." Burns's version ran as follows:

> John Anderson my jo, John,
>   When we were first acquent,
> Your locks were like the raven,
>   Your bonny brow was brent;
> But now your brow is bald, John,
>   Your locks are like the snow,
> But blessings on your frosty pow,
>   John Anderson my jo!
>
> John Anderson my jo, John,
>   We clamb the hill together;
> And many a cantie [merry] day, John,
>   We've had wi' ane another:
> But we maun totter down, John,
>   And hand in hand we'll go,
> And sleep together at the foot,
>   John Anderson, my jo!

Such was the musical and lyrical inspiration for the American version of the song.

O,— John - ny Bull, my jo John, I—

won-der what you mean; Are__ you on for-eign con-quest bent, or what am-bi-tious scheme? Now list to broth-er Jon-a-than, your fruit-less plans fore-go, Re-main on your fast-an-chored isle, O__ John-ny Bull, my jo.

O Johnny Bull, my jo, John, don't come across the main;
Our fathers bled and suffered, John, our freedom to maintain,
And him who in the cradle, John, repelled the ruthless foe,
Provoke not when to manhood grown, O Johnny Bull, my jo.

O Johnny Bull, my jo, John, on Erie's distant shores,
See how the battle rages, and loud the cannon roars;
But Perry taught our seamen to crush the assailing foe,
He met and made them ours, O Johnny Bull, my jo.

What though at Washington a base marauding band,
Our monuments of art, John, destroyed with ruthless hand?
It was a savage warfare, beneath a generous foe,
And brings the more disgrace on you, O Johnny Bull my jo.

O Johnny Bull my jo, John, when all your schemes have failed,
To wipe away the stigmas, John, for New Orleans you sailed;

Far heavier woes await thee John, for Jackson meets the foe,
Whose name and fame's immortal, O Johnny Bull, my jo.

Your schemes to gather laurels here I guess were badly planned;
We have whipped you on the ocean, jo, we have bothered you
  on land:
Then hie thee to old England, John, thy fruitless plans forego,
And haste to thy fast-anchored isle, O Johnny Bull, my jo.

# Mrs. McGrath

During the Napoleonic Era, war was practically continuous. Everywhere in the Western world the cruelty, waste, and inhumanity of war was borne home to millions of people; and it is no accident that a movement for the abolition of war as an instrument of national policy arose in the years immediately following the conclusion of peace in 1815. The peace movement of that day was to constitute an important part of the humanitarian crusade for social reform that gave dignity and meaning to the Jacksonian era.

One of the most poignant judgments upon war and all its works was delivered in the broadside ballad. "Mrs. McGrath," that appeared upon the Dublin streets as early as 1815 and has been sung in Eire ever since. In these years of British rule, poverty-stricken Irish—landless, starving, and oppressed—were forced to become mercenaries of many European powers, including, ironically enough, England, the national enemy. "Mrs. McGrath" expresses the tragedy of a young man mutilated while fighting for the King of England with Wellington in the famous Peninsular Campaign of 1808–1814. This campaign, it will be remembered, was one phase of the huge struggle then being waged with Napoleon.

The dramatic irony, the human sympathy, and the simple lyric of "Mrs. McGrath" illustrate the effectiveness of the broadside ballad at its very best.

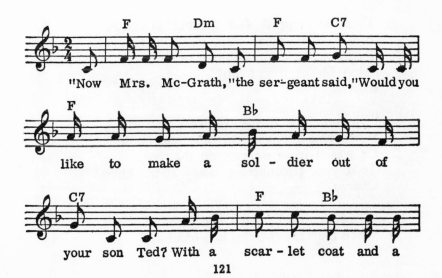

"Now Mrs. Mc-Grath," the ser-geant said, "Would you like to make a sol-dier out of your son Ted? With a scar-let coat and a

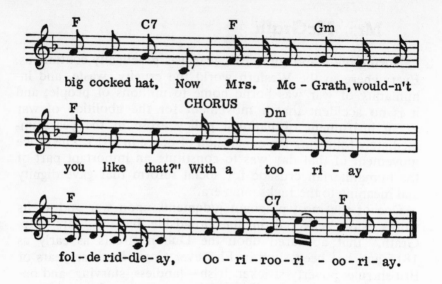

big cocked hat, Now Mrs. Mc - Grath, would-n't

CHORUS

you like that?" With a too - ri - ay

fol - de rid-dle-ay, Oo - ri - roo - ri - oo - ri - ay.

So Mrs. McGrath lived by the seashore
For the space of seven long years or more,
Till a great big ship came a-sailing in the bay:
"Oh it's my son Ted who's been so long away!"
*Chorus*

"Oh captain dear, where have you been,
Have you been a-sailing on the Mediterreen?
And have you any news of my son Ted,
Is the poor boy living, or is he dead?"
*Chorus*

Then up stepped Ted without any legs,
And in their place were two wooden pegs;
She kissed him a dozen times or two,
"Holy Moses, it isn't you!"
*Chorus*

"Oh were you drunk, or were you blind,
When you left your two fine legs behind:
Or was it from walking on the seas,
Took your two fine legs away at the knees?"
*Chorus*

"I wasn't drunk, and I wasn't blind,
When I left my two fine legs behind;

But a cannon ball on the fifth of May
Tore my two fine legs at the knees away."
*Chorus*

"Teddy my dear," the widow cried,
"Your two fine legs were your mother's pride;
These two stumps of a tree won't do at all,
Why didn't you flee from the big cannon ball?"
*Chorus*

"All foreign wars I do proclaim
Against Napoleon and the King of Spain;
And by Heaven, I'll make them rue the time,
When they took the legs from a child of mine,"
*Chorus*

# IV

# JACKSONIAN

# AMERICA

THE END OF THE WAR OF 1812 marked the beginning of a new period in American history. The American people could now devote their full energies and attention to settling and developing the continent which they had won. Thus, 1815 marks the start of an era of unprecedented expansion, which continued in full swing until 1848. This period, 1815–1848, had a unity and a quality of its own, which entitle us to label it "Jacksonian." It possessed many of the attributes associated with Jacksonian democracy: raw materialism, driving expansion, but also generous enthusiasms and reforming zeals. Americans achieved a sense of stability derived from pride in their past and a feeling of abounding confidence in the future. This, of course, would change after 1848 and give way to a vastly different mood. For in the fifties, there was a growing preoccupation with the slavery crisis and a growing conviction of the inevitability of civil war.

In Jacksonian America, national development assumed a sectional form. A single nation was growing, developing, evolving; but it was organized into three clearly differentiated sections, or regions, each with its own distinct patterns of social, political, and economic life.

In the Northeast, the first decisive steps were taken, during this period, toward industrialization. The countryside was beginning to be transformed. Factories were established, canals dug, and railroads built; swarms of immigrants were brought in to do construction work and to man the new machines. In the West, pioneers began to move rapidly toward the Mississippi Valley, pushing back the Indians and founding new states as they went, then leaping across the High Plains into California and Oregon. A new community of free farmers was coming into being to provide wheat for the industrial East and for the world.

In the South, slavery reached its height. Jefferson, years earlier, had dreamed of the day when the slaves would be emancipated and sent back to Africa, leaving the Southland, even as the West, for settlement by free and prosperous white farmers. But with the industrial revolution and its bottomless demand for raw cotton, slavery acquired a new lease on life as slaveowners hastened to move their black chattels into the rich new lands of the Southwest.

The Jacksonian period achieved a deep and abiding expression in the singing of the American people. Each main region—North, West, South—produced new songs which reflected and gave expression to the distinctive features of its own sectional life. America was singing now of its experience and destiny in accents unmistakably American. The old songs, of course, continued to be sung, but new lyrics were being composed, and the nation's musical resources were being marvelously enriched. Immigrants, pouring in, brought their own special contributions with them; and, in the South, the Negro people were creating a new and uniquely American musical idiom that was already beginning to feed back into the singing of white America.

In the following chapter, we shall be concerned with the development of the different aspects of national singing in each of the great sections of the country, taken one by one.

# Sea and Immigration

The period 1814–1860 was the climactic age of sail, an epoch in which American square riggers scoured the world in pursuit of trade and established a reputation for being the swiftest and loveliest vessels afloat. The great opportunities which opened up for the merchant marine during this period were a direct result of the Revolution, which had freed United States commerce from the straitjacket of British domination and laid the globe itself open to American searfaring enterprise. Northerners were not slow to exploit this opportunity. British mercantile policy had fostered the shipbuilding industry in colonial days; a hardy race of skilled seamen, whalermen, and shipbuilders had developed as a result of dozens of harbors sprung up along the navigable rivers and coasts of New England and New York.

Young people, in the age of the square rigger, were lured to sea by the glittering image of adventure and romance which it presented. Here is the testimony of Richard Henry Dana, a Harvard student who served as an ordinary seaman on the merchant ships *Pilgrim* and *Alert* in the years 1834–1836 and recorded his experiences in the classic *Two Years before the Mast*:

There is a witchery in the sea, its songs and stories, and in the mere sight of a ship, and the sailor's dress, especially to a young mind, which has done more to man navies, and fill merchantmen, than all the press-gangs of Europe. I have known a young man with such passion for the sea that the very creaking of a block stirred up his imagination so that he could hardly keep his feet on dry ground; and many are the boys, in every seaport, who are drawn away, as by an almost irresistible attraction, from their work and schools, and hang about the decks and yards of vessels, with a fondness which, it is plain, will have its way.

But the beauty of sail, the grace of a ship's motion, and the boundless expanse of sea and stars and sky—all this was a painted veil. Beyond it lay agonies of toil and heartbreak. "No sooner," continued Dana, "has the young sailor begun his life in earnest, then all this fine drapery falls off, and he learns that it is but work and hardship, after all. *This is the true light in which a sailor's life is to be viewed.*"*

*Two Years before the Mast* (New York: Bantam Books, 1959), 320. Italics not in original.

Manning the great sailing vessels of Dana's time was back-breaking toil. The seaman's calling was especially dangerous, and the whalerman faced a whole series of additional perils inseparable from the hunting of whales and the processing of their carcasses. Voyages lasted for months, sometimes for years. Men had to cope with the despair and homesickness engendered by prolonged periods of exile from native land and loved ones.

Life at sea, as we might expect, produced songs fulfilling a central function in the existence of the people involved. The songs these men created and sang and taught to each other helped them to face and overcome dire, daily peril, to undergo backbreaking toil, to cope with monotony and boredom, to summon inspiration for life from the bottom of their souls, and, above all, to work together.

Again, as might be expected, British and American sea songs had a close affinity to each other, and many of the same ones, with appropriate variations, were sung on board both British and American ships. Though the age of sail has vanished many of the songs to which it gave rise have come down to us. Many seem to possess a mysterious inner life all of their own. They are imbued with a strange sense of the surge of the sea, and of its vastness. Often, they express the sailor's deep inner sadness, the yearning for home, the bitterness that a man feels at scorn and abuse, the immediacy of death.

Seamen sang many songs, and many different kinds of song. Although some were reserved for special occasions or for certain types of work, there were, for the most part, no hard and fast barriers: The same song might be pressed into different kinds of service at different times. But, once this is clearly understood, it is still helpful to divide sea songs, in the most general kind of way, into *shanties* and *fo'c'sle* (forecastle) songs. The shanties are that very large group of songs used as work songs, to help in the performance of a sailor's tasks on, above, or below decks, and at the rowing of the ship's boats. Fo'c'sle songs—or forebitters—were sung in the crew's quarters during watch below, on deck during dogwatches, or during other spells of leisure time. Their purpose was recreational.

The shanties, or work songs, arose out of the requirements of hard physical labor. Such work, if steadily and rhythmically performed, does not exhaust to nearly the same degree as labor devoid of rhythmic flow. Rhythm, when the work is undertaken by gangs, plays the additional role of enabling the group to pull together as one.

An incredible amount of backbreaking labor had to be performed in the course of a single sea voyage. Cargo and supplies had to be loaded, stowed below decks, and unloaded, and this was done by the crew working as a gang with block and tackle. Ballast had to be taken on and dumped off; the heavy cast-iron anchors had to be hove up and let down, a job that, before the coming of steam, could only be performed by gang labor at the capstan. Much work had to be done high above the deck, in the ship's rigging: Sails had to be set, reefed, furled, and bunted in an endless, Sisyphean labor, as the wind conditions changed. The deck itself had to be sanded daily and swabbed for an hour or so at daybreak; the pumps had to be manned and the bilge pumped out both in fair weather and foul. Here again, in the days before steam, the energy was provided by gangs of men pulling at the long pump handles or hauling on ropes attached to the pump's twin flywheels; sails had to be bent on and hauled into position by means of a complex array of sheets, halyards, bowlines, buntlines, and downhauls. All of this work was physically exhausting, and much of it was difficult and dangerous—like hauling on the sheet on the leeward side of a heeling ship with decks awash, or furling the topgallants in an icy gale.

In the course of a long voyage, not only the ship itself, but also the ship's *boats* absorbed vast amounts of labor. This was almost as true for regular merchant ships as it was for whalers. In both situations, the crew was obliged to spend days, weeks, and even months at the oars. Here, again, songs were indispensable, and these boatsongs were as much shanties as anything sung on board the ship itself. Telling of the collection and unloading of hides on the California coast, Dana says:

> The next day the *California* began unloading her cargo; and her boats' crews, in coming and going, sang their boatsongs, keeping time with their oars. This they did all day long for several days, until their hides were all discharged. . . .

Shanties were sung, almost without exception, without instrumental accompaniment. The human voice and the human soul stood unaided against the elements. But the same did not hold for the sailor's recreational songs. On the old sailing vessels, the entire crew was divided into two watches. All hands would be on deck between noon and 8:00 p.m.; thereafter, they would have "watch and watch," that is, alternate spells of deck duty and "watch below." During "watch below," a man was not off duty. He might be called on deck any moment for an emergency in which his help was needed; but, if all went well, the men would have leisure then, on Sundays, and during twilight hours on deck, for sleep, mending of clothes, reading, and singing.

The songs used on such occasions have been called fo'c'sle songs. A sailor's repertoire might include shanties, with whatever modifications seemed appropriate, but also ballads, sentimental ditties, love songs, or anything else that Jack might have learned on shore and brought to sea with him for diversion. The usual instrumental accompaniment was a fiddle or harmonica.

Below we reproduce a small selection of the great and beautiful heritage of song left us from the era of sail, as an introduction to the nature and meaning of seafaring life at that time.

*       *       *       *

One of the major achievements of the American merchant marine in this period, seconded by the British, was the transportation of some four million immigrants to North America. The speed of this operation, the numbers of people involved, and the distance they moved characterize it as one of the greatest movements of peoples which history, until that time, had seen.

This period of immigration is known to historians as "the old immigration" to distinguish it from the even greater flood of humanity that arrived upon American shores in the period 1885–1917. The peoples of the old immigration came from Western Europe, primarily from the British Isles, Eire, Western Germany, and Scandinavia. The musical implications of this were, in the long run, to prove significant. The American musical heritage began to receive a massive infusion of materials not only in English but in other European tongues.

We have chosen to focus upon the Irish as a people whose story is in many ways representative of that of other immigrant peoples, in many ways *typical* of people whose musical contribution was created in a foreign tongue. And, as we have seen, Eire's story, her people, and her music, had become intertwined with American history almost from the beginning.

The Irish, at the opening of the nineteenth century, faced

a bleak future. They might starve slowly on their miserable plots, seek jobs in British textile factories, join the British Army—or they might emigrate. The new Republic in America, the United States, had kicked over the British traces. It was a symbol of equality and freedom. Above all, it offered jobs and bread. Thus, when peace came in 1815, Irish began to stream to New York and New England to dig canals, build railroads, and man cotton factories.

In 1846, famine came to Eire and the stream of emigration turned into a flood. The mass of the Irish people were so poor that only the potato patch stood between them and starvation. But the potato's yield was uncertain. In 1845, the rot set in and did not run its course until 1850. In that five year period, over one and one-quarter million Irish died of cold, hunger, and disease. Over one and one-half million Irish left their native land forever; most of them came to Canada and to the United States. In the following pages, we reproduce a few of the exquisite songs that these people brought with them in the steerage, which express the beauty of their heritage, the sorrow of their life, and the yearning for a happier future. These Irish songs, as we shall see later, were destined to find their way to the remotest corners of the Union.

# Haul on the Bowline

This is one of the oldest, best-known, and best-loved, of the "short haul" shanties, used whenever a short, sharp, powerful pull was needed. The bowline was a rope with an important function on the square sails of medieval ships, but it retained its popularity, over the years, for other short hauls. Simple as it is, the melody conveys a powerful rhythmic thrust. Accent and action are both concentrated on the final *"haul!"*

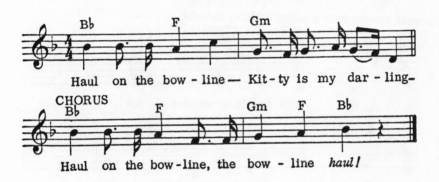

Haul on the bow-line— Kit-ty is my dar-ling—
Haul on the bow-line, the bow-line *haul!*

Haul on the bowline—Kitty comes from Liverpool
*Chorus*
Haul on the bowline—so early in the morning
*Chorus*
Haul on the bowline—the bully mate is snarling
*Chorus*
Haul on the bowline—haul for better weather
*Chorus*
Haul on the bowline—we'll either break or bend her
*Chorus*
Haul on the bowline—the bully ship's a-rolling
*Chorus*
Haul on the bowline—it's a long time to pay day
*Chorus*

# Blood-red Roses

This is a halyard shanty, a type of song used when a steady, intermittent pull was needed, as in hoisting the heavy yards (spars) upon which many of a square-rigger's sails were bent. The hands took their places at the rope, the shantyman, or leader, yelled out the solo, and, as the men came in on the refrain, they hauled with a will. There were two hauls to each refrain. Before the men had finished hauling and singing, the high-pitched cry of the leader would again be heard, giving out on the next line of the song.

SOLO

Our boots and clothes are all in pawn,

CHORUS

Go down, you blood - red ros - es,

SOLO

go down! And it's might - y draft - y

CHORUS

round Cape Horn, Go down, you blood - red ros - es,

SOLO

go down! Oh, you pinks and po - sies,

CHORUS

Go down, you blood-red ros - es, go down!

*Solo*
1. Our boots and clothes are all in pawn
   *Chorus*
   Go down, you blood-red roses, go down!
   *Solo*
   And it's mighty drafty round Cape Horn
   *Chorus*
   Go down, you blood-red roses, go down!
   *Solo*
   Oh, you pinks and posies
   *Chorus*
   Go down, you blood-red roses, go down!
   *Solo*
   Oh, you pinks and posies
   *Chorus*
   Go down, you blood-red roses, go down!

2. You've had your advance and to sea must go
   *Chorus*
   Chasing whales through the frost and snow
   *Chorus*
   Oh, you pinks and posies
   *Chorus*
   Oh, you pinks and posies
   *Chorus*

3. My old mother, she wrote to me
   *Chorus*
   "My dearest son, come home from sea."
   *Chorus*
   Oh, you pinks and posies
   *Chorus*
   Oh, you pinks and posies
   *Chorus*

4. But around Cape Horn we all must go
   *Chorus*
   Round Cape Horn through the ice and snow
   *Chorus*
   Oh, you pinks and posies
   *Chorus*
   Oh, you pinks and posies
   *Chorus*

133

5. Round Cape Horn we all must go
   *Chorus*
   For that is where the whalefish blow
   *Chorus*
   Oh, you pinks and posies
   *Chorus*
   Oh, you pinks and posies
   *Chorus*

6. Just one more pull and that will do
   *Chorus*
   For we're the bullies to kick her through
   *Chorus*

# Leave Her, Johnny, Leave Her

This song, with its soaring chorus, was usually sung as a capstan shanty at the end of a voyage. While entering port and "warping" the vessel alongside the dock, the sailor had the privilege of unloading his feelings about the captain, the mates, the owners, the ship, and the treatment that he had received aboard. Such sentiments, uttered during the course of the voyage itself, would have earned him a flogging or irons. "Leave Her, Johnny, Leave Her," provided the musical form for the seaman's final gripes. It is reproduced here with a few of the seemingly endless verses. Without the full chorus and using only the more discreet verses, the song might also be sung at sea as a halyard shanty.

An immigrant version, evidently inspired by the sailor's, is given on page 150.

leave her, John - ny, leave her! For the
voy-age is done, and the winds don't blow, And it's
time for us to leave her.

She would not wear, and she would not stay,
*Chorus* Leave her, Johnny, leave her!
She shipped great seas both night and day,
*Chorus* And it's time for us to leave her.

*Full Chorus*

It was rotten meat and weevily bread
*Chorus* Leave her, Johnny, leave her!
Eat it or starve, the Old Man said,
*Chorus* And it's time for us to leave her.

*Full Chorus*

Oh the winds were foul and the work was hard,
*Chorus* Leave her, Johnny, leave her!
From Liverpool dock to the Brooklyn yard,
*Chorus* And it's time for us to leave her.

*Full Chorus*

The sails are all furled and the work is all done,
*Chorus* Leave her, Johnny, leave her!
And homeward now we've made our run,
*Chorus* And it's time for us to leave her.

*Full Chorus*

I thought I heard the Old Man say,
*Chorus*   Leave her, Johnny, leave her!
Tomorrow you will get your pay,
Chorus   And it's time for us to leave her.

*Full Chorus*

Now it's time for us to say goodbye,
*Chorus*   Leave her, Johnny, leave her!
The old pierhead is drawing nigh,
*Chorus*   And it's time for us to leave her.

*Full Chorus*

# The Golden Vanity

One of the oldest and most familiar of the traditional songs, "The Golden Vanity" survives on both sides of the Atlantic in dozens of variants. Among ordinary seamen, it was a favorite at both capstan and pump, for it expressed the truth of life at sea: the heroism of sailors, the tyranny of command, the ever-present mystery of the ocean.

Oh, we had a little cabin boy, and boldly up spoke he,
And he said to the captain, "What will you give me,
If I'll swim alongside of the Spanish enemy,
And I sink her in the lowland, lowland low,
     If I sink her in the lowland sea?"

"Of gold and silver I will give you fee,
And my only daughter your bonny bride to be,
If you'll swim alongside of the Spanish enemy
And you sink them in the lowland, lowland, low,
     If you sink them in the lowland sea."

Then the boy bared his breast and overboard sprang he,
And he swam til he came to the Spanish enemy,
Then with his auger sharp in her sides he bored holes three,
And he sank her in the lowland, lowland low,
     He sank her in the lowland sea.

Now some were playing at cards and some were playing at dice,
And some were sitting by giving very good advice,
Until the salt water it flashed into their eyes,
And it sank them in the lowland, lowland low,
     It sank them in the lowland sea.

Then the boy swam back to the cheering of the crew
But the captain would not heed him, for his promise he did rue,
And he scorned his proud entreaties, though full loudly he did
     sue,
And he left him in the lowland, lowland low,
     He left him in the lowland sea.

So the boy swam round til he came to the larboard side,
And to his messmates bitterly he cried,
"Oh messmates pick me up, for I'm drifting with the tide,
And I'm sinking in the lowland, lowland low,
     I'm sinking in the lowland sea."

Then his messmates took him up, and upon the deck he died,
And they sewed him in his hammock, which was so large and
     wide,
And they lowered him overboard, and he drifted with the tide,
And he sank beneath the lowland, lowland low,
     He sank beneath the lowland sea.

# Off to Sea Once More

In the whole range of sea songs that have survived from the age of sail few capture the sailor's mood more effectively than "Off to Sea Once More." Ashore at the end of a long voyage, the sailor has fallen prey to landsharks, both male and female, who have battened upon him and stripped him of his hard-earned, meager pay. In a strange port, without money or friends, he has only one recourse: to go to sea once more. The song, like those of a later day that recount the miner's woes, ends on a theme of warning.

The surge of the sea and the motion of the ship's deck, which do not leave the sailor, even when he is ashore, are echoed here. "Off to Sea Once More" has been found in many variations among British and American seamen, and has been collected on both sides of the Atlantic—in Nova Scotia, Maine, England, and Scotland.

When first I came to Liv-er-pool, I went up-on the spree, My mon-ey at last I spent it fast, got drunk as drunk could be; And when my mon-ey it was all gone, ah, then I want-ed more, For a man must be blind to

140

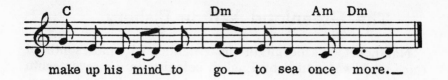

make up his mind to go to sea once more.

2. That night I slept with Angeline, too drunk to roll in bed;
   Me watch was new, and me money too, in the morning
       with 'em she'd fled;
   And as I roamed the streets about, the whores they all
       did roar,
   "There goes Jack Rack, poor sailor lad, he must go to sea
       once more!"

3. I shipped on board of a whaling ship bound for the
       Arctic seas,
   Where the cold wind blows through the frost and snow,
       and Jamaica rum would freeze;
   And worst of all I had no gear, for I'd lost all me
       money ashore,
   Oh, it's then that I wished that I was dead so I'd go
       to sea no more.

4. Some days we were catching whales, me lads, and some
       days we were catching none,
    With a twenty foot oar stuck into our hands from four
       o'clock in the morn,
   And when the shades of night come on, we'd rest on
       our weary oars,
   It was then that I wished that I was dead or safe
       with the gals ashore.

5. Come all ye bold seafaring men, and listen to my song;
   When you come off from your long trips, I'd have you
       not go wrong,
   Take my advice, drink no strong drink, don't
       go roaming on the shore,
   But get married lads, and have all night in, and go
       to sea no more!

# The Greenland Whale Fishery

Nantucket, a sandspit in the Atlantic, 25 miles south of Cape Cod, was settled by English colonists in the seventeenth century. There was no wealth in its barren soil: for two centuries, from the time the English first came there until the Civil War, Nantucket's life was linked with seafaring and the whale fishery. The whale was the island's sole source of livelihood and wealth. Its Quaker people became famous the world over as among the most daring and resourceful seamen the world has seen.

First they killed stranded whales washed up upon their shores—an art the Indians taught them. Then they built schooners and ventured into the seas around; then they cruised north to Greenland and south to the Falklands and ranged the wide Atlantic for their quarry. After the Revolution, they rounded Cape Horn and roamed the vast Pacific from the Bering Strait to the Antarctic, from the Sea of Japan to 'Frisco Bay.

What led the whalemen to the Pacific was the search for the aristocrat of whales, the leviathan of the seas, the sperm. Sperm whales might grow to as much as 100 feet in length, and might weigh as much as ten tons. Killing this monster was a risky business, but the profits were proportionately high. Until the Civil War, the sperm was our principal source of artificial light. Sperm candles, veritable jewels of light, were made from the limpid oil found by the hundred gallons in the whale's head. From his blubber, the casing of fat around the body, huge quantities of oil were extracted to light lamps, lubricate machinery, and process leather.

Until the Revolution, England provided the principal market for Nantucket's oil and candles, but by 1820 the American demand had skyrocketed. Other New England ports, of which the greatest was New Bedford, rushed in to compete with the islanders for the fortunes to be made from this trade. The great age of American whaling had begun.

Once a ship arrived at the hunting grounds, a lookout was set, and the mastheads were manned from sunrise to sundown. Turn and turn about, the crew members stood at the crosstrees, far above the deck and scanned the wide circle of the sea for the telltale spout of the whale when he surfaced, the fluke flung heavenward when he breached. When a whale was sighted, the ship's boats were lowered from their davits. The men took their appointed places and rowed off with harpoons and lances ready for the fray. Indians and Negroes made the most skilled and daring harpooners. The steel barb, mounted on a hardwood shaft, had to be hurled 20 or 30 feet into the side of the whale.

A struck whale might race off across the sea, dragging the boat behind him; or he might turn upon his tormentors and smash their cockleshell in his jaws. Once the whale was killed, in a horrible flurry of gushing blood and boiling spray, and towed alongside, the ship was converted into a factory at sea. The blubber was removed from the carcass, cut up and "tried out"; the precious oil was poured into barrels and stowed away in the hold. An average whale might yield 40 or 50 barrels; the whole process might have to be repeated many times, over a period of months, before the hold was filled, and the ship could weigh anchor and head for home.

"The Greenland Whale Fishery" is a fo'c'sle ballad of English origin, evidently old, since British whalemen were fishing in Greenland waters centuries before Yankees headed for the Pacific. A swift and dramatic statement of whaling life, the song was much loved by American whalemen, who sang it with their own modifications of verse and melody.

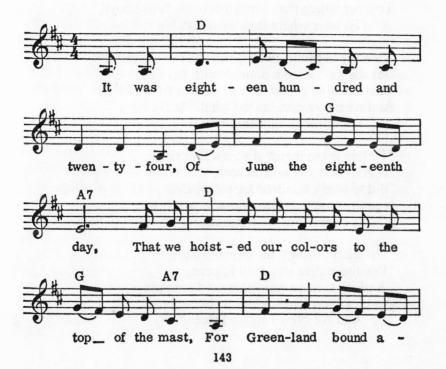

It was eight - een hun - dred and twen - ty - four, Of__ June the eight - eenth day, That we hoist - ed our col - ors to the top__ of the mast, For Green-land bound a -

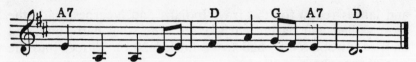

way, brave boys, For‗ Green-land bound a - way.

The lookout at the crosstrees stood,
With a spyglass to his eye,
"There's a whale, there's a whale, there's a whalefish,"
    he cried
"She blows on every hand, brave boys,
    She blows on every hand."

The captain stood at the quarter deck,
And the ice was in his eye,
"Overhaul, overhaul, let your davit tackles fall,
And lower your boats to the seas, brave boys,
    And lower your boats to the seas."

Now the boats got down and the men aboard,
And that whale was still in view,
Resolved, resolved was each whalerman bold,
To steer where that whalefish blew, brave boys,
    To steer where that whalefish blew.

Now the harpoon struck, and the line played out,
But she gave such a flourish with her tail,
That the boat capsized, and we lost four men,
And we never caught that whale, brave boys,
    We never caught that whale.

"To lose those men," the captain cried,
"It grieves my heart full sore,"
"But to lose a hundred barrel whale,
It grieves me ten times more, brave boys,
    It grieves me ten times more."

"Up anchor now," the captain said,
"For the winter star doth appear,
"And it's time to leave this cold cold place,
And for New England steer, brave boys,
    And for New England steer."

# The Banks of Newfoundland

This magnificent foc's'le song and capstan shanty is a saga
of the hardships of the North Atlantic passage, of its howling
gales and storms that inflicted dreadful suffering upon immigrant and sailor alike. Irish sailors, like those mentioned in
the song, served on both the British and the American packet
ships that plied from Liverpool and were in stiff competition
with each other for the transatlantic immigrant trade. "The
Banks of Newfoundland," as might be expected, was popular
on both British and American ships. It captures the spirit of
the roaring winds blowing incessantly through the mountainous spray and the shrouds.

My bul - ly boys of Liv - er - pool, I'd
have you to be - ware,_When you sail on a Yan-kee
pack - et ship, no_ dun - ga - ree jump - ers
wear;_ But have a big mon - key jack-et_ al -
ways at your_com - mand,_For there blows some cold nor'-
west - ers on the_ Banks_of New-found - land._

**CHORUS**

We'll scrape her and we'll scrub her___ With ho-ly—stone and sand,___ And we'll think of the cold nor'-west-ers on the ___ Banks___ of New-found-land.___

2. We had Mike Lynch from Ballynahinch, Pat Murphy
   and some more;
   In the year of eighteen forty-four those seaboys
   suffered sore:
   They pawned their gear in Liverpool and sailed as they
   did stand,
   And there blows some cold nor'westers on the Banks
   of Newfoundland.
*Chorus*

3. We had on board an Irish girl, Bridget Reilly was her name,
   To her I'd promised marriage, on me she had a claim:
   She tore up her flannel petticoat to make mittens for
   my hands,
   Before she'd see her true love freeze on the Banks of
   Newfoundland.
*Chorus*

4. So now it's reef and reef me boys with the canvas frozen
   hard,
   And it's mount and pass every mother's son on a
   ninety foot topsail yard,
   Never mind about boots and oilskins, and haul or you'll
   be damned,
   For there blows some cold nor'westers on the Banks of
   Newfoundland.
*Chorus*

5. I dreamed a dream the other night, I dreamed that
     I was home,
   I dreamed that me and my true love, we was back in
     old Dublin town;
   That we were back on Erin's shore with a jug of ale in hand,
   But then I awoke and my heart was broke on the Banks of
     Newfoundland.
*Chorus*

6. And now we're off the Hook, me boys, and the land's all
     white with snow,
   And soon we'll see the paytable and have all night below;
   And on the docks, come down in flocks, the pretty
     girls will stand,
   "It's snugger with me than it is at sea on the Banks of
     Newfoundland."
*Chorus*

# The Praties They Grow Small

In 1846, in the greatest catastrophe of its long and tragic history, famine came to Eire. Ragged skeletons with staring eyes roamed the countryside, holding out skinny hands for a crust or a blessing. The people died, from exhaustion, starvation, and disease, on the roads, in the fields, and in their cabins. The British Government, which was ultimately responsible for the welfare of its Irish subjects, averted its gaze from this scene of incredible mass suffering with cold indifference.

Mr. Nicholas Cummins, an Irish magistrate, published the following eyewitness account of conditions at Skibbereen, in the County of Cork, in the *London Times* of December 24, 1846:

> Being aware that I should have to witness scenes of frightful hunger, I provided myself with as much bread as five men could carry, and on reaching the spot I was surprised to find the wretched hamlet apparently deserted. I entered some of the hovels to ascertain the cause, and the scenes which presented themselves were such as no tongue or pen can convey the slightest idea of. In the first, six famished and ghastly skeletons, to all appearances dead, were huddled in a corner on some filthy straw, their sole covering what seemed a ragged horsecloth, their wretched legs hanging about, naked above the knees. I approached with horror, and found by a low moaning they were alive—they were in fever, four children, a woman, and what had once been a man.
>
> It is impossible to go through the detail. Suffice it to say, that in a few minutes I was surrounded by at least two hundred such phantoms, such frightful spectres as no words can describe, either from famine or from fever. Their demoniac yells are still ringing in my ears, and their horrible images are fixed upon my brain.
>
> In another case, decency would forbid what follows, but it must be told. . . . I found myself grasped by a woman with an infant just born in her arms and the remains of a filthy sack across her loins—the sole covering of herself and her baby. The same morning the police opened a house on the adjoining lands, which was observed shut for many days, and two frozen corpses were found, lying upon the mud floor, half devoured by rats.

In the years that followed, such scenes would become all too familiar in many parts of Eire.

"The Praties They Grow Small" arose out of sufferings such as these, in the years 1846–1848. Perhaps this song rivals as a lament "Lay This Body Down" (see p. 209 below) in its simplicity and power, its capacity to convey the terrible meaning of agony, oppression, and death in three short stanzas.

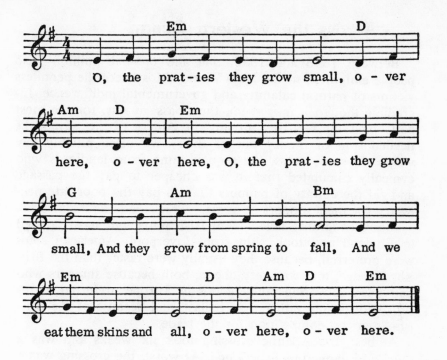

O, the prat-ies they grow small, o - ver here, o - ver here, O, the prat-ies they grow small, And they grow from spring to fall, And we eat them skins and all, o - ver here, o - ver here.

O, I wish that we were geese, night and morn, night and morn,
O, I wish that we were geese,
For they fly and take their ease,
And they live and die in peace, over here, over here.

O, we're trampled in the dust, over here, over here,
O, we're trampled in the dust,
But the Lord in whom we trust,
Will give us crumb for crust, over here, over here.

# Across the Western Ocean

Between 1846 and 1850, one and one-half million Irish people emigrated to the New World. Most were the penniless victims of natural calamity and governmental indifference. Incredible though it may seem, their passage was, for the most part, paid by relatives already in America who saved the needed sum of money out of their own often pitiably low wages. In some cases, the money came from landlords who cynically calculated that it was cheaper to pay the passage and rid the county of paupers than to pay the poor-rate necessary for their support at home.

Many emigrants sailed from Irish ports, but most crossed to England and took ship from Liverpool. American ships were preferred, because they usually were faster than the British. Passage, too, was very cheap, both because shippers who had been delivering bulky goods in Europe preferred to return with people rather than ballast, and because of the British-American competition for the trade.

At best, the Atlantic crossing took six weeks and was a cruel and dangerous experience. At worst, the crossing was a hell on earth, an ordeal of famine, overcrowding, disease, and shipwreck. In those days, neither Washington nor London exercised the least control over conditions prevailing on immigrant boats. In 1847 alone, 17,000 Irish immigrants—one out of every five who embarked upon the transatlantic voyage—died at sea.

"Across the Western Ocean" is an immigrant song set to the tune of "Leave Her, Johnny, Leave Her" (see p. 135 above). Immigrants evidently learned the melody from the sailors.

Oh, the times are hard and the wages are low,
    Amelia, where you bound for?
The Rocky Mountains is my home,
    Across the Western Ocean.

Beware these packet ships I say,
    Amelia, where you bound for?
They'll steal your stores and clothes away,
    Across the Western Ocean.

There's Liverpool Pat with his tarpaulin hat,
 Amelia, where you bound for?
And Yankee John the packet rat,
 Across the Western Ocean.

Father and Mother, say good bye,
 Amelia, where you bound for?
Brother and sister, don't you cry,
 Across the Western Ocean.

# The Farmer's Curst Wife
## (The Devil and the Farmer)

Crossing the Atlantic on the packet ships was, at best, a weary business. Time hung heavy at sea, and in the cramped space between decks the young people sang and danced as best they might. "The Farmer's Curst Wife" was a favorite jig. Widely known throughout the British Isles in one form or another, this song was taken by British and Irish immigrants to all parts of the United States.

2. "See here my good man, I have come for your wife
      Riteful, riteful, titty fie day,
   See here my good man I have come for your wife,
   For she's the bane and torment of your life,"
      With a riteful la, etc.

3. So the Devil he hoisted her up on his hump,
      Riteful, riteful, titty fie day,
   So the Devil he hoisted her up his hump,
   And down to Hell with her he did jump,
      With a riteful la, etc.

4. When they got there the gates they were shut,
      Riteful, riteful, titty fie day,
   When they got there the gates they were shut,
   With a blow of her hand she laid open his nut,
      Riteful la, etc.

5. Two little devils were playing handball,
      Riteful, riteful, titty fie day,
   Two little devils were playing handball,
   "Take her back Daddy, she'll be the death of us all!"
      Riteful la, etc.

6. So the Devil he hoisted her up on his hump,
      Riteful, riteful, titty fie day,
   So the Devil he hoisted her up on his hump,
   And back to earth with her he did jump,
      With a riteful la, etc.

7. "See here my good man, I have come with your wife,"
      Riteful, riteful, titty fie day,
   "See here my good man, I have come with your wife,
   For she's the bane and torment of my life,"
      Riteful la, etc.

8. Now they say that the women are worse than the men,
      Riteful, riteful, titty fie day,
   They say that the women are worse than the men,
   They went down to Hell and got kicked out again,
      Riteful la, etc.

# The Castle of Dromore
## (Caislean Droim an Oir)

"The Castle of Dromore" is a lullaby which people of Irish descent still sing in New England. Traditionally, it is one of the most ancient of Irish songs, dating back to the early middle ages. In Eire, it is still sung in the native Gaelic, but during the nineteenth century, like so many other Gaelic songs, it was translated into English; in this form, it has found its way to England and to the United States.

Oc - to - ber winds la - ment a - round the cas - tle of Dro - more;_ But peace is in her loft - y halls, my dear - est treas - ure store._ Though au - tumn leaves_ may droop_ and die, a bud of spring_ are you _____ Sing - ing hush - a - bye, lull - a - bye, lou lo lan, Sing

hush - a - bye, lou lo lan. (Hum) _____

Bring no ill will to hinder us, my helpless babe and me,
Dread spirits of the black water, Clanowen's wild banshee;
And holy Mary pitying us, in Heaven for grace that is true,
Singing hushabye, lullabye, lou lo lan, sing hushabye lou lo lan.

Take time to thrive my ray of hope in the garden of Dromore,
Take heed young eaglet that thy wings are feathered fit to soar;
A little rest, and then the world is full of work to do,
Singing hushabye lullabye lou lo lan. sing hushabye lou lo lan.

* * *

Tá gaoth an geimread sgaolta fuair,
     Thar timpeall Droim an Óir,
Ach ins an halla taob istigh,
     Ta síochain ann go leor.
Ta gach sean-duilliúr, dul ar crith,
     Ach is óg an leanán thú,
Seinn lóitin is lú lá lú lá ló,
     Seinn lóitin is lú lá ló.


A Róis mo chroi a shlaitin óir
     As garra Droim an Óir,
Bi ag fás go mbeidh gach cleite beag
     Mar sgíatan iolrea mhór.
Is leim ansan ar fuaid an tsaol,
     Oibrig is saothraig clú,
Seinn lóitin is lú lá lú lá ló,
     Seinn lóitin is lú lá ló.

# The Pesky Sarpent

From the end of the War of 1812 to the early fifties, Irish immigrants were streaming into New England to build railroads, dig canals, and man cotton factories. The traditional New England farmer of Yankee stock was on the way out, abandoning his native soil and seeking more fertile land in New York State and points west.

The changing times, the transition of New England from rural to industrial economy, are clearly reflected in the evolution of "Springfield Mountain." We first encountered this song (p. 44 above) as a funeral elegy for a young farmer of Protestant, Anglo-Saxon origin. But in the Jacksonian period, Protestants were being replaced by Catholics, Anglo-Saxons by Gaels, farmers by workers. To these newly arrived Americans, the traditional New Englander was a strange phenomenon. Caricatures, on the Boston stage, of the sanctimonious, high-pitched Yankee hayseeds were sure to evoke hilarious laughter.

Accordingly, "Springfield Mountain" was material made to order for stage comedians seeking to entertain Irish Catholic audiences. The old elegy was cleverly reworked and made its appearance on the Boston music-hall stage in the 1830's under the title "The Pesky Sarpent." The date of its first publication as sheet music was 1840. In one or another version, the story of Timothy Myrick spread across the country and became one of America's most popular songs.

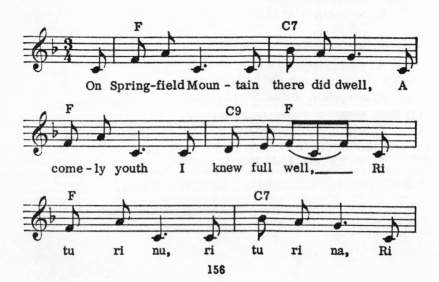

On Spring-field Moun - tain there did dwell, A come - ly youth I knew full well,____ Ri tu ri nu, ri tu ri na, Ri

tu ri nu, ri tu ri na.

2. One Monday morning he did go,
   Down in the meadow for to mow,
      Ri tu ri nu, etc.

3. He scarce had mowed half round the field,
   When a pesky sarpent bit his heel,
      Ri tu ri nu, etc.

4. He took his scythe and with a blow,
   He laid the pesky sarpent low,
      Ri tu ri nu, etc.

5. He took the sarpent in his hand,
   And straitway went to Molly Bland.
      Ri tu ri nu, etc.

6. "Oh, Molly, Molly here you see
   The pesky sarpent what bit me."
      Ri tu ri nu, etc.

7. Now Molly had a ruby lip,
   With which the pizen she did sip.
      Ri tu ri nu, etc.

8. But Molly had a rotten tooth,
   Which the pizen struck and killed 'em both.
      Ri tu ri nu, etc.

9. The neighbours found that they were dead,
   So laid them both upon one bed.
      Ri tu ri nu, etc.

10. And all their friends both far and near,
    Did cry and howl they were so dear.
       Ri tu ri nu, etc.

11. Now all you maids a warning take
    From Molly Bland and Tommy Blake.
       Ri tu ri nu, etc.

12. And mind when you're in love, don't pass,
    Too near to patches of high grass.
        Ri tu ri nu, etc.

# The Westward Movement

In the period between the War of 1812 and the outbreak of the Civil War, westward advance proceeded with impressive speed. Settlers poured through the mountain gaps into the mighty central valley lying between the Appalachians and the Rockies, carried white civilization beyond the Mississippi into Texas, Kansas, Missouri and Iowa, and moved through the last huge barrier of western mountain and desert to found new states in California and Oregon.

In the Jacksonian age, frontiering was a complex and many-sided activity. Far ahead of the main advance ranged the hunter, the lumberman, and the miner, for the first valuable products of the wilderness were furs, timber, and precious metals. Such men were professional pioneers; some were rude farmers, while others were prospectors or land surveyors. They blazed the trails and cleared a path for the advance of the main army of settlers, the mass of small farmers who came west to raise crops, build communities, and found states. These were drawn from the South, the East, and the far corners of Europe not mainly by the lust for gold or quick wealth, but by the most powerful magnet of all, virgin land.

What kind of songs did these pioneers—hunters, lumbermen, and farmfolk—sing? They sang everything which Americans had created or inherited: lullabies, colonial and revolutionary songs, ancient European ballads, sea songs, psalms, and spirituals. This fact is well illustrated in the manuscript song books in which the pioneers painfully copied down for themselves and their children the songs which they treasured. All of our American songs were frontier songs simply because Americans sang them on the frontier.

But the frontier was not only a place where people sang. Frontiering was also an occupation which produced songs that expressed specific aspects of pioneer life and experience. During the Jacksonian period, the frontier produced its own special and unique songs telling of lumbering, hunting, Indian fighting, overlanding, and the gold rush. The body of songs produced by such experiences in this period was very rich: in this section, we shall try to suggest through a small sampling something of its beauty and profundity.

Over the course of time, an idealized image of the frontier has become embodied in literature and raised to the status of a folk myth that exercises a continuing and extraordinary

159

influence. The frontier as embodied in myth is a rich and complex bundle of associations. It represents the simple, unaffected life compared to the complexity and sophistication of civilization, closeness to the serenity of nature—trees, rivers, earth, and stars—compared to the raucous urban community from which the wilderness has been forever banished. The frontier is free in the narrow sense from the endless petty restraints of modern life, and free in the broadest spiritual sense conceivable; for we like to think that this country was settled by free men, and not a few of these were small farmers fleeing westward from the blight of slavery as it advanced through the rich river bottoms of the South. The frontier, we have been taught, is American national identity itself. American experience, for close to three hundred years, has been synonymous with the on-going process of Western movement, with the never-ending struggle to clear, tame, and settle the continent Americans have come to believe that pioneering—with its symbols of ax, cap, cabin, and gun—constituted a uniquely American way of life. This way of life has vanished, but we cling tenaciously to its symbols.

In short, the frontier as crystallized in myth gives form to an American dream of freedom, equality, and happiness that has been sought through all our past and yet remains to be realized. The songs of the frontier do not neglect this dream, but they also emphasize another aspect of frontier life. They tell us that frontiering was a harsh, dangerous, and cruel existence; that its unrelieved toil robbed women of youth, beauty, and even sanity; that it was a brutal battle with the elements, with Indians, with sickness, and with disease; and that it was a moral catastrophe which enslaved men to false and wicked appetites and lured them to their destruction. In song, the settlement of the wilderness appears to be not only a story of epic dimension, but also an American tragedy. There is a deeply human message in this music, for it emphasizes the immense cost involved in clearing the continent and the senseless wastage of a frenzied, hectic, competitive race for wealth.

# The Wisconsin Emigrant

After the War of 1812, the face of New England changed as industrialization advanced. Pioneering fever gripped the boldest and most adventurous; they loaded the wagons, hitched up the oxen, and started West toward New York state and the Northwestern Territory.

Both those who stayed and those who left faced and made a serious decision. In the West lay the promise of virgin fields and rich harvests; toils and hazards still unknown would have to be undergone before the dream of prosperity became a fact. At home, in New England, the soil was undeniably poor and stony, daily labor was hard, and a man's bread was earned by the sweat of his brow; but there was also security. Generations had toiled to make New England productive and beautiful; children grew up in settled surroundings, amid the beloved sights and sounds of home.

"The Wisconsin Emigrant" was collected in Vermont and Massachusetts in the early 1930's by Helen Hartness Flanders; the source for the lyric was A. L. Stewart of West Springfield, Massachusetts, a man then in his nineties who had learned the song in the years before the Civil War. "The Wisconsin Emigrant" is delightful for the frankness and clarity with which it expresses the alternatives between which the New England pioneer of that day was torn.

"Since times are so hard, I've thought, my true heart, Of leaving my ox-en, my plough, and my cart, And a-way to Wis-con-sin, a jour-ney we'd

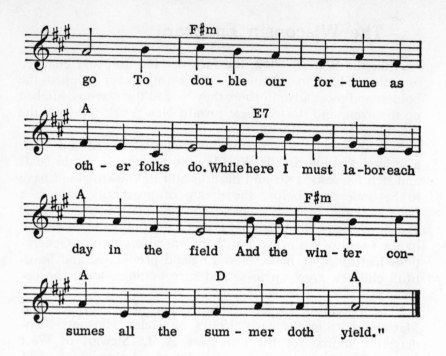

go To dou-ble our for-tune as

oth-er folks do. While here I must la-bor each

day in the field And the win-ter con-

sumes all the sum-mer doth yield."

2. "Oh husband I've noticed with sorrowful heart
   You've neglected your oxen, your plough, and your cart.
   Your sheep are disordered; at random they run,
   And your new Sunday suit is now every day on.
   Oh, stay on the farm and you'll suffer no loss,
   For the stone that keeps rolling will gather no moss." } *bis*

3. "Oh wife, let's go. Oh, don't let us wait.
   Oh, I long to be there. Oh, I long to be great!
   While you some rich lady—and who knows but I
   Some governor may be before that I die?
   While here I must labor each day in the field,
   And the winter consumes all the summer doth yield." } *bis*

4. "Oh husband, remember that land is to clear,
   Which will cost you the labor of many a year,
   Where horses, sheep, cattle, and hogs are to buy—
   And you'll scarcely get settled before you must die.
   Oh, stay on your farm and you'll suffer no loss,  } *bis*
   For the stone that keeps rolling will gather no moss."

5. "Oh wife, let's go. Oh, don't let us stay.
   I will buy me a farm that is cleared by the way,
   Where horses, sheep, cattle, and hogs are not dear,
   And we'll feast on fat buffalo half of the year.
   While here I must labor each day in the field,  } *bis*
   And the winter consumes all the summer doth yield."

6. "Oh husband, remember, that land of delight
   Is surrounded by Indians who murder by night.
   Your house they will plunder and burn to the ground,
   While your wife and your children lie murdered around.
   Oh, stay on the farm, and you'll suffer no loss,  } *bis*
   For the stone that keeps rolling will gather no moss."

7. "Now, wife, you've convinced me. I'll argue no more.
   I never had thought of your dying before;
   I love my dear children, although they are small,—
   But you, my dear wife, are more precious than all.
   We'll stay on the farm, and suffer no loss  } *bis*
   For the stone that keeps rolling will gather no moss."

# Hush, Little Baby

"Hush, Little Baby" is one of the most widely loved, and widely used, American lullabies. Generations of children have been lulled to sleep with it. The version given here was collected by the late John A. Lomax in Alabama.

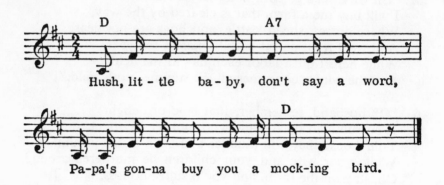

Hush, lit-tle ba-by, don't say a word,

Pa-pa's gon-na buy you a mock-ing bird.

If that mocking bird won't sing,
Papa's gonna buy you a diamond ring.

If that diamond ring turns brass,
Papa's gonna buy you a looking glass.

If that looking glass gets broke,
Papa's gonna buy you a billy goat.

If that billy goat won't pull,
Papa's gonna buy you a cart and bull.

If that cart and bull turn over,
Papa's gonna buy you a dog named Rover.

If that dog named Rover won't bark,
Papa's gonna buy you a horse and cart.

If that horse and cart fall down,
You'll still be the sweetest little baby in town.

Hush little baby don't say a word,
Papa's gonna buy you a mocking bird.

# Let's Go a-Huntin'

This song is as old as the country and followed the frontier all the way to Texas, wherever little boys went out in the woods to hunt. The charming melody of the version given here was recorded by John A. Lomax in Fort Spunky, Texas. The lyric is substantially as it is sung by Bill Bonyun, the New England folksinger. Bill has sung this song to literally thousands of elementary school children in the past decade and tells me that it ranks as "one of the all-time children's favorites." The English "Cutty Wren," from which "Let's Go a-Huntin'" is derived, is a peasant song of elaborate symbolism dating back to a period several hundred years before the founding of the American colonies. Thus, in one form or another, this song has been in continuous oral tradition for the better part of seven centuries and is one of the very oldest in our heritage.

Let's go a - hunt - in', said Risk - y Rob,
Let's go a - hunt - in', said Rob-in to Bob,
Let's go a - hunt-in', said Dan'-l to Jo,
Let's go a - hunt-in', said Bil-ly Bar - low.

2. What shall we hunt for? said Risky Rob,
   What shall we hunt for? said Robin to Bob,
   What shall we hunt for? said Dan'l to Jo,
      Let's hunt for a rat, said Billy Barlow.

3. How shall we kill him? said Risky Rob,
   How shall we kill him? said Robin to Bob,
   How shall we kill him? said Dan'l to Jo,
      Borrow a gun, said Billy Barlow.

4. How shall we haul him? said Risky Rob,
   How shall we haul him? said Robin to Bob,
   How shall we haul him? said Dan'l to Jo,
      Borrow a cart, said Billy Barlow.

5. How shall we divide him? said Risky Rob,
   How shall we divide him? said Robin to Bob,
   How shall we divide him? said Dan'l to Jo,
      Borrow a knife, said Billy Barlow.

6. How shall we cook him? said Risky Rob,
   How shall we cook him? said Robin to Bob,
   How shall we cook him? said Dan'l to Jo,
      Over a fire, said Billy Barlow.

7. I'll roast shoulder, said Risky Rob,
   I'll boil legs, said Robin to Bob,
   I'll bake back, said Dan'l to Jo,
      Tail bone raw, said Billy Barlow.

8. I feel sick, said Risky Rob,
   I gotta bellyache, said Robin to Bob,
   OOOOOOps!! said Dan'l to Jo,
      I feel fine, said Billy Barlow.

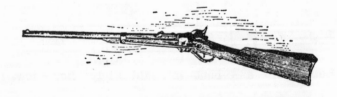

# Skip to My Lou

This was one of the most popular play-party songs in days gone by, and was known throughout the country. To this day, children still skip to it in the streets and playgrounds. Such songs had a special use in frontier communities where revivalist influences were strong. In such communities, says one authority:

> . . . they got around the churches' opposition to square and round dancing by holding play parties, in which they took over the singing games of children, with their skipping, dancing, and marching movements. In these, boys and girls swung one another by the hand and not by the waist, which was forbidden. And thus, since the fiddle was considered the devil's instrument and other musical instruments were scarce, they got along without musicians and callers, giving their own directions for the dance movements by means of the words of the song.*

In "Skip to My Lou," all couples join hands, skip left or right singing the chorus; a lone boy in the center of the ring sings "Lost my partner, what'll I do?" as the group circles, then picks a girl and takes her hand; her first partner goes to the center of the ring as the group sings the chorus, etc.

*Russell Ames, *The Story of American Folk Song* (New York: Grosset & Dunlap, 1955), 65-66.

Skip to my Lou, my dar - ling.

CHORUS

Lou, Lou, skip to my Lou, Lou, Lou,

skip to my Lou, Lou, Lou, skip to my Lou,

Skip to my Lou, my dar - ling.

2. I'll get another one prettier than you (three times)
 Skip to my lou, my darling.
*Chorus*

3. Little red wagon, painted blue (three times)
 Skip to my lou, my darling.
*Chorus*

4. Fly in the sugar-bowl, shoo shoo shoo (three times)
 Skip to my lou, my darling.
*Chorus*

5. Cows in the cornfield, two by two (three times)
 Skip to my lou, my darling.
*Chorus*

6. Skip, skip, skip to my lou (three times)
 Skip to my lou, my darling.
*Chorus*

7. Skip a little faster, that won't do (three times)
 Skip to my lou, my darling.
*Chorus*

## When I Was Single
## The Single Girl

Romance vanished early among pioneer couples. For the woman, it gave way to scouring, cooking, making and mending clothes, caring for children, fetching water, washing dishes, building fires, and tending livestock. It was a life of much toil and little joy that soon robbed a girl of her charms and speeded the process of disillusionment between husband and wife.

Both of the songs reproduced here have been very widely collected. "The Single Girl" has been reported primarily from the South, and is interesting as an early form of the blues. The melody is pentatonic (sung on five notes of the scale) and harmonized with a major chord and the relative minor.

### When I Was Single

When I was sin-gle, O then,___ When
I was sin-gle, O then,___ When
I was sin - gle, my
pock - ets did jin-gle, And I
wish I was sin - gle a - gain.___

CHORUS

I wish I was sin - gle a -
gain, ___ I wish I was sin - gle a -
gain, ___ When I was sin - gle, my
pock - ets did jin - gle, And I
wish I was sin - gle a - gain. ___

I married me a wife, O then,
I married me a wife, O then,
I married me a wife, she's the plague of my life,
And I wish I was single again.
*Chorus*

My wife she died, and O then,
My wife she died, and O then,
My wife she died, and I laughed till I cried,
To think I was single again.
*Chorus*

I married me another, O then,
I married me another, O then,
I married me another, she's the devil's grandmother,
And I wish I was single again.
*Chorus*

Now gather round you young men,
Now gather round you young men,
Be kind to the first, for the next will be worse,
And you'll wish you was single again.
*Chorus*


### The Single Girl

When I was sin-gle, dressed up so fine,

Now I am mar-ried, go rag-ged all the time,

Lord, I wish I was a sin-gle girl a - gain.

When I was single, my shoes they did screek,
Now I am married, Lord, all they do is leak,
Oh Lord, don't I wish I was a single girl again.

Three little babies, crying for bread,
Nothing to give them, I'd rather be dead,
Lord, I wish I was a single girl again.

Dishes to wash, and spring to go to,
When you get married, girls, you got it all to do
Lord I wish I was a single girl again.

When I was single, I lived at my ease,
Now I am married, have a drunkard to please
Lord, I wish I was a single girl again!

171

# The Lumberman's Alphabet
# The Jam on Gerry's Rock

From early colonial days until the end of the nineteenth century, one of the most necessary and most dangerous of frontier occupations was the felling of huge stands of timber in the forests that covered much of America. Wood, in those days, was a raw material even more indispensable than it is now; from it were made homes, furniture, ships, weapons, and tools. Loggers, the professional timbermen, were pioneers among the pioneers. They ranged ahead, at the very outskirts of civilization, to clear the forests and provide abundant logs for the saw mills down river to convert into boards and beams.

The loggers lived in forest camps and worked in gangs. Their home all winter was a rude cabin chinked with moss, and their food was cooked on an open fire. All day they would work in freezing temperatures, felling and topping the pine, and hauling the logs with sled and ox to the river landings. And on the seventh day, if all went well, the time was theirs to patch their clothes, sleep, play cards and drink, or sing. When the thaw set in, in the spring, the loggers brought their rolling, twisting cargo down river to the mills, riding the logs with steel-shod boots, steering them and heading off jams with a peavey—perhaps the most dangerous work that a man might ever do.

The logger's first frontier was New England, New York, and Pennsylvania; from there it leaped to the Lake States, where the huge stands of pine in Wisconsin, Michigan, and Minnesota provided all the lumber the East needed until the end of the nineteenth century, and brought fame to Albany, New York, as the world's greatest lumber market.

We give here two of the best loved of the many lumbermen's songs, both of which have been sung by pioneers clear across the continent. "The Lumberman's Alphabet" is reproduced with a melody transcribed from the singing of Gus Schaffer at Greenland, Michigan in 1938, and recorded by Alan Lomax for the Library of Congress. It probably derives from earlier "Sailor's Alphabet" songs and is to this day an instant favorite with children.

"The Jam on Gerry's Rock" ranks among the most widely sung and deeply felt native American ballads. From a specific accident occurring in the woods—precisely when and where we do not know—it fashions a commentary of universal application on the lumberman's calling. Not only was this song

172

sung in every logging camp in the country, but after the Civil War it migrated to the High Plains to be warbled by cowboys riding the prairie with never a tree in sight. The lyric reproduced here is a composite of many versions; the first melody given, one of the most attractive of many to which the song has been set, is transcribed from the singing of Bill McBride as recorded by Alan Lomax at Mount Pleasant, Michigan; the second melody comes from George Edwards, as collected by Norman Cazden in the Catskills. It is a variant of the Irish "Bonny Boy" (see page 18 above); many of the best singers among the lumbermen were Irish.

### The Lumberman's Alphabet

A is for axe and that we all know,

B is for boy who can use it al - so,

C is for chop-ping we first do be - gin,

D is for dan - ger we of - ten fall in.

CHORUS

Then so mer-ry, so mer-ry, so

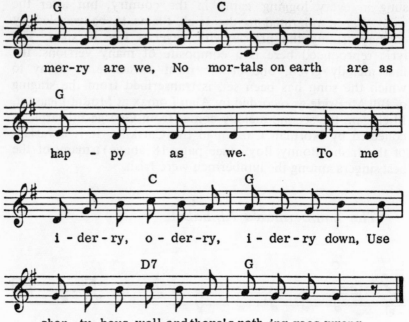

mer-ry are we, No mor-tals on earth are as

hap - py as we. To me

i - der - ry, o - der - ry, i - der - ry down, Use

shan - ty boys well and there's noth-ing goes wrong.

E is for echo that through the woods rang,
And F is for foreman the head of our gang,
G is for grindstone at night we do turn,
And H is for handle that's so smoothly worn.
*Chorus*


I is for iron with which we mark pine,
And J is for jolly boys, all in a line,
K is for keen edge that on our axes we keep,
And L is for lice that keep us from sleep.
*Chorus*


M is for moss that chinks up our camp,
And N is for needle for mending our pants,
O is for owl a-hooting by night,
And P is for pine that we always fall right.
*Chorus*


Q is for quickness we put ourselves to,
And R is for river we haul our logs to,
S is for sled that we haul our logs on,
And T is for team that pulls them along.
*Chorus*

174

U is for uses we set ourselves to,
And V is for valley we haul our logs through,
W is for woods that we leave in the spring,
And now I have sung all that I'm going to sing.
*Chorus*


## The Jam on Gerry's Rock

(1)

Come all of you bold shan - ty boys_ and
list while I re - late The_
tale of one_ young shan - ty boy_ and
his un - time - ly fate; The_
tale of one_ young riv - er man,_ so
man - ly, true and brave, 'Twas

in the jam on Ger - ry's rock __ he

met a wa - tery grave.

(2)

Come, all you jol - ly riv - er lads I'll __

have you to draw near, And lis - ten un - to the

dan - ger which you are going to hear It's

of six jol - ly Ca - na - dian boys who in

vol - un - teer did go For to break the jam on

Ger - ry's rock with their fore-man young Mon - roe.

2. It was on a Sunday morning, in the springtime of the year,
   The logs were piling mountain high; we could not keep
      them clear.
   "Turn out, turn out," our foreman cried, "no reason
      at all to fear,
   We'll break the jam on Gerry's Rock and for Saginaw
      we'll steer."

3. Now some of them were willing, and some of them
      were not;
   To work on jams on Sunday they did not think they
      ought—
   But six of our Canadian boys did volunteer to go
   To break the jam on Gerry's Rock with their foreman,
      young Monroe.

4. They had not rolled off many logs, when the foreman
      he did say,
   "I'll have you boys be on your guard, for the jam will
      soon give way."
   These words were scarcely spoken, when the jam
      did break and go
   And with it went those six brave youths with their
      foreman, young Monroe.

5. Now when the rest of the shanty-boys the sad news came
      to hear,
   In search of their lost comrades to the riverside did steer;
   Six of the mangled bodies a-floating down did go,
   While crushed and bleeding near the bank was that of
      young Monroe.

6. We dragged him from his drowning place, brushed back
      his raven hair
   There was one girl among them, whose sad cries rent
      the air,
   There was one girl among them, a maid from
      Saginaw town,
   Whose moans and cries now rent the skies for her lover
      who was drowned.

7. Miss Clara was a noble girl, the riverman's true friend,
   Who with her widowed mother, lived near the river's bend,
   The wages of her own true love the boss to her did pay,
   And the shanty-boys for her made up a generous purse
      next day.

8. They buried him with sorrow deep, 'twas on the first
      of May—
   Come all of you bold shanty-boys, and for your comrades
      pray,
   Engraved upon a hemlock tree, that by the grave did grow,
   Was the day and the date of the drowning of the
      shanty-boy Monroe.

*The Lumberman's Alphabet* is transcribed by permission from Record AFS L56 in the Archive of Folk Song, Library of Congress. *The Jam on Gerry's Rock* (1) is from the same source; (2) is reprinted from the *Abelard Folk Song Book*, edited by Norman Cazden, by permission of Abelard-Schuman Ltd. All rights reserved, 1958.

# Sioux Indians

The vast stretch of land lying between Canada and the Rio Grande, between the Rockies and the hundredth meridian of longitude, was known before the Civil War as the Great Prairie Wilderness. Grass-covered, arid, and largely treeless, it was inhabited at that time only by nomadic Indians—Sioux, Dakota, Blackfoot, Cheyenne, Arapahoe—and by the buffalo herds which provided their existence. Beyond this sea of grass, to the west, lay the wall of the Rockies; and beyond them, again, huge expanses of desert intervened between the mountains and the Pacific.

The Westward Movement, faced with this formidable barrier to settlement, simply skipped over it. The path to the far West, opened up by the explorations of fur traders, led from Missouri up the Platte River, through South Pass, and down the Snake to the Columbia. It became famous as the Oregon Trail. The magnet that lured immigrants was first the lush, wooded slopes of the Pacific Northwest, and then the prospect of gold in California. During the forties and fifties, settlement of the Far West went rapidly forward in response to both these stimuli.

Emigrant parties assembled at St. Louis or Independence, were provisioned, and moved out along the trail on their 2000-mile journey. Unimaginable hardships attended the travelers. Day after day the sun beat down from a cloudless sky; storms of hail and sleet swept down from the hills. When streams had to be forded, animals were swept away, or wagons sank axle-deep in mud and had to be dragged out by teams of oxen and sweating men. With neither doctor nor remedy at hand, sickness took a heavy toll of children's lives. Indian bands prowled around the caravans and sometimes attacked, decimating the number of pioneers, plundering their possessions, and stampeding their cattle.

"Sioux Indians" is one of the memorable ballads that tell of this frontier ordeal. The version given here is transcribed from the singing of a cowboy as recorded by John A. Lomax for the Library of Congress. The melody is pentatonic, harmonized with minor chord and relative major.

I'll sing you a song though it may be a sad one,——— Of tri-als and trou-bles, and where first be-gun—— I left my dear fam-ily, my friends and my home, A-cross the wide des-erts and moun-tains to roam.——

2. I crossed the Missouri and joined a large train,
   Which bore us o'er mountains and valleys and plains;
   And often at evening out hunting we'd go
   To shoot the fleet antelope and wild buffalo.

3. We heard of Sioux Indians all out on the plain,
   A-killing poor drivers and burning their train,
   A-killing poor drivers with arrow and bow,
   When captured by Indians no mercy they'd show.

4. We travelled three weeks til we came to the Platte,
   We pitched out our tents at the head of the flat,
   We spread out our blankets on the green grassy ground,
   While our horses and oxen were grazing all round.

5. While taking refreshments we heard a loud yell,
   The whoop of Sioux Indians coming out of the dell;
   We sprang to our rifles with a flash in each eye,
   "Boys," says our brave leader, "we'll fight til we die."

6. They made a bold dash and came near to our train,
   The arrows fall round us like hail and like rain,
   But with our long rifles we fed them cold lead,
   Till many a brave warrior around us lay dead.

7. We shot their bold chief at the head of the band,
   He died like a warrior with a gun in his hand;
   When they saw their bold chief laying dead in his gore,
   They whooped and they yelled and we saw them no more.

8. We hitched up our horses and started our train,
   Three more bloody battles this trip on the plain;
   And in our last battle three of our brave boys fell,
   And we left them to rest in a green shady dell.

9. We travelled by days, guarded camp during night,
   Till Oregon's mountains looked high in their might;
   Now at Pocahontas beside a clear stream
   Our journey is ended in the land of our dream.

From Record AAFS L49 in the Archive of Folk Song, Library of Congress.

# The Fools of Forty-Nine
# Santy Anno
# The Dying Californian

Westward expansion was climaxed in the Jacksonian era by the war of 1846–1848, which wrested millions of acres from Mexican possession and brought the rich lands of California into the Union. The value of this act of conquest became immediately apparent when gold was discovered at Sutter's Mill in January, 1848. This was four months after Santa Anna's surrender at Mexico City and a few days before the treaty of peace was signed at Guadeloupe Hidalgo, which formally ceded California to the United States.

Among thousands of people, the discovery of gold sparked a mania for quick and easy wealth, and touched off a wild race for the Far West—overland along the Oregon and California trails, through the fever-ridden swamps of Panama, by boat around Cape Horn. En route, many fell victim to starvation, disease, exhaustion, accident, or shipwreck, and thousands more who reached their destination never found the wealth of their dreams. But so great was the influx of gold-diggers that California was soon ready for statehood. In January, 1848, this Mexican province boasted scarcely 30,000 inhabitants, of whom two-thirds were Mexican or Indian. Two years later, the population had risen to 200,000, and a state constitution had been adopted.

The following is an impressive picture of the passion for gold among the prospectors in the valley of the Sacramento in 1849:

Some, with long-handled shovels, delved among clumps of bushes, or by the side of large rocks, never raising their eyes for an instant; others, with pick and shovel, worked among stone and gravel, or with trowels searched under banks and roots of trees, where, if rewarded with small lumps of gold, the eye shone brighter for an instant, when the search was immediately and more ardently resumed. At the edge of the stream, or knee-deep and waist-deep in water, as cold as melted ice and snow could make it, some were washing gold with tin-pans, or the common cradle-rocker, while the rays of the sun were pouring down on their heads with an intensity exceeding anything we ever experienced at home, though it was but in the middle of April.

The thirst for gold, and the labor of acquisition, overruled all else, and totally absorbed every faculty. Complete silence reigned among the miners; they addressed not a word to each other, and seemed averse to all conversation. All the sympathies of our common humanity, all the finer and nobler attributes of our nature seemed lost, buried beneath the soil they were eagerly delving, or swept away with the rushing waters that revealed the shining treasure.*

The Gold Rush produced many songs; we select for reproduction here three that embody most brilliantly its reckless passions, and comment upon them. "The Fools of Forty-Nine" is a ballad telling of the race across the continent on land and water passages that merely led to death. Appearing in *Put's Original California Songster,* it might be characterized as a magnificent and native American commentary upon Macbeth's great theme:

> And all our yesterdays have lighted fools
> The road to dusty death.

—with the added implication of the chorus that the only wealth men ought to seek is in the salvation of their eternal souls.

The route around Cape Horn was the longest way to California, but it was the wisest. It is celebrated in the beautiful "Santy Anno," which originated among British sailors as a pump shanty. The American version reproduced here gloats over the United States victory over General Santa Anna "on the plains of Mexico"—a victory that laid California open to the Yankees and brought gold within their grasp. As given here, "Santy Anno" is both a shanty and a Gold Rush song. Some of the sailors who sang it were making their last voyage before the mast and would go looking for gold when they reached California.

"The Dying Californian" is a product both of our general ballad tradition and of the revivalist movement that reached its climax in the Jacksonian era. The lyric, based on a letter telling of a New Englander's death at sea while on the way to California, first appeared in the *New England Diadem* in December, 1854. The exquisite melody which we give here was one of several to which the poem was later set. It is taken from the University of Virginia Collection of Folk Music, and was originally printed by George Pullen Jackson in 1940 as No. 36 in his collection of *Down-East Spirituals and Others.* The result may stand as an example of American religious balladry at its best.

---

*Henry Howe, *Historical Collections of the Great West* (N. Y., 1857), 386.

## The Fools of Forty-Nine

When gold was found in . for - ty-eight, the
peo-ple said 'twas gas, And some were fools e -
nough to think the lumps were on - ly brass, But
they soon were sat - is - fied and start - ed off__ to
mine, They bought a ship came round the Horn in the
fall of for - ty - nine. Then they thought of
what they had been told, When they
start - ed aft - er gold, That they

nev - er　in　this world would make a　pile.

2. The poor, the old, the rotten scows were advertised to sail,
   To New Orleans with passengers, but they must come and
     bail,
   The ships were crowded more than full, but some hung on
     behind,
   And others dived off from the wharf and swam till they
     were blind.
*Chorus*

3. With rusty pork and stinking beef and rotten wormy bread
   With captains too that never were as high as the main-
     mast head,
   The steerage passengers would rave and swear they'd paid
     their passage
   They wanted something more to eat besides the lowly
     sausage.
*Chorus*

4. And they begun to cross the plains with oxen, holler and
     haul,
   And steamers they began to run as far as Panama,
   And there for months the people stayed that started after
     gold,
   And some returned disgusted with the lies they had been
     told.
*Chorus*

5. The people died on every route, they sickened and died
     like sheep,
   And those at sea before they were dead were launched into
     the deep,
   And those that died crossing the Plains fared not as well
     as that,
   For a hole was dug and they was dumped along the ter-
     rible Platte.
*Chorus*

## Santy Anno

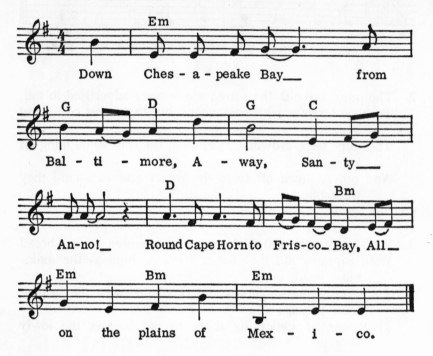

Down Ches-a-peake Bay__ from Bal-ti-more, A-way, San-ty__ An-no!__ Round Cape Horn to Fris-co__ Bay, All__ on the plains of Mex-i-co.

*Chorus*  Then heave her up and away we'll go
Away, Santy Anno!
Heave her up, and away we'll go,
All on the Plains of Mexico.

2. She's a fast clipper ship with a bully crew,
Away, Santy Anno!
A down-east Yankee for a captain too
All on the Plains of Mexico.
*Chorus*

3. There's plenty of gold so I've been told
Away, Santy Anno!
There's plenty of gold so I've been told
All on the Plains of Mexico.
*Chorus*

4. Back in the days of Forty-nine,
Away, Santy Anno!
Those were the days of the good old times,
All on the Plains of Mexico.

186

*Chorus*

5. When Zach Taylor gained the day,
    Away, Santy Anno!
He made poor Santy run away,
    All on the Plains of Mexico.

*Chorus*

6. Santy Anno was a good old man
    Away, Santy Anno!
Till he went to war with Uncle Sam
    All on the Plains of Mexico.

*Chorus*

7. When I leave this ship I'll settle down
    Away, Santy Anno!
Marry a girl named Sally Brown
    All on the Plains of Mexico.

*Chorus*

### The Dying Californian

fold. I am dy - ing, broth - er,
dy - ing, Soon you'll miss me in — your
berth; For my form will soon be —
ly - ing Be-neath the o - cean's brin-y — surf.

Tell my father when you see him
    That in death I prayed for him,
Prayed that I might only meet him
    In a world that's free from sin.
Tell my mother, God assist her
    Now that she is growing old,
That her child would glad have kissed her
    When his lips grew pale and cold.

Listen, brother, catch each whisper
    'Tis my wife I speak of now,
Tell, oh tell her how I missed her
    When the fever burned my brow.
Tell her she must kiss my children
    Like the kiss I last impressed,
Hold them as when last I held them
    Held them closely to my breast.

It was for them I crossed the ocean,
　　What my hopes were I'll not tell;
But they gained an orphan's portion,
　　Yet He doeth all things well;
Tell them I have reached the haven
　　Where I sought the precious dust,
But I gained a port called Heaven
　　Where the gold will never rust.

# Slavery Days

The majority of America's white European immigrants have always been the landless, the hungry, and the poor. That they accepted servitude, as many did in colonial days, was a temporary expedient to cross the wide Atlantic and to get a start in the New World. But black men were brought here by force from Africa, deliberately. They were sold into perpetual bondage that their labor might be used to develop the continent; that they might toil and die so that others might prosper.

To the first white settlers, America seemed a paradise, a land of boundless plenty where the skies were darkened by flocks of birds, where the rivers brimmed with fish, and the fertile earth was veined with precious ores. But, rich though it may have been in natural resources, this land was poor in people. The scattered bands of red men fought the whites, fled, or died; the boundless forests of oak and beech and elm lay silent and deserted. To white men, this absence of labor presented a problem. Some of them sought fortunes from the production and export of commercial crops—rice, sugar, tobacco, wheat, and rum; these fortunes might not be made unless there was ample labor available to clear the trees, plant the land, cultivate the crops, and harvest them.

Not to be denied in their quest for wealth, these whites turned for toilers to the unexplored continent of Africa. Thus, the slave trade arose and endured for nearly four centuries. In this time Christian civilization robbed Africa of perhaps fifty million human beings.

In the seventeenth century, slavery was introduced into all the mainland colonies, but it did not prove very profitable in the North. In the South, it spread like a blight, and a powerful and wealthy class of slaveholders arose. After the Revolution, the Southern United States became the principal source of supply of cotton to feed British, French, Belgian, and American textile factories. Slavery now moved westward by leaps and bounds, always to fresh and virgin lands, to Tennessee, Alabama, Mississippi, Arkansas, Missouri, and Texas.

From the tragic experience of the Negro people under slavery there came a music that enriched American culture immeasurably and was of world significance. Appropriating whatever materials were available—in the Bible, white spirituals, hymns, and secular songs—the genius of an enslaved people fused these with elements of its own African tradition to create an incomparably profound and original expression of the predicament of American man, of man enslaved.

During slavery days, the Negro people created a vast repertoire of song. Much of their secular music, in the form then played and sung, has been lost to us; the majority of the songs that have survived are spirituals. But these spirituals meant far more to the slave than the name implies; that is, devotional songs for church or other solemn occasions. Spirituals were put to the most varied uses: as laments, work songs in the fields and mills, rowing or hauling songs, war songs, lullabies, the special form of sacred dance known as the "shout," and funeral dirges. Spirituals were sung with endless variations of style and tempo, depending on the occasion. As sung by the slaves the spiritual evidently had little in common with the stylized and conventionally harmonized versions that have graced the church services and concert halls of a later age.

The development of the spiritual was linked to one of the Negro people's major cultural achievements under slavery—Christianization. Negroes had begun to move toward protestantism in the days of the great eighteenth century revival of religion known as the "Great Awakening." Jonathan Edwards, most eminent of the American leaders of this Awakening, had noted as early as 1736 the presence of New England slaves in the throngs that attended revival meeings. In 1776 the Methodist bishop, Francis Asbury, recorded that his revival meetings were attended by "hundreds of Negroes . . . with the tears streaming down their faces." After the Revolution, the tempo of this evangelical activity stepped up and continued unabated until the Civil War. White hymns and revival songs, with both music and lyrics, became available to Negro people throughout the nation.

During the eighteenth century the Puritan psalm-singing tradition had been enriched by the importation of hymns, like those of Isaac Watts, and by the beginning of native American composition of religious anthems and odes. The advance of the revivalist movement stimulated the demand for religious music with a propaganda mission and a popular approach to the problem of salvation. For the work of the revivalist movement, numbers of traditional hymns were pressed into service; ordinary folk in newly "awakened" communities began to try their own hands at religious versification.

New lyrics took a passionate approach to the question of sin, conversion, and sanctification. They warned sinners of the reality of death, and the urgent need to prepare for it; they

191

pointed up the certainty of hellfire for the unrepentant and of everlasting damnation for the unregenerate. They told of the experience of conversion and of the raptures of the vision of the Living God. They affirmed faith in Jesus Christ and in the possibility of eternal life.

The revivalists set their lyrics to traditional tunes familiar to and loved by the common people, to tunes overwhelmingly of British folk origin.* As the frontier moved Westward during the Jacksonian era, this type of sacred popular song, or *white spiritual,* became general among frontier folk, both North and South. A vast amount of new song was thus proliferated: hymns of praise, religious ballads, revivalist songs of many types. But this material found a ready audience not only among white farmers, woodsmen, and pioneers, but also among the Negro slaves. Both white and Negro Americans utilized the same musical tradition and lyrics that were, by the 1820's, finding their way with profusion into the songsters. Inevitably, white and Negro people would use the *common* tradition in *different* ways. Both White and Negro spirituals were, as a class, appropriate, profound, and creatively beautiful expressions of the spiritual and intellectual needs of the people who produced them.

Slaveholders were, for the most part, reluctant witnesses of the great movement of religious conversion among their slaves, but they were obliged to make the best of it. It is true that Christian religion could be used, and often was, to inculcate acceptance of one's lot on earth, of obedience to slave masters, of "pie in the sky by and by" as the reward of meekness and obedience here and now. But this is only one side of the matter. Historically, the awakening of the slave to protestantism served the same purpose among Negroes as among white Americans. The religious awakening endowed them with a sense of unity, an interpretation of history, and a readiness to accept sacrifice, struggle, and death for what was right. The connection between the rise of Christianity among the slaves, the massive role played by the Negro people during the Civil War, and the disintegration of chattel bondage *is clear and demonstrable.*

The role played by the spiritual in the education of the Negro slave was unique. Focus and expression of the people's

*"All the known tunes adopted by American religious folk from sources other than British throughout the two-hundred year period under consideration could be counted on the fingers of one hand." George Pullen Jackson, *White and Negro Spirituals* (Locust Valley, N.Y.: 1943), 75.

profoundest beliefs and aspirations, the spiritual bound the race together with a consciousness of its common oppression, human dignity, and destiny. It gave the Negro strength to face the ordeals of life under slavery: the monotony of toil, humiliation, pain, flight and separation, battle, disease and death. It made it possible for human beings to accept their fate when they could do nothing else, and it summoned them to a sustained protest against that same fate whenever the hour struck.

In addition to spirituals, slavery produced many secular songs: dance tunes, corn songs, roustabout songs, and shanties. These were songs of the devil and the flesh. More than one collector has found, to his sorrow, that freedmen or the children of freedmen were reluctant to remember or communicate these pagan ditties. William Francis Allen, a pioneer collector of slave songs during the Civil War, wrote explicitly that it was ". . . no easy matter to persuade them to sing their old songs, even as a curiosity, such is the sense of dignity that has come to them with freedom.* Dorothy Scarborough, another and later collector, tried to coax such songs out of an old man in Birmingham, Alabama, and received the answer: "Yes, mistis, I knows dem. But I ain' gwine backslide by talkin' 'bout 'em. Ef you wants 'reels' you'll have to hunt up some dem young sinner folks. Not me, naw, not me!**

Sea shanties of clearly Negro origin appear elsewhere in this book. Some of the authentic secular songs that have survived slavery days are included in the selection of slave songs that follows.

Until the Civil War, there was but the faintest appreciation among white people of the extraordinary significance of Negro singing. Among the exceptions were the English actress, Frances Ann Kemble, whose comments upon slave songs are reproduced in part below; the Virginia novelist George Tucker; and blackface minstrels, who were quick to realize the extraordinary value of Negro "material" for entertainment purposes. However, Negro song transmitted by these minstrels reaches us in a stereotyped form because it has suffered the distortions that folk music undergoes when exploited for consciously commercial purposes.

The first people to appreciate the national significance of the songs of slavery, and the first to record them, were the fighters against slavery—Northern soldiers, ministers, scholars, and teachers. This work began with the capture of Port

*Slave Songs of the United States (New York, 1867), x.
**On the Trail of Negro Folk Songs (Cambridge, Mass.: 1925), 98.

Royal in 1861 by the Union forces and the liberation of the slave population on the sea islands of that area. In 1862, Secretary of the Treasury Salmon Chase launched an economic plan for these islands, and for the education of the freedman. Northern soldiers, teachers, and social workers hastened South to take part in the project. Among them were a number of skilled amateur musicians: Lucy McKim, daughter of a celebrated Philadelphia abolitionist, who married Wendell, son of William Lloyd Garrison in 1865; William Francis Allen, of Harvard University, one of America's foremost classical scholars; Charles Pickard Ware, son of Henry Ware the well known Unitarian minister of antislavery convictions from Hingham, Massachusetts; and Thomas Wentworth Higginson, also from Massachusetts, who assumed command of the First Carolina Volunteers, a regiment of freedmen who trained at Beaufort, South Carolina, in October 1862.

These people found in the spirituals sung so universally and so freely by the ex-slaves an incredibly vital, moving, and novel form of music. They busied themselves in noting down as much of it as time and other duties permitted. Higginson has left us a number of valuable lyrics and some revealing commentary on the singing of the soldiers, whom, as their commander, he was able to observe very closely. The volume of *Slave Songs* published by Lucy McKim, William Francis Allen, and Charles Pickard Ware in 1867 remains a landmark in the history of American folk music. We have drawn upon it for a number of the beautiful but little known songs that appear in the selection that follows.

# Roll, Jordan, Roll

Lucy McKim called "Roll, Jordan, Roll" "one of the best known and noblest" of the spirituals. Describing the impression that the song made on her friends and herself, she wrote in 1862:

Perhaps the grandest singing we heard was at the Baptist Church, on St. Helena Island, when a congregation of three hundred men and women joined in a hymn:

> Roll, Jordan, roll, Jordan!
> Roll, Jordan, roll!

It swelled forth like a triumphal anthem. That same hymn was sung by thousands of Negroes on the Fourth of July last, when they marched in procession under the Stars and Stripes, cheering them for the first time as the "flag of *our* country." A friend, writing from there, says that the chorus was indescribably grand—"that the whole woods and world seemed joining in that rolling sound."

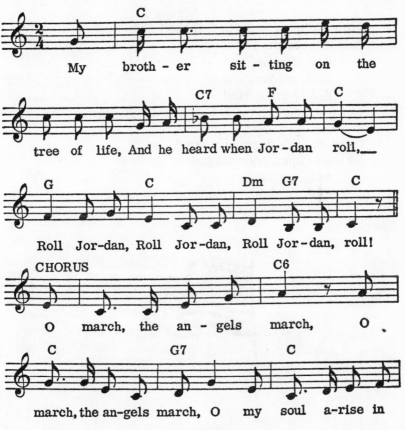

My broth - er sit - ting on the tree of life, And he heard when Jor - dan roll,__ Roll Jor-dan, Roll Jor-dan, Roll Jor-dan, roll!

CHORUS

O march, the an - gels march, O march, the an-gels march, O my soul a-rise in

Heav-en, Lord, For to hear when Jor-dan roll.

My sister sitting on the tree of life,
And she heard when Jordan roll,
    Roll,  Jordan,
    Roll,  Jordan,
    Roll, Jordan, roll!
*Chorus*

Massa Lincoln sittin' on the tree of life,
And he heard when Jordan roll,
    Roll,  Jordan,
    Roll,  Jordan,
    Roll, Jordan, roll!
*Chorus*

Little children, learn to fear the Lord,
And let your days be long,
    Roll,  Jordan,
    Roll,  Jordan,
    Roll, Jordan, roll!
*Chorus*

O, let no false or spiteful word,
Be found upon your tongue,
    Roll,  Jordan,
    Roll,  Jordan,
    Roll, Jordan, roll!
*Chorus*

# Sail, O Believer

For the Negro slave, a spiritual was something to live with, work with, pray with. American rivers and shores echoed to these melodies wherever slave stevedores worked, wherever slave oarsmen plied the longboats sailing from plantation to plantation.

Frances Ann Kemble, famous British actress, who resided in 1839 on her husband's sea island plantations at the estuary of the Altamaha river in Georgia, heard many of these boat songs. Her husband's plantations were on two islands separated by a distance of several miles, and she frequently traveled back and forth by boat. She has left the following commentary on the boat songs she heard:

My daily voyages up and down the river have introduced me to a great variety of new musical performances of our boatmen, who invariably, when the rowing is not too hard, moving up or down with the tide, accompany the stroke of their oars with the sound of their voices. . . . The way in which the chorus strikes in with the burden, between each phrase of the melody chanted by a single voice, is very curious and effective, especially with the rhythm of the rowlocks for accompaniment. The high voices all in unison, and the admirable time and true accent with which their responses are made, always makes me wish that some great musical composer could hear these semisavage performances. With a very little skillful adaptation and instrumentation, I think one or two barbaric chants and choruses might be evoked from them that would make the fortune of an opera.*

"Sail, O Believer" is a boat song that was sung by the slaves on the sea island of St. Helena; its place of origin is in the Hebrides. Changed into a spiritual, it illustrates the remarkable way in which Negro people assimilated the American musical heritage as a means to their own profound and creative expression.

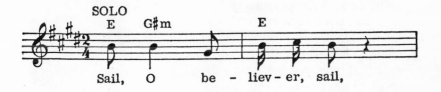

*Journal of a Residence on a Georgian Plantation 1838-1839* (New York: Knopf, 1961), 259-260.

2. Come view the promised land,
    Sail over yonder,
  Come view the promised land,
    Sail over yonder.

3. O brother lend a hand,
    Sail over yonder,
  O brother lend a hand,
    Sail over yonder.

4. O Mary, weep,
    Sail over yonder,
  Bow low, Martha,
    Sail over yonder.

5. For Jesus comes,
    Sail over yonder,
  And Jesus locks the door,
    Sail over yonder.

6. For Jesus comes,
    Sail over yonder,
  And carries the keys away,
    Sail over yonder.

7. Sail, O believer, sail,
    Sail over yonder,
  Sail, O my brother, sail,
    Sail over yonder.

## Poor Rosy

"Poor Rosy" is an excellent illustration of the many-sided nature and uses of the spiritual. "On the water," wrote Lucy McKim, who recorded this song among the slaves of Port Royal, "the oars dip 'Poor Rosy' to an even *andante;* a stout boy and girl at the hominy mill will make the same 'Poor Rosy' fly, to keep up with the whirling stone; and in the evening, after the day's work is done, *heaven shall-a be my home* peals up slowly and mournfully from the distant quarters." Next to "Roll, Jordan, Roll," "Poor Rosy" was evidently an all-time favorite among the sea island slaves whose feelings it so profoundly mirrors. "It can't be sung," a slave woman told Lucy, "without *a full heart and a troubled spirit.*" "Poor Rosy" possesses a deep vitality born of a combination of many moods: the contemplation of bliss, the hatred of evil and human wrong, the brooding expression of the sorrow of life, the dancing sense of tragedy and joy. American ballet, surely, will one day discover and make use of this melody.

The modality of the melody is mixed, that is, it is partly in a major, partly in a minor, key. Throughout the song, neither asserts its dominance. The scale is hexatonic, that is, with six rather than the usual seven tones.

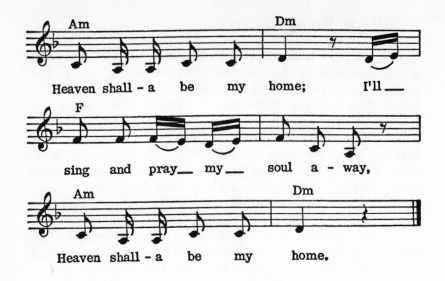

Heaven shall - a be my home; I'll

sing and pray — my — soul a - way,

Heaven shall - a be my home.

2. Got hard trials on my way,
   Got hard trials on my way,
   Got hard trials on my way,
       Heaven shall-a be my home.
   O when I walk and talk with God
       Heaven shall-a be my home.
   O when I walk and talk with God,
       Heaven shall-a be my home.

3. I got troubles on my way,
   I got troubles on my way,
   I got troubles on my way,
       Heaven shall-a be my home;
   Before I stay in hell one day,
       Heaven shall-a be my home.
   I'll sing and pray my soul away,
       Heaven shall-a be my home.

4. River Jordan, I'm bound to go,
   River Jordan, I'm bound to go,
   Rivér Jordan I am bound to go,
       Heaven shall-a be my home.
   Before I stay in hell one day.
       Heaven shall-a be my home.
   I'll sing and pray my soul away,
       Heaven shall-a be my home.

5. Brother Robert, I'm bound to go,
   Brother Robert, I'm bound to go,
   Brother Robert, I am bound to go,
       Heaven shall-a be my home
   O when I walk and talk with God,
       Heaven shall-a be my home,
   O when I walk and talk with God,
       Heaven shall-a be my home.

6. Sister Lucy, I'm bound to go,
   Sister Lucy, I'm bound to go,
   Sister Lucy, I am bound to go,
       Heaven shall-a be my home
   Before I stay in hell one day,
       Heaven shall-a be my home
   I'll sing and pray my soul away,
       Heaven shall-a be my home.

7. Poor Rosy, poor gal,
   Poor Rosy, poor gal,
   Rosy stole my poor heart,
       Heaven shall-a be my home.
   Oh, when I walk and talk with God
       Heaven shall-a be my home.
   Oh, when I walk and talk with God,
       Heaven shall-a be my home.

# Bound to Go

"Bound to Go," collected by C. P. Ware and W. F. Allen on St. Helena Island, is another example of a spiritual that served a practical purpose both as boat song and as marching song. Its rousing melody is that of an old sea shanty, "A Long Time Ago." The combination of this with the slave lyric produces a song of great spiritual as well as rhythmic impact.

I build my house up-on the rock,

O yes, Lord! No wind, no storm can

blow it down, O yes, Lord.

CHORUS

March on, mem-ber, bound to go;

Been to the fer-ry, bound to go;.

Left St. Hel-e-na, bound to go,

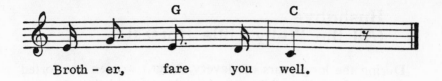

Broth - er, fare you well.

2. I build my house on shifting sand,
      O yes, Lord!
   The first wind come he blow him down,
      O yes, Lord.
*Chorus*


3. I am not like that foolish man,
      O yes, Lord!
   Who built his house upon the sand,
      O yes, Lord.
*Chorus*


4. One morning as I was walkin' along,
      O yes, Lord!
   I saw the berries a-hangin' down,
      O yes, Lord.
*Chorus*


5. I pick the berries and I suck the juice,
      O yes, Lord!
   He sweeter than the honeycomb,
      O yes, Lord.
*Chorus*


6. I took them, brother, two by two,
      O yes, Lord!
   I took them, sister, three by three,
      O yes, Lord.
*Chorus*

# Hushabye
## (All the Pretty Little Horses)

During the long years of slavery, Negro women comforted and cared for white children while their own babies lay unwatched in the shacks and fields. "Hushabye" is both lullaby and lament that comes down to us from slavery days through oral tradition. It has been found in various forms in many parts of the South.

Hushabye,
Don't you cry,
Go to sleepy, little baby;
Way down yonder,
In the meadow,
There's a poor little lambie,
The bees and the butterflies
Pickin' out his eyes,
The poor little thing cries "Mammy!"
Hushabye,
Don't you cry,
Go to sleepy, little baby.

# Sold Off to Georgy

"Sold Off to Georgy" is both lament and boat song. Conceivably it is among the very first slave songs to be noted down. George Tucker, a Virginia novelist, gave both words and music in his book, *The Valley of Shenandoah*, published in 1824. The melody uses only four tones, and is perhaps sung to best effect entirely unaccompanied. If an accompaniment is used, only one chord is required—in the setting given here, D minor. I cannot really justify the G minor chord that I have added, except that it heightens the sadness of the mood.

Farewell, ole plantation,
    Oho! Oho!
Farewell, de ole quarter,
    Oho! Oho!
An' daddy, an' mammy,
    Oho! Oho!
An' massa an' missus,
    Oho! Oho!

My dear wife and one child,
    Oho! Oho!
My poor heart is breaking,
    Oho! Oho!
No more shall I see you,
    Oho! Oho!
Oh, no more for ever,
    Oho! Oho!

# Hangman, Slack on the Line

The Negro people in slavery not only borrowed the melodies and lyrics of the white spirituals and turned them to their own creative purposes, but also drew upon the rest of the song heritage which had been brought from Europe, and which belongs to all Americans. And, of course, as Negro people sang these old songs, they modified them, rhythmically, melodically, lyrically.

"Hangman" is an excellent example of this process of borrowing and creative adaptation. Compare the Negro version of this children's favorite with the traditional version given on p. 14 above. Like the white version, this one also comes from Florida.

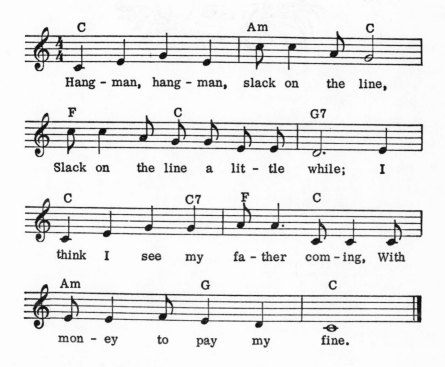

Hang - man, hang - man, slack on the line,
Slack on the line a lit - tle while; I
think I see my fa - ther com - ing, With
mon - ey to pay my fine.

2. O father, father, did you bring me money,
      Money to pay my fine?
   Or did you come here to see me die
      On this hangman's line?

3. No, I didn't bring you money,
   Money to pay your fine,
   But I just came here, to see you die,
   Upon this hangman's line.

*repeat sequence with mother, brother, sister,
and lover; the last of these concludes with*

15. True love, I got gold and silver,
    Money to pay your fine;
    How could I bear to see you die
    On this hangman's line?

From Dorothy Scarborough's *On the Trail of Negro Folk Songs*, Harvard University Press. Copyright 1925 by Harvard University Press, 1953 by Mary McDaniel Parker.

# Lay This Body Down

Colonel Thomas Wentworth Higginson, commander of the First South Carolina Volunteers, took down the lyrics of this song from the singing of his freedmen soldiers during the Civil War. He termed it "a flower of poetry in that dark soil."

"Lay This Body Down" is a spiritual that was also used as a boat song and a funeral chant. It is, perhaps, one of the most consummately simple and profound laments in the whole range of our music and literature. To the high wailing notes of this song, the sea island slaves were laid to rest in graveyards without fence or mark whose very location remains to this day forgotten.

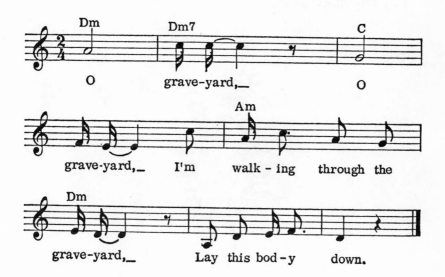

I know starlight,
I'm walking through the starlight,
Lay this body down.

I know moonlight,
I'm walking through the moonlight,
Lay this body down.

I lie in the grave,
I'm lying in the graveyard,
Lay this body down.

209

O graveyard, O graveyard,
I'm walking through the graveyard,
Lay this body down.

I go to judgment
In the evening of the day,
Lay this body down.

Your soul and my soul
Will meet on that day,
Lay this body down.

Graveyard, O graveyard,
I'm walking through the graveyard,
Lay this body down.

# Jimmy Rose

Dorothy Scarborough learned this dance song from Dr. John A. Wyeth of Texas, who spent his childhood and youth on a large plantation during slavery days and learned much about Negro music and musical instruments from the slaves themselves.

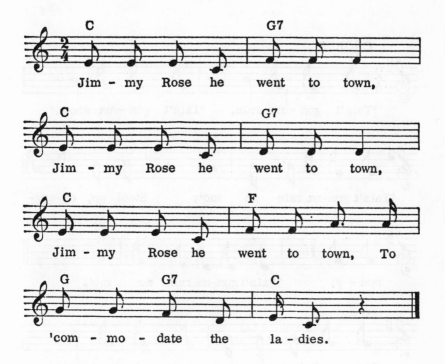

Jim - my Rose he went to town,
Jim - my Rose he went to town,
Jim - my Rose he went to town, To
'com - mo - date the la - dies.

Fare ye well, ye ladies all,
Fare ye well, ye ladies all,
Fare ye well, ye ladies all,
God Almighty bless you.

From Dorothy Scarborough's *On the Trail of Negro Folk Songs*, Harvard University Press. Copyright 1925 by Harvard University Press, 1953 by Mary McDaniel Parker

# T'ain't Gonna Rain No Mo'

Dorothy Scarborough describes this as "a famous old dance song, well known especially in Texas." It was a natural for minstrel shows, and in the 1920's became popular around the world—with different lyrics—on 78 r.p.m. records. It is thus notable as one of the few dance songs of slavery days that has been in continuous oral tradition since that time.

'Tain't gon - na rain, 'Tain't gon - na snow,
'Tain't gon-na rain no mo'; Steal up, ev-ery-
bod - y, T'ain't gon-na rain no mo'.
Ole cow died at the mouth of the branch,
T'ain't gon-na rain no mo'. The buz-zards had a
pub - lic dance, 'Tain't gon-na rain no mo'.

*Chorus*

What did the blackbird say to the crow?
    'Tain't gonna rain no mo'.
'Tain't gonna hail and 'tain't gonna snow,
    'Tain't gonna rain no mo'.

*Chorus*

Gather corn in a beegum hat,
    'Tain't gonna rain no mo'.
Oh massa grumble if you eat much of that,
    'Tain't gonna rain no mo'.

*Chorus*

Two, two, and round up four,
    'Tain't gonna rain no mo'.
Two, two, and round up four,
    'Tain't gonna rain no mo'.

*Chorus*

Six, two, and round up four,
    'Tain't gonna rain no mo'.
Six, two, and round up four,
    'Tain't gonna rain no mo'.

*Chorus*

# The Rose of Alabama

The words and music of this song were published as sheet music in Boston in 1846, after it had become part of the repertoire of a minstrel troupe known as the "Ethiopian Serenaders." The words, by Silas S. Steele, were set to a melody which was described in the *Negro Song Book* of 1848 as "a sweet and genuine plantation air, fresh from the fields." "The Rose of Alabama" remained popular for a number of years and was a favorite of Southern soldiers during the Civil War.

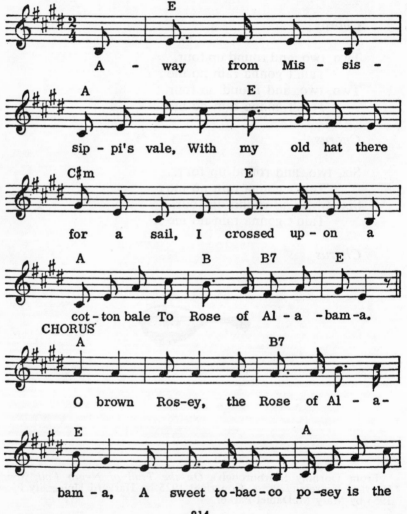

Rose of Al - a - bam-a, A sweet to-bac-co po -sey is the Rose of Al - a - bam-a.

I landed on the sandbank,
I sat upon a hollow plank,
And there I made the banjo twank,
  For Rose of Alabama.

*Chorus*

I asked her to set down where she please,
So cross my legs she took her ease,
"It's good to go upon the knees,"
  Says Rose of Alabama.

*Chorus*

The river rolled, the crickets sing,
The lightning bug he flashed his wing,
And like a rope my arms I fling
  Round Rose of Alabama.

*Chorus*

I hug so long I cannot tell,
For Rosey seemed to like it well,
My banjo in the river fell,
  Oh Rose of Alabama.

*Chorus*

Like alligator after prey,
I plunge in, but it float away,
And all the time it seemed to say,
  "Oh Rose of Alabama."

*Chorus*

And every night in moon or shower,
To hunt that banjo for an hour,
I meet my sweet tobacco flower,
  My Rose of Alabama.

*Chorus*

215

# V
# THE
# CIVIL
# WAR

THE CIVIL WAR resembled the Revolution and the War of 1812 in that it produced many topical songs designed to meet the urgent needs of the moment: to celebrate victory, fortify convictions, taunt the enemy, steel the soul for battle, and provide solace. It was a time when literary and musical activity flowered with a great intensity.

Thousands of ordinary, anonymous Americans—soldiers, civilians, nurses, housewives, and ministers—wrote these songs and verses, which were often sung to traditional ballad tunes. Numbers of these songs were printed as broadsides and circulated in factory, field, and camp by the tens of thousands of copies. Here, the Civil War continued and enriched the broadside ballad tradition of colonial and early national times. Professional songwriters also turned to writing war songs and found a wide and ready market for their compositions. Much money was made by publishers, especially in New York and Philadelphia, from the distribution and sale of low-priced popular songbooks and sheet music.

Notwithstanding its grandeur, much of this Civil War material has vanished from popular tradition. It is obscurely preserved in the music files, broadside, songster, and manuscript collections of public and university libraries and private homes. Yet, from a historical viewpoint, this heritage has an immense significance. The story of the Civil War may quite literally be told through its songs: there was hardly a battle that did not produce at least one major song, and many battles gave rise to several or even innumerable songs.

At a deeper level, the music of the Civil War provides a commentary on human life and fate; it gives us a key to the moods, thoughts, and agonies of a generation of Americans. The Civil War was also remarkable because for the first time hundreds of thousands of Negro Americans were fighting in it for freedom as free men. White soldiers listened to the singing of Negro troops and were deeply moved by the experience. The war, indeed, produced the first major impact of Negro singing upon the nation.

Some of the greatest freedom songs that we inherit were created in the fires of this war. Here, we reproduce a few of the songs that generally but vividly outline the story of the conflict, and that tell something of the moods and experiences which so many of the lyrics then written sought to express.

# The Northern Bonny Blue Flag

When Fort Sumter fell before the cannon of the rebellious South on April 12, 1861, Northerners flocked to the colors in a blaze of passion. Though many of them felt that slavery was wrong, few foresaw that the main purpose of the war would be the ending of slavery. What most people cared about was the defense of the Union, its unity, its sovereignty, and its flag. This simple and dignified lyric by Isaac Ball, set to a traditional Irish tune, expressed the Union mood in the early months of the conflict. It also provided an answer to the popular Confederate song that boasted a single star on the "bonny blue flag" of secession, and that proclaimed, as the purpose of the war, the defense of Southern property and rights.

We're fight - ing for our Un - ion, We're
fight - ing for our trust, We're
fight - ing for that hap - py land, Where
sleeps our fa - thers' dust. It
can - not be dis - sev - ered, Though it

cost us blood-y wars, We
nev-er can give up the land Where
floats the Stripes and Stars. Hur-rah! hur-rah! For
e-qual rights, hur-rah! Hur-
rah! for the good old flag, That
bears the Stripes and Stars.

We do not want your cotton,
    We care not for your slaves,
But rather than divide this land,
    We'll fill your Southern graves.
With Lincoln for our Chieftain,
    We'll bear our country's scars,
We'll rally round the brave old flag
    That bears the Stripes and Stars.

*Chorus*

## The Bonny Blue Flag (Southern)

We are a band of brothers,
    And native to the soil,
Fighting for the property
    We gained by honest toil;
And when our rights were threatened,
    The cry rose near and far:
"Hurrah for the Bonny Blue Flag
    That bears a single star!"

                 (abridged)

# Song of the Southern Volunteers

In 1861, the *volunteer* was the hero, and many of the songs told of volunteering, or urged it. "The Song of the Southern Volunteers," with its sense of loneliness underlying a pose of bravado and its haunting refrain, has been widely found throughout the South. To this day, the melody is a favorite with children.

CHORUS

We go walk‑ing on the green grass, thus, thus, thus: Come all ye fair and pret‑ty maids, and walk a‑long with us; So pret‑ty and so fair as you take your‑selves to be, I'll choose you for a part‑ner, come walk a‑long with me.

I would not marry a lawyer, who's pleading at the bar,
I'd rather marry a soldier boy who wears a Southern star,
Soldier boy, etc.

*Chorus*

I would not marry a doctor who tries to heal the sick,
I'd rather marry a soldier boy who marches double quick,
Soldier boy, etc.

*Chorus*

222

I would not be a lady that Southrons call a belle,
I'd rather be a soldier boy and hear the Yankees yell,
Soldier boy, etc.
*Chorus*

I would not be a nursemaid and hear the children squall,
I'd rather be a soldier boy and face a cannon ball,
Soldier boy, etc.
*Chorus*

I would not be a farmer who's toiling in the sun,
I'd rather be a soldier boy and see the Yankees run,
Soldier boy, etc.
*Chorus*

I would not be a miller who grinds the people's grain,
I'd rather be a soldier boy who walks through wind and
    rain,
Soldier boy, etc.
*Chorus*

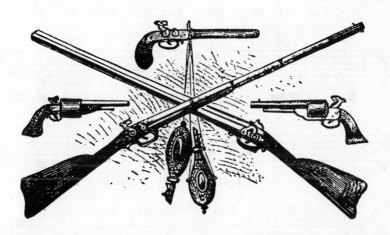

# Flag of the Free

Among the first of the Union volunteers to rush to the colors were Irish immigrants. Few brought antislavery convictions with them from the Old World; most knew little about the Negro and cared less. But they loved their adopted land, and its cause was theirs. Irish were also to be found in the Confederate forces, though to a lesser extent. One way or the other, they filled graves on every battlefield in the Civil War.

"Flag of the Free" was a recruiting song. It was set to one of the loveliest of Gaelic melodies, "Eibhleen a Ruin" (Treasure of My Heart), a love song of beauty and simplicity. In the middle of the eighteenth century, Lady Caroline Keppel had set English lyrics to "Eibhleen," and it became known to the English-speaking world, including the United States, as "Robin Adair." Then, the Civil War inspired the writing of a uniquely American lyric.

Could we de-sert you now, Flag of the Free; When we a sol-emn vow, Flag of the Free, You from all harm to save, Made when we crossed the wave, And you_ a_ wel-come gave, Flag of the Free?

2. Are we now cowards grown,
         Flag of the Free?
   Would we you now disown,
         Flag of the Free?
   You to whose folds we've fled,
   You in whose cause we've bled,
   Bearing you at our head,
         Flag of the Free?

3. Could we desert you now,
         Flag of the Free,
   And to black traitors bow,
         Flag of the Free?
   Never! through good and ill,
   Ireland her blood will spill,
   Bearing you onward still,
         Flag of the Free.

# The Yankee Man o' War

The Civil War began in a light-hearted mood. The bands played, the men marched in their bright uniforms, the flags waved, and the girls flocked around. It would be easy, thought the Northerners, to teach the rebels a lesson in one summer's campaign, and be home again before winter set in. But this rosy dream was soon shattered by the Battle of Manassas, or First Bull Run, in July, 1861. The first test of strength saw the Union troops streaming back to Washington, hanging their heads in shame.

If the North was to face stern trials by land, it retained control of the navy from the very beginning of the conflict. This would prove a decisive factor in the eventual Union victory. In 1861, Abraham Lincoln threw a tight blockade around the Southern coasts; as the stranglehold tightened, overseas trade, the Confederacy's windpipe, was throttled.

"The Yankee Man o' War" is taken from the manuscript ballad book of James Ashby of Holt County, Missouri, the entry dated May 7, 1876. The theme of a young man's parting from his sweetheart was a familiar one in British broadside ballads; only minor changes were needed to produce a song appropriate to the Civil War. The ancient melody with which the lyrics are here linked is a variant of "The Lowlands of Holland," a traditional ballad that tells of a lover departed and lost at sea.

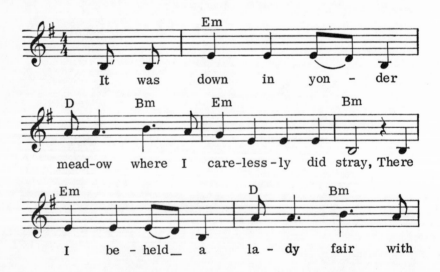

It was down in yonder mead-ow where I care-less-ly did stray, There I be-held a la-dy fair with

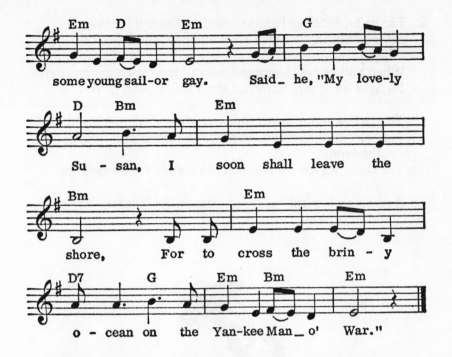

some young sail-or gay. Said he, "My love-ly
Su - san, I soon shall leave the
shore, For to cross the brin - y
o - cean on the Yan-kee Man o' War."

2. Young Susan she fell weeping, "Young sailor," she did say,
   "How can you be so venturesome and throw yourself away?
   For by the time I'm twenty-one I shall receive my store,
   So Willie, do not venture on the Yankee Man o' War."

3. "O Susan, lovely Susan, the truth to you I'll tell;
   The South she has insulted us, the North she knows it well.
   I may be crowned with laurels just like some jolly tar;
   And I'll face the forts of the rebels on the Yankee
       Man o' War."

4. "How can you be so venturesome for to face the Southern
       foes?
   When they are far in battle, love, they never take a man;
   And from some bloody weapon you might receive a scar,
   So Willie, do not venture on the Yankee Man o' War."

5. "O Susan, lovely Susan, the time will quickly pass;
   Let's go down to the ferryhouse and take the parting glass;
   My shipmates they are waiting to row me from the shore,
   And it's for America's glory on the Yankee Man o' War."

6.  The sailor took his handkerchief and tore it into two,
    Saying "Susan, you may keep one half, the other I'll keep
        for you
    When bullets may surround me and the rebel cannon roar,
    I'll fight for lovely Susan on the Yankee Man o' War."

7.  Then a few more words together, then she let go his hand;
    The jolly crew surrounded him and rowed him from
        the land.
    The sailor waved his handkerchief when far away from
        shore,
    And Susan blessed her sailor love on the Yankee
        Man o' War.

From *Ballads and Songs Collected by the Missouri Folk-Lore So-ciety*, edited by H. M. Belden. University of Missouri Studies: Columbia, Missouri, 1955. Reprinted by permission.

# The Homespun Dress

The South could and did run the blockade, could harass Northern commerce with its raiders and privateers, and could even sink battleships like the *Cumberland*. But without British help the South could not break the blockade. As the war went on, and the Northern stranglehold tightened, Southerners either had to go without, or make for themselves. Southern women took to weaving homespun, and this symbolic act of dedication to country soon found expression in song. "The Homespun Dress" was evidently popular in the South before the end of the war, and by 1865 was sufficiently well known to be published in New York. Frank Moore, famous Civil War song collector, gives the following account of how the song came into his possession:

> The accompanying song was taken from a letter of a Southern girl to her lover in Lee's army, which letter was obtained from a mail captured on Sherman's march through northern Alabama. The materials of which the dress alluded to is made are of cotton and wool, and woven on the hand-loom, so commonly seen in the houses of the South. The scrap of a dress, enclosed in the letter as a sample, was of a gray color, with a stripe of crimson and green—quite pretty and creditable to the lady who made it.
>
> The lines are not a false indication of the universal sentiment of the women of the South, who by the encouragement they have extended the soldiers and the sacrifices they have made, have exercised an influence which has proved of the greatest importance to the rebels, and have shown what can be accomplished by united effort on the part of the gentle sex.*

O yes, I am a Southern girl,
 And glory in the name,
I boast of it with greater pride
 Than glittering wealth and fame.
I envy not the Northern girl
 Her robes of beauty rare
Though diamonds deck her snowy neck
 And pearls bestud her hair.

*Chorus*

  Hurrah, hurrah, for the sunny South I say,
  Three cheers for the homespun dress
  The Southern ladies wear.

*\*The Civil War in Song and Ballad* (New York, 1865), 174.
For the melody, see pp. 218-9, "The Bonny Blue Flag."

229

Now Northern goods are out of date,
    And since old Abe's blockade,
We Southern girls can be content
    With goods that Southrons made,
We send our sweethearts to the war,
    But girls never you mind,
Your soldier love will not forget,
    The girl he left behind.

*Chorus*

The Southern land's a glorious land
    And has a glorious cause,
Three cheers, three cheers for Southern rights
    And for the Southern boys;
We scorn to wear a bit of silk,
    A bit of Northern lace,
But make our homespun dresses up,
    And wear them with a grace.

*Chorus*

And now young man a word for you
    If you would win the fair,
Go to the field where honor calls,
    And win your lady there.
Remember that our bravest smiles
    Are for the true and brave,
And that our tears are all for those
    Who fill a soldier's grave.

*Chorus*

# On to Richmond!

In the spring of 1862, General George McClellan, the dashing commander of the Army of the Potomac, took the initiative after months of inactivity. Afraid to launch a direct attack on the Confederate capital of Richmond, McClellan instead worked out an elaborate flanking movement. He took his army by sea down the Virginia coast, and landed it between the York and James rivers. "On to Richmond!" yelled the newspapers.

As the Union troops moved ponderously forward, Robert E. Lee was placed in command of the Southern forces. At the end of June, 1862, Lee drove off McClellan in the famous and bloody series of engagements known as the Seven Days' Fight. The South rightly celebrated a brilliant victory with a very catchy song.

"Well,__ we have the na-vy an'__ we have the men, For-ward, on to Rich-mond, to storm the reb-el den, On to Rich-mond, so ear-ly in the morn-in', On to

Rich-mond!" I heard the Yan-kees say.

"We'll flank it on the North an' we'll shell it on the South,
We'll storm it on the East an' we'll run the rebels out,
On to Richmond, so early in the mornin',
On to Richmond!" I heard the Yankees say.

Lee was in the center an' Jackson in the rear,
An' on the right and left side the noble hills appear,
Longstreet he had to travel, an' branches had to cross,
An' old McGruder was about to give the Yankees grass.

It was about the first of June when the balls began to fly,
The Yankees took an' wheeled about an' changed their
    battle cry,
"Off from Richmond, so early in the mornin',
Down to the gunboats! Run boys, run."

Florida is a-hunting, an' a huntin' through the brush,
The rebels are in earnest, push boys, push,
The Louisiana Legion, Butler was the cry,
The Texas Rangers comin', fly boys, fly.

Virginia is a-comin' with her death-defying steel,
Georgia is a-chargin' across the swamps and fields,
"Off from Richmond, so early in the mornin',
Down to the gunboats, run boys, run."

"The Palmetto rebels is now upon the trail,
And the Arkansas devils want to ride us on a rail,
Never mind your knapsacks, never mind your guns,
A-fightin' these rebels it ain't no fun."

McClellan is a humbug and Lincoln is a fool,
All of them is liars of the highest greeting school,
A home was the promise, an' every man a slave,
You better run North, or you'll all find a grave.

# General Lee's Wooing

By the summer of 1862, the North had scored a number of victories in the West and had taken New Orleans, but the South remained undefeated. The Union's hour of peril was at hand. Lee, having blunted McClellan's offensive in the Seven Days' Fight, began the attack. He swept northward, defeated Pope at Manassas, and placed himself astride the Potomac west of Washington. The world held its breath. If Lee could not be stopped as he headed toward Maryland and Pennsylvania, the end of the war was near.

General McClellan rallied the Union forces and met Lee at Antietam Creek in Maryland on September 17, 1862. Neither side could claim victory in the horrible carnage, but Lee suffered a severe check and was obliged to fall back. On September 24, Abraham Lincoln issued the first Emancipation Proclamation promising freedom to all slaves in States still in rebellion on January 1, 1863.

An anonymous Northern soldier wrote "General Lee's Wooing" following the battle of Antietam. These verses, among the finest penned during the war, illuminate in a single flash the meaning of the struggle at Antietam Creek. It was a battle worthy of commemoration, for it proved to be a decisive turning point in the war. Emancipation of the slaves gave the country a crusading cause, rallied the flagging energies of the North, won the sympathy of the world, and brought tens of thousands of black recruits into armies shaken by ghastly losses. British recognition of the South and her intervention in the South's behalf were alike ruled out. Confederate hopes of victory received a crushing blow.

My Mar - y -land, my Mar - y -land, I
bring thee pres - ents fine, A daz-zling sword with

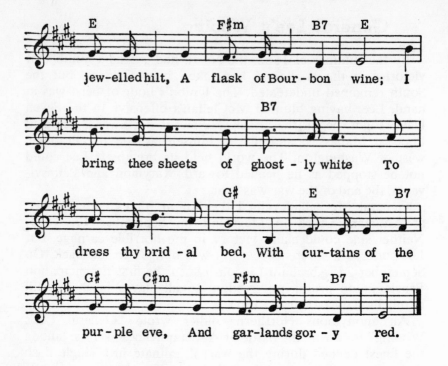

jew-elled hilt, A flask of Bour-bon wine; I

bring thee sheets of ghost-ly white To

dress thy brid-al bed, With cur-tains of the

pur-ple eve, And gar-lands gor-y red.

My Maryland, my Maryland,
   Sweet land upon the shore,
Bring out thy stalwart yeomanry,
   Make clean the threshing floor.
My ready wains lie stretching far
   Across the fertile plain,
And I among the reapers stand
   To gather in the grain.

My Maryland, my Maryland,
   I fondly wait to see
Thy banner flaunting in the breeze,
   Beneath the trysting tree.
While all my gallant company
   Of gentlemen with spurs,
Come tramping, tramping o'er the hills,
   And tramping through the furze.

My Maryland, my Maryland,
   I feel the leaden rain,
I see the winged messenger,
   Come hurling to my brain.
I feathered with thy golden hair,
   'Tis feathered now in vain,
I spurn the hand that loosed the shaft
   And curse thee in my pain.

My Maryland, my Maryland,
   Alas the ruthless day,
That sees my gallant buttonwoods
   Ride galloping away;
And ruthless for my chivalry,
   Proud gentlemen with spurs,
Whose bones lie stark upon the hills,
   And stark among the furze.

# What Gives the Wheat Fields Blades of Steel?

On January 1, 1863, the slaves were freed. This day saw the dawning of a new idea in the United States: that in this land the destinies of Negro and white are forever linked, that the white man may never be wholly free while the Negro remains a slave.

On this day, Lincoln inscribed upon the Union banners the message that slavery was the enemy and that its extinction was necessary for the survival of the Union. This, too, was the message of the great antislavery hymn, "What Gives the Wheat Fields Blades of Steel?" by John Greenleaf Whittier, composed in 1862, and set to the tune of Martin Luther's "A Mighty Fortress is our God." It mirrored the new mood and understanding that would sustain the Union soldiers to the end.

We wait beneath the furnace-blast
        The pangs of transformation:
Not painlessly doth God recast
        And mould anew the nation.
                Hot burns the fire
                Where wrongs expire;
                Nor spares the hand
                That from the land
Uproots the ancient evil.

The hand-breadth cloud the sages feared
        Its bloody rain is dropping;
The poison plant the father spared
        All else is overtopping.
                East, West, South, North,
                It curses the earth;
                All justice dies
                And fraud and lies
Live only in its shadow.

What thought the cast-out spirit tear
        The nation in his going?
We who have shared the guilt must share
        The pang of his overthrowing!
                Whate'er the loss
                Whate'er the cross
                Shall they complain
                Of present pain
Who trust in God hereafter?

(abridged)

237

# Freedom Songs

Frederick Douglass, runaway slave and leader of the Negro, urged his people to rally to the Union cause and take arms to win freedom. By so doing, said he, they would win for themselves "the gratitude of our country and the best blessings of posterity through all time." The Negro people responded to his call and flocked to the colors. Over 100,000 of them actually served in the armed forces. Lincoln himself acknowledged that their contribution was decisive.

The great spirituals of slavery days went to battle with tens of thousands of Negro soldiers who fought the Confederacy and laid down their lives for the Stars and Stripes. New songs, too, were born of the new mood generated by emancipation and the war itself. We have space for only three of these here: "Many Thousand Gone" and "Oh, Freedom!" express the Negro's reaction to the end of slavery and the birth of a new vision of happiness, and rank among the great freedom songs of the modern era. "Song of the Freedmen" first appeared in the popular songsters in 1864 and was evidently a marching favorite of the Negro soldiers.

## Many Thousand Gone

No more auc - tion block for me, No more, no more; No more auc - tion block for_ me, Man - y thou - sand gone.

No more peck of corn for me,
No more, no more;
No more peck of corn for me,
Many thousand gone.

No more driver's lash for me,
No more, no more;
No more driver's lash for me,
Many thousand gone.

No more pint of salt for me,
No more, no more;
No more pint of salt for me,
Many thousand gone.

## Oh, Freedom!

Oh,____ free-dom! oh,____ free-dom!
Oh, free-dom o - ver me; And before I'll be a slave, I'll lie
bur - ied in my grave, And go
home to my Lord and____ be free.

2. No more moaning, no more moaning,
   No more moaning over me;
   And before I'll be a slave,
   I'll lie buried in my grave,
   And go home to my Lord, and be free.

3. No more mourning, no more mourning,
   No more mourning over me;
   And before I'll be a slave, etc.

4. No more weeping, no more weeping,
   No more weeping over me;
   And before I'll be a slave, etc.

5. No more sighing, no more sighing,
   No more sighing over me;
   And before I'll be a slave, etc.

6. Oh, what singing, oh, what singing,
   Oh, what singing over me;
   And before I'll be a slave, etc.

7. Oh, what shouting, oh, what shouting,
   Oh, what shouting over me;
   And before I'll be a slave, etc.

8. Oh, freedom! Oh, freedom!
   Oh, freedom over me;
   And before I'll be a slave, etc.

## Song of the Freedmen

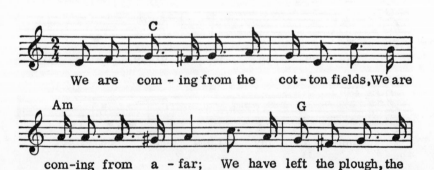

We are com-ing from the cot-ton fields, We are
com-ing from a - far; We have left the plough, the

240

hoe, the axe, And we are going to war. We have

left the old plan - ta - tion seat, The

sug-ar and the cane, Where we worked and toiled with

wea - ry feet, In sun and wind and rain.

CHORUS

Then come a - long my boys, O,

come, come a - long, Then come a-long my

broth - ers, O come, come a - long. We are

com - ing from the cot - ton fields, We are

com-ing from a - far; We have left the plough, the

hoe, the axe, And we are going to war.

We will leave our chains behind us, boys,
    The prison and the rack;
And we'll hide beneath a soldier's coat
    The scars upon our back;
And we'll teach the world a lesson soon,
    If taken by the hand,
How night shall come before 'tis noon
    Upon old Pharaoh's land.
*Chorus*

# A Plaint

After Antietam, the Union again took the offensive and tried to break through to Richmond, but sustained enormous losses without good result. In May, 1863, Lee stopped the Union armies at Chancellorsville and, repeating the feat of the previous year, at once passed over to the attack. Again the grey tide rolled northward, up the Shenandoah Valley, past Washington, into Pennsylvania; and again the Union braced itself for a decisive struggle. Three days of bloody conflict at Gettysburg in July, and Lee's army was broken. Long lines limped south; the wounded and the dying left bloody tracks in the dust. But Gettysburg was only a partial victory, for the Southern armies were broken, not destroyed. A long, heartbreaking struggle still lay ahead.

By spring of 1864, Lincoln was ready for the final offensive. Grant came to Washington and assumed command of all Federal forces; his plan was to pin Lee down in Virginia with the Army of the Potomac while the Army of the Cumberland slashed through Georgia deep in the Confederate rear. One of the best of the songs that told of Grant's last Virginia campaign is a Southron's lament that, as far as we know, was not set to music. A. E. Townsend's "Plaint" over the havoc of war in his native Virginia is reproduced below.

> Alas! for the pleasant peace we knew
> In the happy summers of long ago,
> When the rivers were bright and the sky was blue
> By the homes of Henrico.
> We dreamed of wars that were far away
> And read, as in fable, of blood that ran
> Where the James and Chickahominy stray,
> Through the groves of Powhatan.
>
> 'Tis a dream come true, for the afternoons,
> Blow bugles of war by our fields of grain,
> And the sabres sink as the dark dragoons
> Come galloping up the lane;
> The pigeons have flown from the eaves and tiles,
> The oat-blades have grown to blades of steel,
> And the Huns swarm down the leafy aisles
> Of the grand old commonweal.

They have torn the Indian fisher's nets
Where the gray Pamunkey goes toward the sea,
And blood runs red in the rivulets
That babbled and brawled in glee;
The corpses are strewn in Fair Oak glades,
The hoarse guns thunder from Drewry's Ridge,
The fishes that played in the cool deep shades
Are frightened from Bottom Bridge.

I would that the years were blotted away,
And the strawberries green in the hedge again;
That the scythe might swing in the tangled hay,
And the squirrels romp in the glen;
The walnuts sprinkle the clover slopes
Where graze the sheep and the spotted steer,
And the winter restore the golden hopes
That were trampled in a year.

# Roll, Alabama, Roll

Throughout the war, the Confederacy with the aid of a number of cruisers built in British yards, harassed Union commerce. One of the most notorious of these raiders was the *Alabama,* which for two years roamed the high seas taking prize ships and sinking Northern craft.

The *Alabama* met her end on June 19, 1864, when the U.S. man o' war *Kearsarge* ran her down and sank her off the port of Cherbourg in Normandy. Hundreds of Southern sailors lost their lives in the brief but disastrous encounter.

William H. Cushman, chief engineer of the *Kearsarge,* wrote to his mother the following laconic description of the engagement:

We have met the celebrated "pirate Alabama" and *sunk* her, after 1 hour and 30 minutes hard fighting. She came out of Cherbourg, about 10 a.m. accompanied by the *Couronne,* a French ironclad; when at about one mile she commenced firing at 11 a.m., we waited 20 minutes until we got the range we wanted, then commenced. After firing 1 hour and 5 minutes we had the pleasure of seeing her haul down her flag (it had been twice shot down) and then surrender. Before we could launch our two good boats to get them to her, she sunk beautifully. We had hardly got warmed up and expected to fight several hours. Only 3 of our men wounded, one quarter gunner lost his arm (of the three), an officer wounded. We picked up 6 officers and 69 of the men.*

Cushman's share of the prize money given as a reward for this feat was $5,800. Officers received a disproportionate share of such bonus pay provided by the government or various American cities and this often caused resentment among the enlisted men. This is well expressed in the following anecdote that went the rounds during the war. A vessel was about to go into action, and one sailor lad was on his knees. An officer sneeringly asked him, if he was afraid?

"No, I was praying," was the response.

"Well, what were you praying for?"

"Praying," said the sailor, "that the enemy's bullets may be distributed the same way as the prize money is, *principally among the officers.*"

"Roll, Alabama, Roll" tells the story of the *Alabama* and its fate clearly, dispassionately, and concisely. The tune is that of a roustabout song and halyard shanty "Roll the Cotton Down." "Roll, Alabama, Roll" itself continued in use as a halyard

*Cherbourg. June 19, 1864. In *Letters and Papers Relating to the Sinking of the Confederate Cruiser Alabama.* Library of Congress, Division of Manuscripts.

shanty. Stan Hugill relates that he heard a variant of this song in Gisborne, New Zealand in 1925. The husband of the lady who sang it for him had been a seaman on the *Alabama*.

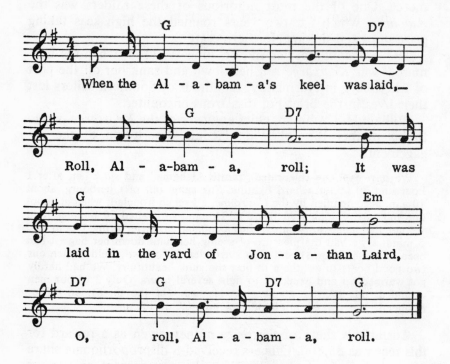

When the Al - a - bam - a's keel was laid,—
Roll, Al - a-bam - a, roll; It was
laid in the yard of Jon - a - than Laird,
O, roll, Al - a - bam - a, roll.

2.  It was laid in the yard of Jonathan Laird,
    Roll, Alabama, roll;
    It was laid in the town of Birkenhead,
    O, roll, Alabama, roll.

3.  Down the Mersey ways she rolled then,
    Roll, Alabama, roll;
    Liverpool fitted her with guns and men,
    O, roll, Alabama, roll.

4.  From the Western Isles she sailed forth,
    Roll, Alabama, roll;
    To destroy the commerce of the North,
    O, roll, Alabama, roll.

5. To Cherbourg port she sailed one day,
        Roll, Alabama, roll;
    To take her count of prize monnay,
        O, roll, Alabama, roll.

6. Many a sailor lad he saw his doom,
        Roll, Alabama, roll;
    When the Kearsarge hove in view,
        O, roll, Alabama, roll.

7. A ball from the forward pivot that day,
        Roll, Alabama, roll;
    Shot the Alabama's stern away,
        O, roll, Alabama, roll.

8. Off the three mile limit in '64,
        Roll, Alabama, roll;
    The Alabama sank to the ocean floor,
        O, roll, Alabama, roll.

# Sherman's March to the Sea

The two phases of Grant's plan of attack were launched simultaneously. While Grant crossed the Rapidan and headed into the wilderness, Sherman advanced down the railroad from Chattanooga to Atlanta. In September, 1864, began the famous march to the sea, cutting a swath of desolation 60 miles broad and 300 miles long through central Georgia to Savannah. Sherman reached his objective on the Georgia coast in December, 1864 and then turned north.

News of Sherman's advance preceded him. In Charleston jail, hundreds of ragged Federals eagerly awaited deliverance. One of them, Lieutenant S. H. M. Byers, composed "Sherman's March to the Sea." The simple but imaginative lyric was frequently sung to the tune of "Rosin the Beau," a much parodied Irish melody that finds in the poem here reproduced its perfect mate. This song was seized upon in the North and became a smash hit, appearing in songsters and song sheets by the hundred thousand copies.

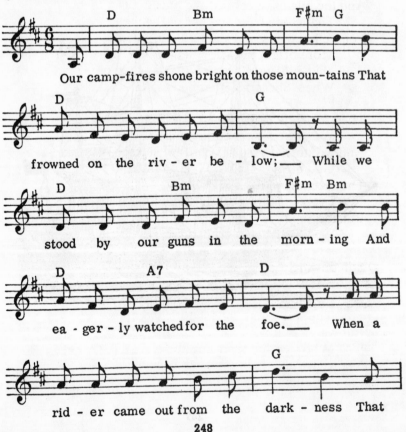

Our camp-fires shone bright on those moun-tains That
frowned on the riv - er be - low;__ While we
stood by our guns in the morn - ing And
ea - ger - ly watched for the foe.__ When a
rid - er came out from the dark - ness That

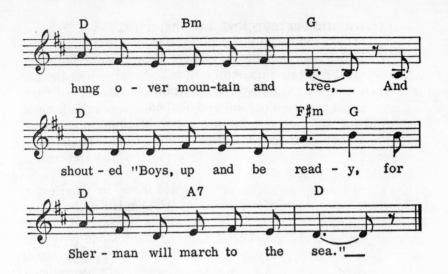

hung o-ver moun-tain and tree,__ And
shout-ed "Boys, up and be read-y, for
Sher-man will march to the sea."__

Then cheer upon cheer for bold Sherman
    Went up from each valley and glen,
And the bugles re-echoed the music
    That came from the lips of the men.
For we knew that the stars on our banner
    More bright in their splendor would be,
And that blessings from Northland would greet us,
    When Sherman marched down to the sea.

Then forward, boys, forward to battle,
    We marched on our wearisome way,
And we stormed the wild hills of Resaca,
    God bless those who fell on that day!
Then Kenesaw, dark in its glory
    Frowned down on the flag of the free,
But the East and the West bore our standards
    And Sherman marched down to the sea.

Still onward we pressed, til our banners
    Swept out from Atlanta's grim walls,
And the blood of the patriot dampened
    The soil where the traitor's flag falls;
But we paused not to weep for the fallen,
    Who slept by river and tree,
Yet we twined them a wreath of laurel
    As Sherman marched down to the sea.

O proud was our army that morning,
  That stood where the pine proudly towers,
When Sherman said "Boys, you are weary,
  This day fair Savannah is ours."
Then sung we a song for our chieftain
  That echoed o'er land and o'er lea,
And the stars on our banner shone brighter,
  When Sherman marched down to the sea.

# The Southern Girl's Reply

Grant's offensive lasted for almost one year, from May 1864 to April 1865. The Federals paid in blood for every inch of Southern soil; but the more that died, the more came. Seemingly, there was no end to the blue-clad swarm seeking graves in Southern earth. Grant led his soldiers to victory, and death. They adored him and died for him. As they marched down the Southern lanes and stormed the Southern trenches, his name was on their lips.

> "Our army has a leader now," they sang,
> "That's gallant, true, and brave;
> Though many a one we've had before
> Has proved himself a knave,
> And honesty's been laid aside
> While scrambling after pelf,
> As one by one we've found them out,
> And laid them on the shelf.
>
> "Hurrah! Hurrah! Hurrah!
> For Grant's the man to lead the van,
> The rest are all too slow;
> But let old Grant down on them come,
> Away the rebels go."

One year of bitter fighting, and the Confederacy lay in ruins. On Palm Sunday, April 9, 1865, Robert Lee, in tears, rode out to his men and told them that the war was at an end. They would ride home in defeat; at the end of the road, they would find poverty, ashes, and despair.

Slavery had divided the American people. Years would pass before a common love of freedom could reunite them. And there would be, as a Southern girl sang to her Northern wooer, a legacy of blood and bitterness in a divided land. This song, to the tune of the "Bonny Blue Flag" (see p. 218), was first published in 1865. It has been in continuous oral tradition since that time.

> I cannot listen to your words,
> The land's too far and wide,
> Go seek some happy Northern girl
> To be your loving bride.
> My brothers they were soldiers;
> The youngest of the three
> Was slain while fighting by the side
> Of General Fitzhugh Lee.

Hurrah, hurrah,
For the sunny South I say,
Three cheers for the Southern girl
And the boy that wore the Gray.

My lover was a soldier too,
  He fought at God's command;
A sabre pierced his gallant heart,
  You might have been the man;
He reeled and fell but was not dead,
  A horseman spurred his steed,
And trampled on his dying brain—
  You might have done the deed.

Hurrah, hurrah, etc.

They left his body on the field,
  Who the fight this day had won,
A horseman spurred him with his heel,
  You might have been the one.
I hold no hatred in my heart,
  Nor cold and righteous pride,
For many a gallant soldier fell
  Upon the other side.

Hurrah, hurrah, etc.

But still I cannot take the hand
  That smote my country sore,
Or love the foe that trampled down
  The colors that she wore;
Between my heart and yours there runs
  A deep and crimson tide,
My lover's and my brothers' blood
  Forbids me be your bride.

Hurrah, hurrah, etc.

# VI

# Between
# The
# Civil War
# And The
# First
# World War

THE PERIOD BETWEEN the Civil War and the First World War was in some ways analogous to the Jacksonian era, but on a more stupendous scale. At the end of the war, in 1865, America turned with a kind of frenzy to economic expansion. Industrialization, given great impetus by the war, now proceeded with breath-taking speed. By 1900, the United States had forged to the top as the world's greatest power. By almost any standard of economic measurement—steel, coal, and oil production, railroad mileage, number of industrial workers, commercial turnover, and aggregate national income—she was ahead of Great Britain and Germany, her principal competitors.

At the same time, the Westward Movement continued and was brought to a close. In these years, the frontier pushed up the westward slopes of the Mississippi Valley, on to the High Plains. The fabulous Cattle Kingdom, comprising parts of Texas, Oklahoma, Colorado, Kansas, Nebraska, Wyoming, and Montana, developed because of the demand for meat to feed America's teeming industrial population. The age of the cowboy came and went. Hard on the heels of the cattle men came farm settlers with plough and barbed wire, tearing up the grass-lands and putting tens of thousands of acres under wheat. By 1917, the frontier disappeared. Steam tractors crawled over the vast expanses where once the buffalo had roamed, where Sioux and Apache had hunted, and where the buckaroos had rounded up their herds.

The era of the cowboy and of open grazing had come to a close by 1890, adding its own never-fading aura to the legend of pioneering romance. But there was little romance in the lives of the factory workers of the East or middle-West. American industry was open shop. Long hours, cruel exploitation, dangerous conditions, and searing poverty were the order of the day. Nor was the average farmer, especially in newly settled areas, much better off. Though American farming in this period became enormously productive as new power machinery was introduced, large numbers of farmers failed to secure any noticeable advantage. The hardest lot of all was reserved for the new immigrants, flooding in by the million from Southern and Eastern Europe to man the mines, mills, and factories, and, as aliens, to toil in grime to create wealth they would not live to share. All these people in the ranks of the dispossessed, farmers, workers, immigrants, watched with angry eyes the pyramiding fortunes of industrial millionaires and the rise of gingerbread palaces of ostentatious splendor.

Some of the songs that arose from the experiences and struggles of workers and farmers and the moods that these express receive attention in the first part of the following chapter. Much of this music-making followed a tradition with which we are now familiar: Traditional melodies and literary forms were used to create new songs expressive of new situations. Many cowboy songs, for example, were set to readily identifiable English or Irish tunes brought to the High Plains from homes in the South or East. What changed were the things about which cowboys sang and the trotting rhythms to which the words were set.

But with the immigrants in this period it was rather different. Millions of people coming into this country after the Civil War from Southern and Eastern Europe brought with them their own heritage of language, song, music, and dance; these were seen now on American soil for the first time in all their wonderful variety. *All of this is part of the American heritage simply because it is here.* American culture, one may predict, will not become truly unique, truly national, until it has learned to absorb and utilize the gifts that these immigrants brought with them. For they are as surely part of the

American bone, fiber, and spirit as the British and Irish heritage that began to root itself in the colonies nearly 300 years before. The existence of the vast but relatively unknown immigrant heritage constitutes an "underground stream" in American culture, a stream private to the groups that preserve and cherish it, but not yet common to all of us.

To make this point concretely and to illuminate the nature and beauty of the "undiscovered" heritage, the second part of this chapter is devoted to immigrant songs. We focus first of all upon the songs of the Jewish people who, between the years 1880 and 1917, came to our Eastern cities from Russia, Poland, Austria-Hungary, and the Ukraine. We may regard the singing of these people to be representative of the mood and fate of many other immigrants who came from the same area during the same period. These songs reveal a new kind of American music that was then coming into being: Jewish immigrants utilized their own musical and literary heritage to express the meaning of the new American experience which they were called upon to undergo.

In these same years, French-speaking immigrants from Canada began to filter down in large numbers into New England to work in the lumber woods, take up farms, and find jobs in the textile factories.* They brought with them elements of the French-Canadian song heritage which, in its own way, rivals that of the British in extent and importance. We have chosen two songs from the great French tributary of the "underground stream" to illustrate, again as concretely as possible, what we mean by this phrase.

The main barrier to our appreciation and use of the immigrant element of national song is a barrier of language; their mood and meaning has to be recreated in the English idiom. This fact underscores the existence of one of the cultural frontiers of our own time.

For the Negro people, the period from 1863 to 1868 represented a climax in the struggle to win freedom and full equality as American citizens. In 1867, Congress framed the Fourteenth Amendment, conferring American citizenship on ex-slaves and their descendants, and guaranteeing them broad political rights under the Constitution. In the years 1867 and 1868, all the Southern states redrafted their own constitutions

*French Canadians [Acadians] would have migrated to the British seaboard colonies during the eighteenth century, but the path was blocked at that time by imperial policy; and so these people entered the United States at the other extremity, via New Orleans.

to bring them into line with the new Federal requirements. For the first time, Negro citizens sat side by side with whites in the state legislatures and in the national Congress.

The bright hopes raised by these years faded rapidly before the harsh counterattack of the unreconstructed Southerners. Over the years, Negroes, with the complicity of the Republican Party, the Congress, and the Courts, were again forced back into the status of helots—hewers of wood and drawers of water for whites, aliens in their own land. In the late 1890's, a cast-iron system of segregation was imposed throughout the South by law; by the turn of the century, the region once again exhibited the most odious features of racism and human exploitation that had flourished during slavery days.

Abandoned and forgotten, the Negro people lived on. Negro prisoners toiled like slaves on the roads and railroads, in the river bottoms, on the levees, in the prison farms and camps. Negro croppers worked day after day like slaves from sunup to sundown, chopping and picking cotton in fields that were not theirs. The tragic destiny and the despair of an oppressed people found expression in profound and beautiful songs: chain-gang songs, prison songs, spirituals, bad-man ballads, shouts, field hollers, and blues. These will receive as much attention as space permits in the third section of the following chapter.

# Farmers and
# Workers

The High Plains had always been the home of wandering bands of Indians: Blackfoot, Cheyenne, Crow, Arapaho, Osage, Nez Perce, Apache, Mandan, Arikara, Pawnee, and many more. These people lived by hunting the buffalo or antelope, gathering berries and roots, and planting corn and squash. Their homes were earth lodges and tepees. Their tools, until the coming of white men, were of bone and stone, their weapons, the bow and arrow and the club.

At the end of the Civil War, the age of steel moved swiftly westward into this prehistoric land. By 1869, the Union Pacific railroad had spanned the central plains through Nebraska and Wyoming, utilizing an army 10,000 strong of track-laying, bridge-building Irish. By 1872, the Atchison, Topeka, and Santa Fé and the Kansas Pacific, had been driven clear across Kansas.

These lines produced a revolution in the life of the High Plains. The buffalo were exterminated; the Indians were broken and their remnants swept into reservations. Stockyards were established at the railheads in Abilene, Newton, Dodge City, Ogalalla, and Ellis, so that Western beef could be hauled to Chicago and the hungry markets of the East. Drovers from the South Texan borderlands began to drive their herds of long-horn cattle up to the railhead cattle towns, over the long trails that led clear through Texas and Indian Territory, or up the Pecos River through New Mexico and Colorado. Between 1866 and 1890, the age of the cowboy and the long trails came and went; during this time 6 million head of Texan longhorns, at the very least, were driven northward either to provide meat for the markets and the Indian reservations or stock the grass-lands of Montana, Wyoming, the Dakotas, New Mexico, and Colorado.

During these years the cattle kingdom of the open grass-lands came and went in a flash, leaving its own ineffaceable imprint on the national memory. This was an epic of frontier life, and the cowboy was its hero. It was a hardy, dangerous, and challenging existence which kindled, as did the sea years before, a passion in the hearts of adventurous youth; and it was a way of life which only the toughest and most skilful could survive. The trails along which the huge herds had to be driven covered many hundreds of miles of open territory. Rivers had to be forded, sometimes in flood; stampedes had to be met and checked; cattle thieves and Indians had to be fought and driven off. The cowboy was in the saddle day after day for many hours; his moments of rest were few.

From the life of the range and the open ranch arose the cowboy's songs. Like the sailor and lumberjack before him, he had songs both for work and for relaxation. His saddle songs, as might be expected, grew out of the familiar heritage of Irish and English singing which immigrant families brought with them into the West, and which he had learned at his mother's knee. Naturally, modifications occurred; rhythms were molded by the tempo of a horse's stride, and new lyrics were created to express the special joys and fears, the special impact of a horseman's life. Cowboys, too, had songs for the bunkhouse and the camp fire; here, the singing of old ballads, traditional songs, and sentimental ditties was interspersed with endless tales and yarns. The favorite cowboys' ballads told of bold, adventurous men, pioneers and outlaws, like, for example "Sioux Indians" (page 179), or "Brennan on the Moor" (page 264). "The Jam on Gerry's Rock" (page 175) was especially well liked, for the tale it told of death by drowning was only too familiar to men obliged to ford endless swirling streams on their long drives.

The cowboy was a romantic figure from the age of rural America that, by the end of the nineteenth century, was vanishing forever. The swift advance of industrialization and the rise of giant business corporations had a dramatic impact on the American social structure. At the opening of the Civil War, the majority of Americans had still been country dwellers, living upon the land; but in 1917 this was no longer so. The census of 1920 revealed that one-half the population lived in urban communities, that they were dependent for their livelihood on daily labor in mines, offices, and factories, and on the railroads, and that most of them lived in grimy industrial towns.

The huge working class that had thus arisen—by 1917 the industrial army numbered well over 15 million workers—was composed partly of European immigrants and partly of farm people who had fled to the cities. The working class was a very heterogeneous group: not more than one worker in five was a member of the trade union movement. Organization had been slowed by the fierce competition of huge numbers of poor, ignorant immigrants arriving each year, by the avariciousness of employers and their savagely anti-union policies, and by the indifference of conservative trade-union leaders to the plight of the downtrodden and exploited masses.

This period, by and large, was one of terrible suffering for working people, and often of brutal strife between them and their employers. Numerous ballads were created to express the experiences which American workers and their families suffered; they told of the calamities and the tragedies of the worker's life: factory fires and accidents, coal mine disasters, railroad smash-ups, unemployment, hunger, and hard times, strike battles, the murder of union organizers, the destructiveness of floods. The songs were topical and usually set to traditional tunes, including gospel songs, hymns, and spirituals. A few of the best of these are included in the section that follows.

# I Ride an Old Paint

This song was originally published in Carl Sandburg's *American Songbag* and comes from Margaret Larkin of New Mexico. It was a favorite of Woody Guthrie's and is perhaps one of the most entrancing of all cowboy songs.

snuf - fy    Are    rar - in'    to    go.

Old Bill Jones had two daughters and a song,
One went to Denver and the other went wrong.
His wife she died in a poolroom fight,
Still he sings from morning till night.

*Chorus*

Oh, when I die, take my saddle from the wall,
Put it on my pony, and lead him from his stall.
Tie my bones to his back, turn our faces to the West,
And we'll ride the prairie that we love the best.

*Chorus*

# The Colorado Trail

This love song, perhaps one of the finest that we have, was also published in Carl Sandburg's *American Songbag*. It was learned by Dr. T. L. Chapman from a cowboy patient in a Duluth, Minnesota hospital.

Eyes like the morn-ing star, Cheeks like a rose,
Ann-ie was a pret-ty girl, God Al-might-y knows;
Weep all you lit-tle rains, Wail, winds,_wail,
All a-long, a-long, a-long, the Col-o-rad-o Trail.

# Goodbye, Old Paint

This famous saddle song and dance song was first collected by John A. Lomax before the first World War, and is transcribed here from Lomax's recording of a Montana cowboy. It's a good song for improvising and goes jogging on forever.

Good - bye, old Paint, I'm a-leav - in' Chey - enne, Good - bye, old Paint, I'm a-leav - in' Chey - enne.

1. I'm leav - in' Chey-enne, I'm off to Mon - tan' Good-
2. I'm a - rid - in' old Paint, I'm lead - in' old Dan,

bye, old Paint, I'm a - leav - in' Chey - enne.

Goodbye, old Paint, I'm a-leavin' Cheyenne,
Goodbye, old Paint, I'm a-leavin' Cheyenne.
I'm off to Montan' to throw the houlihan,
Goodbye, old Paint, I'm a-leavin' Cheyenne.

Goodbye, old Paint, I'm a-leavin' Cheyenne,
Goodbye, old Paint, I'm a-leavin' Cheyenne.
They feed in the coulees, they water in the draw,
Goodbye, old Paint, I'm a-leavin' Cheyenne.

263

# Brennan on the Moor

This is one of the best-known Irish "bad man" ballads. It tells of a hero dear to the hearts of his countrymen because he roamed the wild hills rather than submit to British tyranny. It was popular among cowboys both as a bunkhouse and saddle song.

It's a - bout a bold high - way - man my sto - ry I will tell, His name was Will - ie Bren - nan, and in Ire - land he did dwell; 'Twas up - on the Kil - wart Moun - tains he be - gan his wild ca - reer, And man - y a rich gen - tle - man be -

fore him shook with fear, It was

CHORUS

Bren-nan on the moor,

Bren-nan on the moor, Bold,—

gay, and un-daunt-ed stood young

Bren-nan on the moor.

One day upon the highway young Brennan he went down,
He met the mayor of Cashel five miles outside the town;
Now the mayor he knew Willie, "And I think," says he,
Your name is Willie Brennan, you must come along
     with me,

*Chorus*

Now Willie got his blunderbuss, my story I'll unfold,
He caused the mayor to tremble and deliver up his gold,
Five thousand pounds was offered for his apprehension
     there,
But he with horse and saddle to the mountains did repair,

*Chorus*

Now Willie is an outlaw all on some mountain high,
With infantry and cavalry to take him they did try,
But he laughed at them and scorned them, until,
     as it was said,
By a false-hearted woman he was cruelly betrayed,

*Chorus*

Now Willie hung at Clonmel, in chains he swung and
     died,
But still they say that in the night, some do see him ride;
They see him with his blunderbuss, and on the midnight
     chill,
Along the Clonmel highway rides Willie Brennan still,

*Chorus*

# The Farmer Is the Man

The period from the early 1870's to the middle 1890's was one of great unrest among Western and Southern farmers, but primarily among pioneer farmers on the wheat-producing frontier, in the vast new prairie states of the Dakotas, Kansas, Nebraska, Minnesota, Wyoming, and Montana. Declining prices for wheat and cotton on the world market coupled with the extortionate practices of railroads, speculators, and middlemen, combined to produce a series of political explosions among the farmers that culminated in the Populist movement of 1890–1896. Many songs were produced by the farmers who were both musical and militant. Among the best known is "The Farmer Is the Man," an anonymously composed ditty that reflects Jeffersonian sentiments about the primary importance and worth of the farmer in society. The song expresses, in musical form, the famous phrase uttered by William Jennings Bryan in his 1896 "Cross of Gold" speech:

. . . The great cities rest upon our broad and fertile prairies. Burn down your cities and leave our farms, and your cities will spring up again as if by magic; but destroy our farms and the grass will grow in the streets of every city in the country.

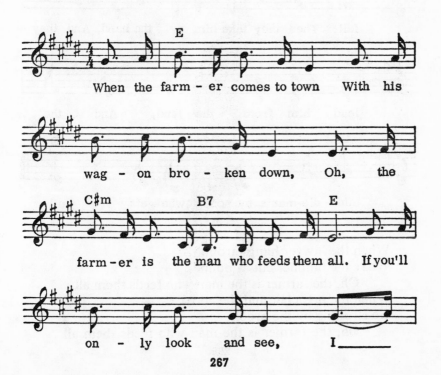

When the farm - er comes to town    With his
wag - on bro - ken down,    Oh, the
farm - er is    the man who feeds them all.    If you'll
on - ly look    and see,    I_____

think you will a - gree, That the

A　　　　　　　B7　　　　　E CHORUS

farm - er is the man who feeds them all. The

G#m　　　　　　　　　　　B7

farm - er is the man,_____ The

E　　　　B7　　E

farm - er is the man, Lives on cred - it till the

Bm　　　　　　　　E

fall; Then they take him by the hand, And they

lead him from the land, And the

A　　　　　　　B7　　　　　　　E

mid - dle-man's the one who gets it all.

When the lawyer hangs around,
While the butcher cuts a pound,
　　Oh, the farmer is the man who feeds them all.
When the preacher and the cook
Go strolling by the brook
　　Oh, the farmer is the man who feeds them all.

268

*Chorus*

When the banker says he's broke
And the merchant's up in smoke,
They forget that it's the farmer feeds them all.
It would put them to the test
If the farmer took a rest;
     Then they'd know that it's the farmer feeds them all.

*Chorus:*    The farmer is the man,
             The farmer is the man,
             Lives on credit til the fall;
             With the interest rate so high,
             It's a wonder he don't die,
             For the mortgage man's the one who gets it all.

# Peter Emberley

Peter Emberley was born in 1863 at Alberton, Prince Edward Island. The ruined homestead on this beautiful coast may still be seen. In 1880, when he was 17, Peter left home and found work as a lumberman in the New Brunswick woods in the valley of the Southwest Miramichi. In the winter of that year, he was fatally injured at Parker's Ridge while loading logs and was taken to Boiestown to die.

John Calhoun, a Boiestown farmer and songwriter, composed this ballad which soon achieved a wide popularity among the people of the Miramichi. That it has served for nearly a century to keep fresh the memory of this youth among the people of New Brunswick and Maine attests to its power. In recent years, the simple wooden cross in the Boiestown Catholic Cemetery was replaced by a stone memorial; the red earth of Prince Edward Island was brought there and scattered upon the grave.

The melody to which the lyric is here set is a variant of "The Bonny Boy" and "The Jam on Gerry's Rock" (pages 18 and 175). All three songs lament the death of a young man in the prime of life; but unlike the other two "Peter Emberley" has had little currency outside of Maine and the Maritime Provinces of Canada.*

My name is Pe - ter Em - ber-ley___ As ___ you may un - der -

*Stewart Holbrook [*The American Lumberjack* (New York: Collier Books, 1962) page 129] calls this ballad the "ultimate in bathos." But he only reproduces one verse of the lyric, and that in a corrupted form. He would have found a Maine version, very close to Calhoun's original, in Phillips Barry, *The Maine Woods Songster* (Cambridge, Mass.: Powell Printing Co., 1939). 68-69.

stand; I was born on Prince Ed - ward's
Is - land, Close by the o - cean
strand; In eight - een hun -dred and
eight - y When the flow-ers bore a bril - liant
hue, I left my na - tive
coun - te - ree,_My_ for - tune to pur - sue.

I landed in New Brunswick,
    That lumbering counteree,
I hired for to work in the lumber woods
    On the Sou'west Miramashee;
I hired for to work in the lumber woods
    Where they cut the tall spruce down,
It was loading two sleds from a yard
    I received my deathly wound.

There is danger on the ocean
    Where the seas roll mountain high,
There is danger on the battlefield
    Where the angry bullets fly,

There is danger in the lumber woods,
     And death lurks solemn there,
And I have fallen victim
     Unto its monstrous snare.

Here's adieu unto my father,
     It was him that drove me here.
I thought it very cruel of him,
     His treatment was severe;
For it is not right to impress a boy,
     Or try to keep him down,
For it oft times drives him from his home
     When he is far too young.

Here's adieu unto my greatest friend,
     I mean my mother dear,
Who reared a son that fell as quick
     As he left her tender care;
It's little she thought not long ago,
     When she sang a lullaby,
What country I might travel in,
     Or what death I might die.

Here's adieu unto a younger friend,
     My Island girl so true;
Long may she live to grace the soil
     Where my first breath I drew;
The world will roll on just the same
     As before I passed away:
What signifies a mortal man
     When he lies in the clay?

Here's adieu unto Prince Edward's Isle,
     That garden in the seas;
No more I'll roam its flowery banks
     Or enjoy a summer's breeze;
No more I'll watch those gallant brigs
     As they go sailing by,
With streamers floating in the wind
     Far above their canvas high.

But now before I pass away
    There is one more thing I pray,
I hope some holy father
    Will bless my silent grave;
Near by the city of Boiestown
    Where my mouldering bones do lie,
Awaiting for my Savior's call
    On that great rising day.

Transcribed from the singing of Marie Hare of Strathadam, New Brunswick, at the Seventh Annual Miramichi Folksong Festival, Newcastle, New Brunswick, August 19, 1964.

# Hard Times in the Mill

This song arose out of the open shop conditions of textile mills in the South around the turn of the century, when the 12 hour day, starvation wages, and child labor were still the rule.

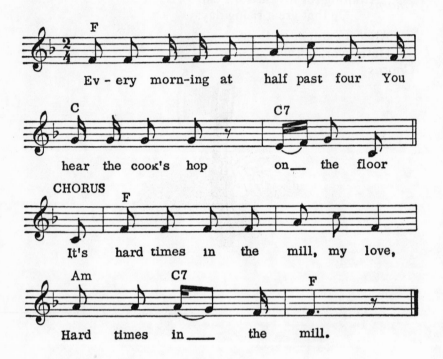

Ev - ery morn-ing at half past four You hear the cook's hop on the floor

**CHORUS**

It's hard times in the mill, my love, Hard times in the mill.

2. Every morning just at five
   You gotta get up, dead or alive.
*Chorus*

3. Every morning at six o'clock
   Two cold biscuits, hard as a rock
*Chorus*

4. Every morning at half-past nine
   The bosses are cussin' and the spinners are cryin'.
*Chorus*

5. They docked me a nickel, they docked me a dime,
   They sent me to the office to get my time.
*Chorus*

6. Cotton mill boys don't make enough,
   To buy them tobacco and a box of snuff.
*Chorus*

7. Every night when I get home,
   A piece of corn bread and an old jawbone.
*Chorus*

8. Ain't it enough to break your heart?
   Hafta work all day until it's dark.
*Chorus*

# The Shoofly

The mines in the anthracite coal region of Pennsylvania were opened up before the Civil War by Welsh immigrant miners. Civil War times and the burgeoning demand for fuel for the blast furnaces brought about an immigration of German and Irish workers into the area; and at the end of the conflict, large numbers of Slavic immigrants arrived. The many nationalities involved and the plentiful supply of workers made it easy for the coal corporations to break unions, drive down wages, and convert the anthracite region into a center of poverty, bitterness, and despair. The United Mine Workers did not win a permanent footing in Eastern Pennsylvania until after World War I.

Many songs from this period tell of the hazards and hardships of a miner's life and of the sorrows that his women and children had to endure. Songs and ballads were spread far and wide through the mine regions by itinerant singers (often blinded or crippled miners) and through broadsides. "The Shoofly" dates from the hard times of the 1870's. George Korson, who collected this song tells us: "It was made by a village schoolmaster, Felix O'Hare, who put into it the anxiety and despair that followed the closing of the small mine at Valley Furnace in the Schuylkill Valley in 1871."

The Shoofly was a neighboring colliery, also closed down.

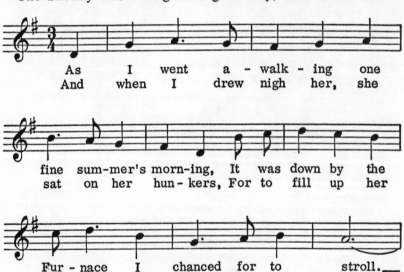

As I went a-walk-ing one
And when I drew nigh her, she

fine sum-mer's morn-ing, It was down by the
sat on her hun-kers, For to fill up her

Fur-nace I chanced for to stroll.____
scut-tle she had just be-gun,____

I es - pied an old la - dy, I'll
And to her - self she was

swear she was eight - y, At the foot of the
sing - ing a dit - ty, And these are the

dirt banks a - root - ing for coal;____
words the old la - dy did sing:____

CHORUS
A - cry - ing, "Och - one! sure, I'm

near - ly dis - tract -ed,____ For it's

down by the Shoo-fly they cut a bad

vein;____ And since they con - demned the old

slope at the Fur - nace, __ Sure_ all me fine

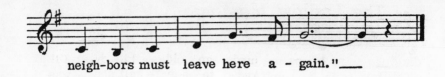

neigh-bors must leave here a - gain."___

2. " 'Twas only last evenin' that I asked McGinley
     To tell me the reason the Furnace gave o'er.
   He told me the company had spent eighty thousand,
     And finding no prospects they would spend no more.
   He said that the Diamond it was rather bony,
     Besides too much dirt in the seven foot vein;
   And as for the Mammoth, there's no length of gangway,
     Unless they buy land from old Abel and Swayne."

*Chorus*

3. "And as for Michael Rooney, I owe him some money,
     Likewise Patrick Kearns, I owe him some more;
   And as for old John Eagen, I ne'er see his wagon,
     But I think of the debt that I owe in the store.
   I owe butcher and baker, likewise the shoemaker,
     And for plowin' me garden I owe Pat McQuail;
   Likewise his old mother, for one thing and another,
     And to drive away bother, an odd quart of ale."

*Chorus*

4. "But if God spare me children until the next summer,
     Instead of a burden, they will be a gain;
   And out of their earnin's I'll save an odd dollar,
     And build a snug home at the 'Foot of the Plane.'
   Then rolling in riches, in silks, and in satin,
     I ne'er shall forget the days I was poor,
   And likewise the neighbors that stood by me children,
     Kept want and starvation away from me door."

*Chorus*

Reprinted by permission of the Johns Hopkins Press from *Pennsylvania's Songs and Legends,* edited by George Korson. The Johns Hopkins Press, Baltimore, Maryland, 1949. © Copyright by George Korson.

# The Ludlow Massacre

The Ludlow massacre of April, 1914 epitomizes the era of the open shop when employers exercised an absolute and despotic rule over their industrial serfs; obliged the workers to live in vile company shacks and buy their food in company stores at company prices; and surrounded their people with spies and thugs who watched their movements and intimidated them.

In the coal fields of Las Animas and Huerfano counties, Colorado, John D. Rockefeller and his Colorado Iron and Fuel Co. ruled the lives of thousands of Americans of Greek, Italian, Slav, and Mexican descent. In September, 1913, these workers marched out of the company shacks and took shelter in tent colonies. They were striking in protest against a total denial of personal rights and the violation by the operators of state laws regulating conditions of work in the mines, and for the recognition of their chosen union, the United Mineworkers of America.

All winter long the strike continued, and the workers held out in their tents. In April 1914, Company B of the state militia, recruited mainly from company strongarm men, moved into the Ludlow colony with machine guns and coal oil. When the flaming slaughter was over, 21 people were dead; 13 were children, 2 were women. Louis Tikxas, a mineworkers' leader, and three miners were taken prisoner and murdered by the militiamen in cold blood. The massacre precipitated a general rebellion of Colorado miners which was only put down with the aid of Federal troops.

Woody Guthrie, who wrote the ballad that we reproduce here, was born in Oklahoma in 1912 and grew up in the open shop era that lasted into the early '30's. In the twentieth century, the American labor movement has produced no balladeer whose genius compares to his.

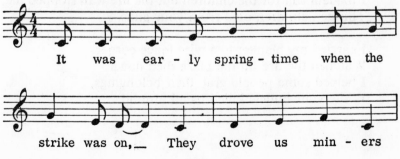

It was ear - ly spring - time when the strike was on, __ They drove us min - ers

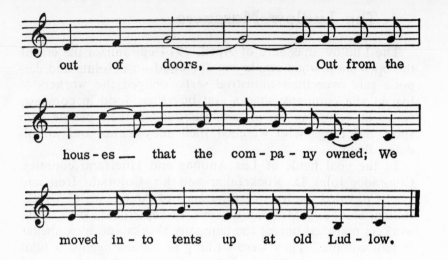

out of doors, _____ Out from the
hous-es ___ that the com-pa-ny owned; We
moved in-to tents up at old Lud-low.

I was worried bad about my children,
Soldiers guarding the railroad bridge;
Every once in a while the bullets would fly,
Kick up gravel under my feet.

We were so afraid you would kill our children,
We dug us a cave that was seven foot deep,
Carried our young ones and a pregnant woman
Down inside the cave to sleep.

That very night you soldiers waited,
Until us miners was asleep;
You snuck around our little tent town,
Soaked our tents with your kerosene.

You struck a match and the blaze it started;
You pulled the triggers of your gatling guns;
I made a run for the children but the fire wall stopped me,
Thirteen children died from your guns.

I carried my blanket to a wire fence corner,
Watched the fire till the blaze died down;
I helped some people grab their belongings,
While your bullets killed us all around.

I never will forget the look on the face,
Of the men and women that awful day,
When we stood around to preach their funerals
And lay the corpses of the dead away.

We told the Colorado governor to phone the President,
Tell him to call off his National Guard;
But the National Guard belonged to the Governor,
So he didn't try so very hard.

Our women from Trinidad they hauled some potatoes
Up to Walsenburg in a little cart;
They sold their potatoes and brought some guns back
And they put a gun in every hand.

The state soldiers jumped us in the wire fence corner;
They did not know that we had these guns.
And the red-neck miners mowed down these troopers,
You should have seen those poor boys run.

We took some cement and walled the cave up
Where you killed these thirteen children inside;
I said "God bless the mine workers' union,"
And then I hung my head and cried.

# Solidarity Forever

The Industrial Workers of the World was organized in 1905 by radical and labor groups intent upon organizing the masses of unskilled and semiskilled workers into a single industrial union regardless of race, creed, or color. Its songster, *IWW Songs*, first appeared in 1906 and over the years was expanded to include lyrics by Ralph Chaplin, Joe Hill, James Connell, and others. Undoubtedly the best of these songs is "Solidarity Forever." Written by Chaplin in 1915, and sung to the tune of "John Brown's Body," it continues to be reproduced until the present time in the *AFL-CIO Songbook,* an official publication of the American labor movement.

1. When the union's inspiration through the worker's blood shall run,
    There can be no power greater anywhere beneath the sun.
    Yet what force on earth is weaker than the feeble strength of one?
    But the union makes us strong.
*Chorus:* Solidarity forever!
    Solidarity forever!
    Solidarity forever!
    For the union makes us strong.

2. They have taken untold millions that they never toiled to earn,
    But without our brain and muscle not a single wheel could turn.
    We can break their haughty power, earn our freedom when we learn
    That the union makes us strong.
*Chorus*

3. It is we who ploughed the prairie, built the cities where they trade,
    Dug the mines and built the workshops, endless miles of railroad laid,
    Now we stand outcast and starving midst the wonders we have made,
    But the union makes us strong.
*Chorus*

4. In our hands is placed a power greater than their hoarded
        gold,
    Greater than the might of armies magnified a thousand
        fold
    We can bring to birth a new world from the ashes of the
        old,
    For the union makes us strong.
*Chorus*

# Immigrants

Between 1890 and 1914, a total of 15 million people immigrated to the United States. The immigrants—Italians, Poles, Russians, Ukrainians, Czechs, Greeks, Hungarians, and Rumanians—came primarily from Eastern and Southern Europe. One and one-half million of them, or roughly 10 per cent, were Jews.

The last and greatest wave of Jewish migration to America began in 1881. The Jewish people came here principally from the Polish provinces which Russia had acquired as the result of the partition of Poland in 1772. Since that time, the Tsars had established and maintained in Poland a pale of Jewish settlement beyond which Jews were forbidden to go; and they had hounded these people with a bitterly repressive policy which included the direct instigation of pogroms, or massacres, of the helpless minority. In 1881, the assassination of Alexander II touched off a new wave of violence against the Jews and produced the passage of laws imposing new and ferocious restrictions upon them. Large scale migration to America set in and continued without letup until the outbreak of World War I.

The everyday language of the Polish and Russian Jews was Yiddish, a dialect originating with the Jewish settlements in medieval Germany, which the Jews retained as they were driven eastward. The songs of these Yiddish-speaking people were born of the bitterness of poverty and oppression; they drew upon both the Jewish literary and musical heritage as well as Slavic melody to express a many-sided picture of Jewish life. These songs—love songs, lullabies, street songs, ballads—came to the New World with the immigrants. Virtually erased by Hitler and Himmler's nearly total massacre of the Jewish population of Europe, these Yiddish songs constitute a precious part of the American heritage that is preserved in its fullness only here.

In Poland, many of the Jews had been village or small town handicraftsmen; in the United States, they found work at first principally in the clothing industry. Their first experience of America was in the sweatshops and tenements of New York City's lower East Side. Here they were crammed into slums that gave the City's Jewish quarter the dubious fame of having the densest population per square mile in the world. They lived and toiled amid what one observer described as "the endless panorama of the tenements, rows upon rows, between stony streets, stretching to the north, to the south, to the west, as far as the eye reaches."* Here, in dingy, crowded, airless rooms, men, women, and children worked for endless hours, sewing and cutting garments for a pittance.

The first Jewish immigrants found themselves at the mercy of the "sweater," the middleman who gave out the work, set the wages, and took the profit from selling the product of their labor to finishers. The sweater's power lay in the mass of ignorant immigrants arriving daily on these shores with the immediate, pressing need for shelter and bread. As Jacob Riis wrote in 1890:

As long as the ignorant crowds continue to come and to herd in these tenements, his grip can never be shaken off. And the fresh supply across the seas is apparently inexhaustible. Every fresh persecution of the Russian or Polish Jew on his native soil starts greater hordes hitherward to confound economic problems, and to recruit the sweater's phalanx. The curse of bigotry and ignorance reaches half way across the world, to sow its bitter seed in fertile soil in the East Side tenements.**

"Ot Azoy" and "Mein Yingele" deal directly with the immigrant's experience. The first tells of the weary lot of the Jewish handicraftsman and of the inevitable struggle to set a limit to his toil which resulted in the first victories of unionization in the Jewish garment unions. "Mein Yingele," was written by an immigrant, Morris Rosenfeld, in 1887. It tells its own story of the hardship that long hours of labor in the garment factories inflicted upon working people by denying them the simplest rights and pleasures of life. This song, in the course of time, found its way back to Yiddish-speaking people in Europe and achieved an international renown. "Schlof Mayn Kind," with lyrics by Sholom Aleichem, tells the familiar tale of the woman with little children, waiting anxiously for a letter from America. When will papa write? Is he still living? When will the family be reunited? "Papir Iz Doch Vays" is among many exquisite love songs which the immigrants brought with them to the New World.

*Jacob Riis, *How the Other Half Lives* (New York: Sagamore Press, 1957), 87.
**Ibid, 90.

## Ot Azoy Neyt A Shnayder
### (Weary Days Are a Tailor's)

CHORUS

Wea-ry days are a tai-lor's, Wea-ry days are his. Wea-ry days are a tai-lor's, Wea-ry days are his.

From dawn til dusk he sews a-way, A cent and a song are all his pay.

*Chorus*

From dawn till dusk he sits and sews,
Hunger and pain are all he knows.

*Chorus*

From dawn till dusk we work away,
Time was, we worked a twelve-hour day.

286

*Chorus*
> The union broke the twelve-hour day,
> Brought us shorter hours and better pay.

* * *

*Chorus*
> Ot azoy neyt a shnayder,
> Ot azoy neyt er doch!

> Er neyt un neyt a gantse voch,
> Fardint a gildn mit a loch!

*Chorus*
> A shnayder neyt un neyt un neyt,
> Un hot kadoches, nit kayn brot!

*Chorus*
> Farayorn, nit haynt-gedacht!
> Hob mir gehorevet fun acht bis acht!

*Chorus*
> Ober die struksie hot ongemacht,
> Mir arbetn shoyn mer nit fun acht biz acht!

### Schlof Mayn Kind
### (Sleep, My Child)

Sleep, my child, my sweet, my pret-ty one,

Sleep, my dar-ling, sleep. Sleep, my life, my
sweet, my pret-ty one, Sleep, my dar-ling___
son. Sleep, my life, my sweet, my pret-ty one,
sleep my dar-ling___ son.

By your cradle sits your mama,
    Sings a song and weeps.
One day you will understand.
    Why your mama weeps.

Daddy's gone to America,
    Daddy's gone far away.
He has left us here a-waiting!
    Sleep, my darling babe.

In that far-off land, they say,
    Everyone is blest.
In that promised land, they say,
    Weary folk find rest.

Daddy will send us twenty dollars,
    And his picture too.
If he's living, sure he'll fetch us,
    We'll start life anew.

He will hug us, he will kiss us,
    He will leap for joy!
I will stand there, stand there quietly.
    Tears will stream down.

While we wait his happy message,
  Sleep, my darling, do.
Sleep, my darling, since you're little,
  And I watch over you.

*    *    *

Schlof mayn kind, mayn treyst mayn sheyner,
  Schlof-zhe zunenyu.
Schlof mayn lebn, mayn kadish eyner,
  Schlof-zhe, lyu-lyu-lyu.

Bay dayn vigl zitst dayn mame
  Zingt a lid un veynt.
Du vest amol farshteyn mistame,
  Vos zi hot gemeynt.

In Amerike ist der tate,
  Dayner, zunenyu,
Du bizt noch a kind les-ate,
  Schlof-zhe, lyu-lyu-lyu.

In Amerike iz far yedn
  Zogt men, gor a glik.
Un far yedn, a gan-eydn,
  Gor epes antik.

Er vet shikn tsvantsig doler,
  Zayn portret dertsu,
Un vet nemen, lebn zol er!
  Undz ahintsutsu.

Er vet chapn undz un kushn,
  Tantsn azh far freyd!
Ich vel kvaln trern gisn,
  Veynen shtilerheyt.

Biz es kumt dos gute kvitl,
  Schlof-zhe zunenyu.
Schlofn iz a tayer mitl,
  Schlof-zhe, lyu-lyu-lyu.

## Mayn Yingele
### (My Little Son)

I have a lit-tle son,— A lit-tle boy so fine, And when I look at him I think, The whole wide world is mine. Rare-ly do I set eyes on him While he's play-ing in broad day-light; I watch him on-ly while he sleeps, I see him on-ly at night.

At dawn my work drives me away,
And keeps me long from home;
My flesh and blood is strange to me,
My son's a joy unknown.

I stumble home in black despair
Through all my empty days
To hear my weary wife describe
How sweetly my child plays.

290

I stand and watch my sleeping son,
My heart is still and sad;
I listen to his murmuring lips
That ask: "Where is my Dad?"

I stand and watch my sleeping son,
And my soul is torn with pain:
One day, my child, you will awake,
But I'll not come again.

\* \* \*

Ich hob a kleynem yingele,
A zunele gor fayn.
Ven ich derze im, dacht sich mir,
Di gantse velt is mayn!

Nor zeltn, zeltn, ze ich im,
Mayn sheynem, ven er vacht.
Ich tref im imer schlofndig,
Ich ze im nor baynacht.

Di arbet traybt mich fri aroys,
Un lozt mich sper tsurik.
O, fremd is mir mayn eygn layb,
Mayn eygn kind's a blik.

Ich kum tsuklemterheyd aheym,
In finsternish gehilt,
Mayn bleche froy dertseylt mir bald
Vi fayn dos kind zich shpilt.

Ich shtey bay zayn gelegerl,
Un her un ze un sha . . .
A troym bavegt di lipelech:
O, vu iz, vu iz Pa?

Ich blayb tsuveytogt un tsuklemt
Farbitert un ich kler:
Ven du ervachst amol, mayn kind,
Gefinstu mich nit mer.

## Papir Iz Doch Vays
### (Silver Is the Daylight)

Sil - ver is the day - light, and

blue is the sea, Bright is the

new love, you have brought to me; Let me

stay near you al - ways,

Let our fin - gers twine, Let me kiss your

rose-red lips; let me call you mine.

Last night I went to a wedding, I danced through the night.
A thousand thousand pretty girls danced in my sight;
A thousand thousand pretty girls, but none like you so fair,
With your black and dancing eyes and your black
      and dancing hair.

I find you everywhere, in earth, sea and sky.
My love torments me as the world goes by;
My love torments me always, as I stand alone and gaze,
At the black and sparkling vault, where I sing my song
     of praise.

Oh God in Heaven, grant me my cherished dream!
Not pearls nor rubies that vain and falsely gleam,
Grant me a hut for my palace, where my love and
     I may be,
In the green and peaceful meadow, where the silver
     streams flow free.

Papir iz doch vays un tint iz doch shvarts,
Tsu dir mayn zis lebn, tsit doch mayn harts.
Ich volt shtendig gezesn draw teg nochanand
Tsu kushn dayn sheyn ponim un tsu halt dayn hant.

Nechtn baynacht bin ich oyf a chasene geven,
Fil sheyne meydelech hob ich dort gezen.
Fil sheyne meydelech—tsu dirkumt nisht gor—
Mit dayne shvartse eygelech un dayne shvartse hor.

Dayn talye, dayn mine, dayn eydeler tason,
In hartsn brent a fayer, men set es not on.
Nito aza mentsh, vos zol filn vi es brent,
Der toyt un dos lebn iz bay Got in di hent.

Ach du liber Got, her oys mayn farlang,
Dem oysher gistu kovid, mit asheynem gang—
Oy, mir, gib a shtibele oyf dem groz dem grinem
Az ich mit mayn zis-lebn zoln voynen derinen.

  *Ot Azoy Neyt a Shnayder, Schlof Mayn Kind, Mayn Yingele,* and
*Papir Iz Doch Vays* are reprinted by permission of Schocken Books from
*A Treasury of Jewish Folk Songs,* by Ruth Rubin. Copyright © 1950 by
Schocken Books Inc., New York. Translation from the Yiddish by John
Anthony Scott.

# Son Petit Jupon
## Isabeau S'y Promène

The ancestors of the French Canadians came from France's coastal provinces of Normandy and Brittany; in the New World, they settled on shores and islands washed by the waters of the St. Lawrence and the Atlantic. Thus, it is not surprising that many of these people's loveliest songs involve the sea.

Both in Canada and Louisiana, many songs of French origin have survived, and in addition a new, specifically French-American body of song has been created. The two songs reproduced here may both be considered of Canadian origin, though both, in one form or another, are still sung in France. Both are ballads that survive in the singing of French-Americans in the United States. "Son Petit Jupon" tells its charming story with delicacy and humor; the melody is sung on the five-note pentatonic scale, and is evidently very old; it is only one of numerous variants to which the lyric has been set. "Isabeau S'y Promène" tells a tragic story with a lightness of touch and subtlety of expression that effectively accents its sadness. It may be considered a masterpiece of ballad form. The melody is in the Dorian mode (D to D on the white keys of the piano); its original harmonic "feel" will be destroyed if it is accompanied with chords whose notes lie outside the scale as here used. I learned this version of the song from the singing of Mrs. Leo Mitchell of Newcastle, New Brunswick; it was one of her favorites from a childhood spent on the Magdalen Islands, off the New Brunswick coast.

### Son Petit Jupon
### (The Little Dress of Gray)

Mon père n'av - ait fil -
My fa - ther had no

le que moi, Mon père n'av -
daugh - ter but me, My fa - ther

294

ait fil - le que moi, Or donc, sur
*had no daugh-ter but me, And once he*

**REFRAIN**

la mer il m'en - voie, Ma - rie Ma - de -
*sent me out to sea, Mar - y Ma - de -*

leine, son p'tit jup - on de
*leine, In her lit - tle dress of*

laine, Ma - rie, Ma - rie Ma - de -
*gray, Mar - y, Mar - y Ma - de -*

lon, son tout pet - it jup - on.
*lon, Is she going to come my way?*

Or, donc, sur la mer il m'envoie
Or, donc, sur la mer il m'envoie,
Le marinier qui m'y menoit,
*Refrain*

Le marinier qui m'y menoit,     (*bis*)
Il devint amoureux de moi,
*Refrain*

Il devint amoureux de moi,     (*bis*)
Souvent de moi il s'approchoit,
*Refrain*

Souvent de moi il s'approchoit,     (*bis*)
Il dit: "Ma mie, embrassez-moi,"
*Refrain*

Il dit: "Ma mie, embrassez-moi,"     (*bis*)
"Non, non, monsieur, je n'oserois,"

*Refrain*

Non, non, monsieur, je n'oserois," *(bis)*
Car si mon papa il savoit,"
*Refrain*

Car si mon papa il savoit, *(bis)*
Fille battue ce serait moi,"
*Refrain*

"Fille battue ce serait moi, *(bis)*
Mais, ma'moiselle, qui lui diroit?"
*Refrain*

\*     \*     \*

And when he sent me out to sea, *(twice)*
The sailor who was with me,
*Refrain*

The sailor who was with me, *(twice)*
With his affections was too free,
*Refrain*

With his affections was too free, *(twice)*
He often came and stood by me,
*Refrain*

And when he was as close as this, *(twice)*
He said, "My fair, give me a kiss,"
*Refrain*

"Give me a kiss, you are so fair," *(twice)*
"No, no, my friend, I would not dare,"
*Refrain*

"No, no, my friend, I would not dare, *(twice)*
For if my papa were to hear,"
*Refrain*

"For if my papa were to hear, *(twice)*
He would chastise me, I do fear,"
*Refrain*

"He would chastise you, you do fear, *(twice)*
But, ma'moiselle, he is not near!"
*Refrain*

296

## Isabeau S'y Promène *(Isabel)*

I - sa - beau s'y pro - mè - ne
*I - sa - bel was a - walk - ing*

Le long de son jar - din,___ Le long de
*Down in the gar-den green,___ Down in the*

son jar - din Sur le bord de l'île,___
*gar-den green At the is-land's edge,___*

Le long de son jar - din Sur le bord de
*Down in the gar - den green By the wa - ter-*

l'eau, Sur le bord du vais - seau.___
*side Where the tall___ ships ride.___*

2. Elle fit un rencontre
   De trente matelots,
   De trente matelots
       Sur le bord de l'île,
   De trente matelots
       Sur le bord de l'eau,
       Sur le bord du vaisseau.

3. Le plus jeune des trente
   Il se mit a chanter,
   Il se mit a chanter
       Sur le bord de l'île,

Il se mit a chanter
     Sur le bord de l'eau,
     Sur le bord du vaisseau.

4. "La chanson que tu chantes,
     Je voudrais la savoir,
     Je voudrais la savoir
          Sur le bord de l'île,
     Je voudrais la savoir
          Sur le bord de l'eau
          Sur le bord du vaisseau."

5. "Embarque dans ma barque,
     Je te la chanterai,
     Je te la chanterai
          Sur le bord de l'île,
     Je te la chanterai
          Sur le bord de l'eau,
          Sur le bord du vaisseau."

6. Quand ell' fut dans la barque,
     Ell' se mit a pleurer.

7. "Qu'avez-vous donc la belle,
     Qu'a'-vous a tant pleurer?"

8. "Je pleur' mon anneau d'or,
     Dans l'eau-z-il est tombé."

9. "Ne pleurez point la belle,
     Je vous le plongerai."

10. De la première plonge,
     Il n'a rien ramené.

11. De la seconde plonge
     L'anneau-z-a voltigé.

12. De la troisième plonge
     Le galant s'est noyé.

\*   \*   \*

2. She met a band of sailors
   While she was walking there.
   While she was walking there
      At the island's edge,
   While she was walking there
       By the waterside
       Where the tall ships ride.

3. The youngest of the sailors
   He sang a song of love.
   He sang a song of love
      At the island's edge,
   He sang a song of love
       By the waterside
       Where the tall ships ride.

4. "Your song is such a sweet one,
   I'd like to sing it too.
   I'd like to sing it too
      At the island's edge,
   I'd like to sing it too
       By the waterside
       Where the tall ships ride."

5. "Come with me to my tall ship
   And I'll sing you my song.
   And I'll sing you my song
      At the island's edge,
   And I'll sing you my song
       By the waterside
       Where the tall ships ride."

6. She went on board that tall ship,
   But soon began to cry.
   But soon began to cry
      At the island's edge,
   But soon began to cry
       By the waterside
       Where the tall ships ride.

7. "What's wrong, my pretty lady,
   That makes you so lament?
   That makes you so lament
      At the island's edge,

299

That makes you so lament
    By the waterside
    Where the tall ships ride?"

8.  "I'm weeping for my gold ring
    That in the water fell.
    That in the water fell
        At the island's edge,
    That in the water fell
        By the waterside
        Where the tall ships ride."

9.  "Oh, do not cry my lady,
    I'll fetch it back for you.
    I'll fetch it back for you
        At the island's edge,
    I'll fetch it back for you
        By the waterside
        Where the tall ships ride."

10. He dived into the ocean,
    But came up with no ring.
    But came up with no ring
        At the island's edge,
    But came up with no ring
        By the waterside
        Where the tall ships ride.

11. The next time that he dived there
    The golden ring did gleam.
    The golden ring did gleam
        At the island's edge,
    The golden ring did gleam
        By the waterside
        Where the tall ships ride.

12. The third time that he dived there,
    The youth no more was seen.
    The youth no more was seen
        At the island's edge,
    The youth no more was seen
        By the waterside
        Where the tall ships ride.

*Son Petit Jupon* and *Isabeau S'y Promène* translated from the French
by John Anthony Scott.

# The Negro People

The Civil War destroyed slavery, but it did not bring to the Negro the freedom for which he had given his blood. In the years that followed the conflict, the Federal Government made many promises to the Negro of full rights, citizenship, land, education, human dignity, and freedom. By the end of the nineteenth century, these promises had been repudiated. A relatively small number of Southern whites continued, as before the Civil War, to control the economic resources of the South and, above all, the land. This fact alone doomed the Negro to a role of continued subordination and inferiority in the Southern system. Between the end of Reconstruction (usually dated from the disputed Hayes-Tilden election of 1876–1877) and the end of the century the Negro fell, or was pushed, back into a voteless, nameless, landless, rightless, poverty-stricken obscurity. Negro men, women, and children lived on in the draughty shacks of slavery days, picking cotton in the fields from sunup to sundown for a bare existence.

Segregation was so fundamental a feature of slave life that it endured long after the institution of slavery itself had been abolished. At the end of the nineteenth century, the Southern states enacted segregation codes that gave the explicit sanction of law to traditional Southern practices. Desperately afraid that the Negro might break out of the isolation imposed upon him and play a new and creative role in the political life of the section, Southern legislators passed laws that openly forbade the Negro to soil the white man's world. A Negro could not drink at the same fountain, sit in the same school, eat at the same table, or ride in the same car, as a white person; and he could not marry a white woman.

Retribution for the Negro who "got out of line" was swift. After the Civil War, the practice of leasing out convicts to private companies for forced labor became widespread. The most trifling offense might spell a sentence of months of work on the roads and the railroads, in the mines or on the levees.* Utilization of convicts in this way not only enriched the private operator but also reduced taxation. The leasing system encouraged wild irresponsibility and horrifying brutality in the use and abuse of human beings; even when it fell into

*Convicts were sometimes used as strikebreakers, e.g., by the Knoxville, Tennessee, Iron Company, 1877–1892. It is instructive that the free miners not only fought the use of scabs, but also protested the barbaric cruelty with which, as they asserted, the convicts were treated.

disuse, Southern states continued to operate their penal institutions on a strict commercial basis and to subject prisoners to the cruelty of a system of forced labor that differed little in substance from the regime of slavery itself. Negro prisoners, in the long years between the Civil War and the First World War, had no rights that a guard need respect. Negro life was cheap; no one cared whether a Negro lived or died, so long as he worked.

Creatively and spiritually, in these years, the Negro people rose far above their tormentors. They created a music unrivaled in the wide spectrum of American singing for its expressiveness, poignancy, humanity, and beauty. This was a music of work songs, spirituals, and blues.

The work songs included chain gang and prison songs, which fulfilled, collectively, a function central to traditional song: to enable people to face and overcome the intolerable ordeals of life, summon inspiration from the depths of the soul, survive, and endure. The singing was, of necessity, unaccompanied except for the rhythms or stresses that might be beaten out by hammer, pick, ax, or shuffling feet. With the blues it was different; they constituted a profoundly personal expression of the misery and humiliations which men and women had to endure daily, a personal statement of human feelings about life and its manifold injustices. The blues were leisure time songs, and therefore accompaniment was both possible and natural. Here, the guitar, which had made its first appearance on American soil before the Civil War, was called into service. To the Negro people goes the honor of making it a native American instrument. Southern blues singers worked out accompaniments in which the guitar not only was used with extraordinary sophistication, but also assumed the role of a second voice. The first, and perhaps the greatest, of the blues singers were country people, often blind or crippled, who wandered from place to place and sang for their living. In the course of time, the blues, like jazz, went to town undergoing as it did so, a gradual change. Spirituals, too, continued to be sung, as in the days before the Civil War, and to perform much the same many-sided function: part devotional music, part work song, part lament.

In the pages that follow, we have tried to select a few of the songs that convey most perfectly the mood and meaning of these years.

# Pick a Bale o' Cotton

"Pick a Bale o' Cotton" was a favorite of Huddie Leadbetter ("Leadbelly"), the great Southern singer. Its lively rhythm was well calculated to lighten the monotonous, day-long labor of chopping or picking. For children, it was a natural for dancing and skipping. Recently, American folksingers have taken it to the Soviet Union, where it has proved enormously popular.

2. A me an' my wife can
   Pick a bale o' cotton,
   A me an' my wife can
   Pick a bale a day.
*Chorus*

3. A me an' my girl can
   Pick a bale o' cotton,
   A me an' my girl can
   Pick a bale a day.
*Chorus*

4. A me an' my friend can
   Pick a bale o' cotton,
   A me an' my friend can
   Pick a bale a day.
*Chorus*

5. A me an' my pappa can
   Pick a bale o' cotton,
   A me an' my pappa can
   Pick a bale a day.
*Chorus*

6. You got to jump down turn around
   Pick a bale o' cotton,
   You got to jump down turn around
   Pick a bale a day.
*Chorus*

# No More Cane on This Brazos

"No More Cane on This Brazos" is a cane-cutting song from the Texan sugar lands and is believed by some to rank with the most sublime songs ever created or sung in the United States. Few songs express more clearly the meaning of human bondage on the Texas and Mississippi plantations *after* the Civil War, when prisoners were leased out to private land-owners and driven until they were blind, mad, or dead.

There ain't no\_\_\_\_ more\_ cane on\_\_\_\_ this
Bra - zos,\_\_\_ Oh \_\_\_\_
\_\_\_\_ They done grind it all\_\_ in mo-las-
ses, Oh\_\_\_\_

2. Now cap'n, doncha do me like you done poor Shine,
   Oh—
   You done drive that bully till he went stone blind,
   Oh—.

3. Oughta come on the river in 1904.
   Oh—
   You could find a dead man on every turn row,
   Oh—.

305

4. Oughta come on the river in 1910,
    Oh—
    They was drivin' the women jes' like the men,
    Oh—.

5. Now, wake up, dead man, help me drive my row,
    Oh—
    Wake up, dead man, help me drive my row,
    Oh—.

6. Wake up, lifer, hold up yo' head,
    Oh—
    You may get a pardon, and you may drop dead,
    Oh—.

7. Go down, ole Hannah, doncha rise no mo',
    Oh—
    If you come back, bring the Judgment Day,
    Oh—.

8. There ain't no more cane on this Brazos,
    Oh—
    They done grind it all in molasses,
    Oh—.

9. Some in the prison and some on the farm,
    Oh—
    Some in the fields and some goin home,
    Oh—.

# Another Man Done Gone

"Another Man Done Gone" is a simple, haunting, and incomparably beautiful melody transcribed from the singing of Vera Hall of Livingston, Alabama, as recorded by John A. and Alan Lomax for the Library of Congress Archive of American Folk Song.

An-oth-er man done___ gone,_____ An-oth-er man___ done gone___ From the coun-ty farm, An-oth-er man done gone.

2. I didn't know his name,
   I didn't know his name,
   I didn't know his name,
   I didn't know his name.

3. He had a long chain on,
   He had a long chain on,
   He had a long chain on,
   He had a long chain on.

4. He killed another man,
   He killed another man,
   He killed another man,
   He killed another man.

5. I don' know where he's gone,
   I don' know where he's gone,
   I don' know where he's gone,
   I don' know where he's gone.

6. I'm gonna walk your road,
   I'm gonna walk your road,
   I'm gonna walk your road,
   I'm gonna walk your road.

7. Another man done gone,
   Another man done gone
   From the county farm,
   Another man done gone.

From a 78 r.p.m. recording in the Archive of Folk Song, Library of Congress.

# Godamighty Drag

"Godamighty Drag" was learned by Alan Lomax from the singing of Augustus (Track Horse) Haggerty in the Huntsville, Texas Penitentiary. Lomax writes of song and singer:

Track Horse was a powerful, stocky Negro with a wonderful smile, a beautiful voice, and the gift of leadership. When he took the lead in a work song, his buddies sang like demons, and the chips spun through the air like flecks of brown foam. This was his favorite work song— I suspect his own composition. . . . Songs like this helped to clear the live-oaks off the rich river bottom land of Texas, and thus to create the cotton plantations that enriched the state.*

*"Texas Folk Songs," sung by Alan Lomax. Tradition 1029.

2. Done tole me they'd pardon me
   O lawdy,
   Done tole me they'd pardon me
   O o my Lord.
   By next July sir,
   O lawdy,
   By next July sir,
   O o my Lord.

3. July and August
   O lawdy,
   July and August,
   O o my Lord.
   Done come and gone sir,
   O lawdy,
   Done come and gone sir,
   O o my Lord.

4. Left me here rolling
   O lawdy,
   Left me here rolling
   O o my Lord.
   On this ole farm sir,
   O lawdy,
   On this ole farm sir,
   O o my Lord.

5. Gonna write to the Governor
   O lawdy,
   Gonna write to the Governor
   O o my Lord.
   See if he'll help me
   O lawdy,
   See if he'll help me
   O o my Lord.

6. Mamma and pappa
   O lawdy,
   Mamma and pappa,
   God amighty God knows!
   Done tole me a lie, sir,
   O lawdy,
   Done tole me a lie, sir,
   O o my Lord.

7. Done tole me they'd pardon me
        O lawdy,
   Done tole me they'd pardon me,
        O o my Lord.
   Fore next July, sir,
        O Lawdy,
   Fore next July sir
        O o my Lord.

Collected, adapted and arranged by John A. Lomax and Alan Lomax. © Copyright 1941 Ludlow Music, Inc., New York, N.Y. Transcribed from the singing of Alan Lomax by John Anthony Scott. Used by permission.

# No More, My Lord

"No More, My Lord" is transcribed from a recording made by Alan Lomax in 1947 at the Mississippi State Penitentiary at Parchman. It is a good example of a spiritual that is also a work song; one in which the stroke of the ax on the downbeat is an integral part of the melody. "No More, My Lord" has a deceptive simplicity that conceals an extraordinary musical sophistication. The melody, tranquil and serene, ranks among the finest in our heritage. Compare it to "Sold Off to Georgy," page 206 above. There is similarity, and also development.

have _____ made    me __ glad.
me _____ where    He's __ gone?
you  may  find,    find Him there.

1. I found in Him
   A resting place
   And he have made me glad.

2. Jesus the man
   I am looking for,
   Can you tell me
   Where He's gone?

3. Go down, go down
   Among floweryard
   And perhaps you may find,
   Find Him there.

Collected, adapted and arranged by Alan Lomax. © Copyright 1947 Essex Music Ltd., London, England. All publication rights controlled by Ludlow Music, Inc., New York, N. Y. for the U.S.A. and Canada. Transcribed by John Anthony Scott from "Negro Prison Songs," Tradition Records 1020. Used by permission.

# Settin' Side That Road

This piece is transcribed from the singing of Godar Chalvin of Abbeville, Louisiana; with three lines to the stanza, it is written in the classic blues form. The song is included here as an example of "rural blues" that directly and obviously illustrates the connection between the man's predicament and his musical complaint.

I'm set - tin' side that road__ with a

ball and chain on my leg;__ I'm

set - tin' side that road__ with a

ball and chain on my leg;__

If I had my way__ I'd

catch - a that west - bound train.

That judge give me six months because I didn't wanna
   work;
That judge give me six months because I didn't wanna
   work;
That judge give me six months because I didn't wanna
   work;

I'm settin' side that road, etc.

Transcribed by John Anthony Scott from "A Sampler of Louisiana
Folksongs," a publication of the Louisiana Folklore Society, collected
and edited by Dr. Harry Oster, Louisiana State University. Used by
permission of Dr. Oster and the Louisiana Folklore Society.

# The Ballad of the Boll Weevil

At the beginning of the twentieth century the plight of Southern cotton farmers was aggravated by the spread of the boll weevil, an insect blight that entered Texas from Mexico in 1892; between 1900 and 1922, it took a tremendous annual toll of the United States cotton crop. This misfortune fell with a special impact on the poor Negro tenants and croppers of Mississippi, Alabama, Louisiana, Georgia, and South Carolina. Many of them were ruined and after 1909 began to move northward in large numbers to seek jobs. From this time dates the rapid growth of the ghettoes of Chicago and New York.

"The Ballad of the Boll Weevil" has been found in dozens of variants throughout the South, wherever the cotton farmer suffered from the weevil's depredations. We reproduce two of these variants: the first, a commonly sung version of the ballad, and the second a slow, haunting melody transcribed from the singing of Vera Hall of Livingston, Alabama, as recorded by John A. Lomax in the 1930's for the Library of Congress.

(1)

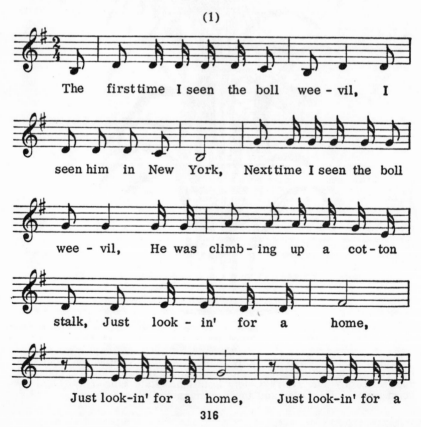

The first time I seen the boll wee - vil, I seen him in New York, Next time I seen the boll wee - vil, He was climb - ing up a cot - ton stalk, Just look - in' for a home, Just look-in' for a home, Just look-in' for a

316

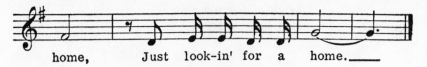

home,          Just look-in' for a home.____

The first time I seen the boll weevil,
He was settin' on the square,
The next time I seen the boll weevil,
He had all his family there,
    Just lookin' for a home, etc.

The farmer took the boll weevil
And buried him in the sand,
Boll weevil said to the farmer,
"I'll stand it like a man,
    It'll be my home," etc.

Then the farmer took the boll weevil,
And left him on the ice,
Boll weevil say to the farmer,
"This is mighty cool and nice,
    It'll be my home," etc.

Farmer said to the boll weevil
"I see you at my door,"
"Yessir," said the boll weevil,
"I been here before,
    I'm gonna get your home," etc.

Boll weevil say to the farmer,
"You can ride in your Ford machine,
When I get through with yo' cotton,
Can't buy no gasoline,
    Won't have no home," etc.

The farmer say to the merchant,
"I want some meat and meal,"
"Get away from here you son of a gun,
Got weevils in yo' field,
    Gonna get yo' home," etc.

If anyone should ask you
Who it was that wrote this song,
Tell him 'twas a dark-skinned farmer
With a pair of blue duckin's on,

Lookin' for a home,
Just lookin' for a home, etc.

(2)

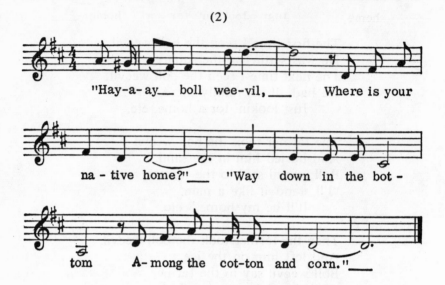

"Hay-a-ay boll wee-vil, Where is your na-tive home?" "Way down in the bot-tom A-mong the cot-ton and corn."

First time I seen the boll weevil,
He's settin' on the square;
Next time I seen him,
He had his family there.

Boll weevil here,
Boll weevil everywhere;
They done ate up all the cotton and corn,
All but that new ground square.

Well, the farmer asked the merchant
Uh—for some meat and meal.
"T'ain't nothing doin', old man;
Boll weevil's in your field."

"Hay-a-ay boll weevil,
Where is your native home?"
"Way down in the bottom
Among the cotton and corn."

*The Ballad of the Boll Weevil* (1) and (2) from Record AFS L51
in the Archive of Folk Song, Library of Congress.

# Ragged and Dirty Blues

This is a blues of migrant workers shaken loose from their little holdings, going from job to job in the lumbering camps, on the levees, moving north toward the cities. It evidently had a wide circulation. Blind Lemon Jefferson brought the song from Texas to Chicago and recorded it there for Paramount in the 1920's under the title "Broke and Hungry." William Brown of Clarksdale, Mississippi recorded another version for the Library of Congress Archive of American Folksong in 1942. The version given here is transcribed from the singing of John W. Scott in 1964.

Well I'm rag - ged, I'm hun-gry, I'm dirt - y too; I'm rag - ged, well I'm broke, and I'm dirt - y too. If I clean up, sweet ma - ma, can I stay all,_ all night_ with you?_____

2. Well I'm motherless, I'm fatherless, I'm sisterless, I'm
    brotherless too;
    I'm motherless, I'm fatherless, I'm sisterless, I'm
    brotherless too.
    That's why I tried so hard (mmm) to make this, this trip
    with you.

3. Well they tell me that graveyard is a long ole lonesome
place.
That graveyard, well, it's a long ole lonesome place;
They put you six foot under, (mmm) then they throw
clay in your face.

4. Well I'm tired of living, honey, I don't know what to do;
I'm tired of living, honey, I don't know what to do.
Your tired of me (mmm) and I'm—I'm tired of you.

5. Well I'm goin' to leave you, honey, even if I have to
ride that line;
I'm goin' to leave you, honey, and I'll have to ride that line.
You can just remember one thing, babe (mmm) I don't,
no I don't mind the dyin'.

6. Well down that road somewhere, honey, down that road
somewhere;
Down that road somewhere, well down that road
somewhere,
I'll find me a good woman (mmm), I won't have to
roam, roam no more.

# Yonder Come Day

Along the coast of South Carolina and Georgia stretches a chain of islands—St. Helena, Sapelo, St. Simons, Cumberland, and many more—famous before the Civil War for the production of "sea island cotton," from which long-staple cloth of the finest quality was woven. Over the years, the plantations of this area fell upon evil days; but economic decay and natural isolation encouraged the continuation of the traditional singing of the Negro people, slaves and the descendants of slaves, who lived there. In the 1930's Lydia Parrish, a Northern woman, came to live on St. Simons, organized a group known as the Sea Island Singers, and transcribed and eventually published their music. Here, therefore, we can study a singing tradition that has continued uninterrupted since slavery days.

"Yonder Come Day" is a Sea Island spiritual that probably came into use in the years following the Civil War. Traditionally, it is sung by the people, who are Baptists, at the end of a night-long service. The melody is on four notes only, and a conventional harmonic accompaniment is impossible; the best instrument to use would be a flute or recorder.

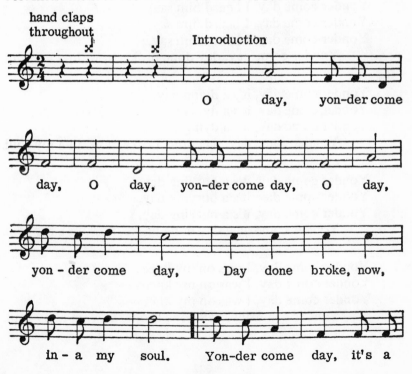

judg-ment day, Yon-der come day, it's a

judg-ment day, Yon-der come day, it's a

judg-ment day, Yon-der come day,

day done broke, now, in-a my soul.

Yonder come day, I heard him say,
Yonder come day, I heard him say,
Yonder come day, I heard him say,
    Yonder come day, day done broke, now, in-a my soul.

Yonder come day, it's a dying day,
Yonder come day, it's a dying day,
Yonder come day, it's a dying day,
    Yonder come day, day done broke, now, in-a my soul.

Yonder come day, it's a burying day,
Yonder come day, it's a burying day,
Yonder come day, it's a burying day,
    Yonder come day, day done broke, now, in-a my soul.

Yonder come day, I was on my knees,
Yonder come day, I was on my knees,
Yonder come day, I was on my knees,
    Yonder come day, day done broke, now, in-a my soul.

Yonder come day, I heard him say,
Yonder come day, I heard him say,
Yonder come day, I heard him say,
    Yonder come day, day done broke, now, in-a my soul.

Yonder come day, that's a New Year's day,
Yonder come day, that's a New Year's day,
Yonder come day, that's a New Year's day,
    Yonder come day, day done broke, now, in-a my soul.

Yonder come day, woncha come on, child,
Yonder come day, woncha come on, child,
Yonder come day, woncha come on, child,
    Yonder come day, day done broke, now, in-a my soul.

Yonder come day, I was on my knees,
Yonder come day, I was on my knees,
Yonder come day, I was on my knees,
    Yonder come day, day done broke, now, in-a my soul.

Yonder come day, I heard him say, *etc.*

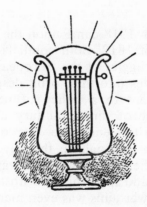

# VII
# BETWEEN
# TWO
# WORLD
# WARS

THE WAR OF 1914–1918 came upon the world about a century after the War of 1812. Both conflicts had their origin in the life-and-death struggles of the European powers, and both drew the United States into their orbit despite an official governmental commitment to a policy of neutrality or, at the very least, avoidance of direct military involvement. There, however, the similarities end. The War of 1812 accelerated the rise of American nationalism, the development of American industry, and the triumphant westward sweep of immigrants and pioneers; and all of this notwithstanding the fact that none of the nation's war aims was even mentioned in the terms of peace. The war of 1914–1918, by contrast, ended with the ignominious collapse of the German enemy and a total military victory that was spelled out starkly in the terms of peace imposed on the vanquished. Yet this victory ushered in a period of national doubt, frustration, bitterness, and confusion rarely equaled in the annals of a civilized people and surpassed only by the mood of black despair that prevailed in Germany itself.

Stranger still, a brief period of hectic prosperity culminated in the most frightful economic catastrophe in American history, the crash of 1929, and the ensuing Great Depression. There had, of course, been previous crashes and previous depressions. This one capped them all in length of duration, numbers of unemployed, the stubbornness with which it resisted treatment, and the sheer mass of human misery and wastage which it imposed.

In 1932, Franklin D. Roosevelt was elected President by a landslide vote; he received a mandate from the American people to effect economic recovery through emergency measures, by utilizing the full powers of the Federal Government. Thus was ushered in the New Deal and, more generally, the Roosevelt era. Roosevelt's tenure of office, from 1933–1945, covered a whole epoch in the life and experience of the nation. It witnessed the rebirth of hope and of a will to struggle against economic and social calamity. This new mood was generated in no small part by the dynamic quality of Roosevelt's leadership and by the bold experimental federal program which he unfolded.

American life in these years moved forward in the ominous shadow of Adolf Hitler. Aflame with Napoleonic ambition, Hitler achieved supreme power in Germany in 1933, established the Third Reich, and immediately set out to tear up the iniquitous Versailles Treaty, conquer Europe, and dominate the world. The regime that he created committed in the 12 short years of its existence acts of barbaric cruelty that characterize it as the most abominable tyranny ever inflicted upon man. By the same token, it was a monument to the bankrupt statesmanship of the Western Powers who had within the space of two decades from the imposition of the Versailles peace permitted the resurrection of the imperialist monster whose earlier annihilation had cost 10 million lives.

In the 1930's the presence of Hitler dominated the world; one cannot understand American life and experience at this time without constant reference to that fact. Similarly, it is not possible to understand American development in the early national period (1783–1815) without reference to the Franco-British struggle in general, and Napoleon in particular. After 1933, as after 1914, the United States gradually emerged from its posture of isolation from European military conflicts and shifted its weight to the weaker side (the Western Allies) in order to prevent the destruction of the international balance of power. The conflict became both total and global in 1942 when the Fascist Powers (Germany, Italy, Japan) found themselves aligned against the Allied nations coalition led by the United States, the Soviet Union, Great Britain, and China. It then became America's destiny to play a part in preventing the engulfment of the globe by Hitler and his allies. For the victory of Fascism over the Allied nations would most certainly have obliterated for an indefinite period of time the very possibility of human progress.

The songs of this stormy period between the beginning of World War I and the end of World War II mirror not only the despair and confusion, but also the hopes and struggles of millions of Americans. We reproduce in the following pages a few of the most expressive from the rich treasury of these years.*

*The development of the blues in this period as a form of folk song would require a book in itself. See Chapter VI, above, and Paul Oliver, *The Meaning of the Blues* (New York: Collier Books, 1963).

# When Johnny Comes Marching Home
# Johnny, I Hardly Knew You

On April 2, 1917 President Woodrow Wilson went before Congress to ask for a declaration of war against Germany. The reason given was the violation of the rights of neutrality and freedom of the seas; since February of that year the Germans had waged unrestricted submarine warfare in an effort to achieve the effective blockade of British and French coasts. Vessels approaching British, French, or Irish ports were liable to be sunk at sight.

In point of fact, the United States had leaned openly toward the Franco-British side from the very start of the conflict in 1914 and had provided, during the first three years of the war, massive material and financial aid to the Western belligerents. American leadership saw in Germany the most menacing threat to the United States as a world power and was determined to reduce it. To Wilson, a more compelling reason for entry into the war than the submarine issue was the imminent collapse of the Russian front. This, coupled with German preparations for an all-out offensive to break the deadlock in the West and growing signs of Allied military exhaustion, was no doubt decisive in bringing about direct American intervention.

Wilson stated his war objective in purely altruistic terms. "We fight," said he, "for the ultimate peace of the world and for the liberation of its peoples, the German people included; for the rights of nations great and small and the privilege of men everywhere to choose their way of life and of obedience. The world must be made safe for democracy."

The American Army landed in France in 1918 more than half a million strong; and it was a singing Army. Traditional marching songs were pressed into service; music hall hits won popularity with the soldiers, including of course contributions from the British and the French. *When Johnny Comes Marching Home* falls into the first of these categories; it first made its appearance during the Civil War and won increasing popularity as the years went by. It is attributed to an Irish-American bandmaster, Patrick S. Gilmore. An Irish version, *Johnny, I Hardly Knew You,* was probably inspired by the American song. *Johnny,* in other words, began life as a war song and then turned into a protest against war; it is the latter version that finds most popularity with folk song audiences today. *Mrs. McGrath* (see p. 121 above) is another example of a traditional song used during World War I, but in this case the process was reversed. It started life as a protest against war, but Irish troops pressed it into service as a marching song, speeded up the slow tempo, and sung it with rollicking abandon.

## When Johnny Comes Marching Home

The old church bell will peal with joy,
    Hurrah, hurrah!
To welcome home our darling boy,
    Hurrah, hurrah!
The village lads and lasses say
    With roses they will strew the way,
And we'll all feel gay when Johnny comes marching
    home.

Get ready for the Jubilee,
    Hurrah, hurrah!
We'll give the hero three times three,
    Hurrah, hurrah!
The laurel wreath is ready now
    To place upon his loyal brow,
And we'll all feel gay when Johnny comes marching
    home.


## Johnny, I Hardly Knew You
(to the same tune: slow tempo)

*Refrain:*  With your guns and drums and drums and guns,
        Haroo, haroo,
            With your guns and drums and drums and guns,
        Haroo, haroo,
            With your guns and drums and drums and guns
        The enemy nearly slew you,
        Oh Johnny dear, you look so queer,
            Johnny, I hardly knew you.

1.  Where are your legs with which you run,
        Haroo, haroo,
    Where are your legs with which you run,
        Haroo, haroo,
    Where are your legs with which you run
        When first you went to carry a gun;
    I fear your dancing days are done,
        Johnny, I hardly knew you.
*Refrain*

2.  And where are your eyes that looked so mild
        Haroo, haroo,
    And where are your eyes that looked so mild
        Haroo, haroo,

And where are your eyes that looked so mild
      When you first my innocent heart beguiled—
*And why did you run from me and the child?*
      Johnny, I hardly knew you.
*Refrain*


3.  You haven't an arm and you haven't a leg,
      Haroo, haroo,
  You haven't an arm and you haven't a leg,
      Haroo, haroo,
  You haven't an arm and you haven't a leg
      You're an eyeless boneless chickenless egg;
  You'll have to be put with a bowl to beg,
      Johnny, I hardly knew you.
*Refrain*


4.  'Tis glad I am to see you home,
      Haroo, haroo,
  'Tis glad I am to see you home,
      Haroo, haroo;
  'Tis glad I am to see you home
      Safe from the is!ands of Ceylon,
  So low in the flesh so high in the bone,
      Johnny, I hardly knew you.
*Refrain*

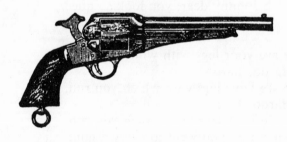

# Mademoiselle from Armentières

This World War I vaudeville hit became a great favorite with British and American troops. Over the years, it has exhibited an irrepressible vitality. It proliferated endless (and often unprintable) lyrics during World War I; and it continued to grow during World War II as another generation of G.I.'s in France added yet more (and often unprintable) verses to the list. Even so, the uses of the song were not yet exhausted. When World War I was over *Mademoiselle* immigrated to the United States with the returning soldiers; in the labor struggles of the twenties and thirties, she made her appearance on the picket lines with verses such as these:

> The bosses are taking it on the chin, parlez-vous,
> The bosses are taking it on the chin, parlez-vous,
>     The bosses are taking it on the chin
>     Because the strikers won't give in,
> Inky dinky parlez-vous.

In the versions reproduced here World War I lyrics are followed by World War II additions.

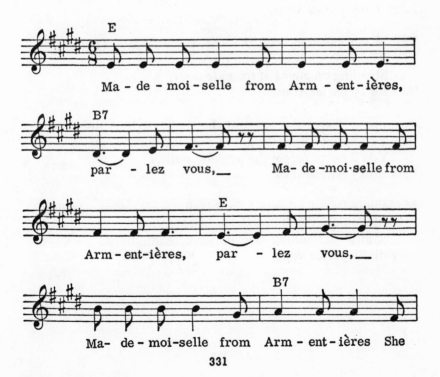

Ma - de - moi - selle from Arm - ent - ières,
par - lez vous,___ Ma - de - moi - selle from
Arm - ent - ières, par - lez vous,___
Ma - de - moi - selle from Arm - ent - ières She

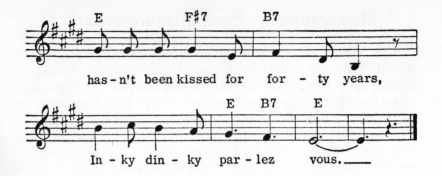

has - n't been kissed for for - ty years,

In - ky din - ky par - lez vous.___

## World War I:

Oh farmer, have you a daughter fair, parlez-vous   (*twice*)
    Oh farmer have you a daughter fair
    Who can wash a soldier's underwear,
Inky dinky parlez-vous.

The officers get all the steak, parlez-vous   (*twice*)
    The officers get all the steak
    And all we get is the belly-ache
Inky dinky parlez-vous.

The M.P.'s say they won the war, parlez-vous   (*twice*)
    The M.P.'s say they won the war
    Standing on guard at the cafe door,
Inky dinky parlez-vous.

You might forget the gas and the shell, parlez-vous   (*twice*)
    You might forget the gas and shell,
    You'll never forget the mademoiselle,
Inky dinky parlez-vous.

Mademoiselle all dressed in black, parlez-vous   (*twice*)
    Mademoiselle all dressed in black
    'Cause her soldier boy he never came back,
Inky dinky parlez-vous.

## World War II:

Our top-kick there in Armentières, parlez-vous
Our top-kick there in Armentières, parlez-vous,
    Our top-kick there in Armentières
    Soon broke that spell of forty years,
Inky dinky parlez-vous.

She might have been young for all we knew, parlez-vous
She might have been young for all we knew, parlez-vous
    She might have been young for all we knew
    When Napoleon flopped at Waterloo
Inky dinky parlez-vous.

She got the palms and the Croix de Guerre, parlez-vous *(twice)*
    She got the palms and the Croix de Guerre
    For washing soldiers' underwear,
Inky dinky parlez-vous.

The second lieutenants are at it again, parlez-vous *(twice)*
    The second lieutenants are at it again
    They're winning the war with a fountain pen,
Inky dinky parlez-vous.

The general got the Croix de Guerre, parlez-vous *(twice)*
    The general got the Croix de Guerre,
    The son of a gun wasn't even there,
Inky dinky parlez-vous.

Oh mademoiselle from Gay Paree, parlez-vous *(twice)*
    Oh mademoiselle from Gay Paree
    You certainly played hell with me,
Inky dinky parlez-vous.

# Pack Up Your Troubles

This was a popular song among both British and American troops in World War I. But it has retained a permanent appeal among children. Over the years, it has lightened the homeward tramp of many a footsore Cub Scout.

Pack up your trou - bles in your old kit bag, And smile, smile, smile! While you've a Lu - ci - fer to light your fag, Smile boys, that's the style; What's the use of wor - ry - ing, It nev - er was worth while; So pack up your trou - bles in your old kit bag, And smile, smile, smile!

# Wandering

The collapse of Germany in 1918 and the return of peace ushered in a period of uneasy transition in American life. Prosperity mingled with poverty, complacency with a sense of rootlessness and drift, law-abiding morality with the lawless gangsterism of the prohibition era. The most exciting singing of these years was that of workers, Negroes, and the poor. Bitter labor struggles led to new picket line and union songs, notably amid the poverty-stricken mining communities of Appalachia. The urbanization of America and the urbanization of the blues proceeded apace.

The precarious prosperity of the twenties vanished in 1929 with the stock market crash of October 24. America spun down into the depths of depression. Factories, banks, schools closed. Thousands lost their homes. The streets were black with homeless men and women. At the depth of the depression, in 1932, some 14 million people were out of work and near starvation. Tens of thousands of these wandered back and forth across the country, living off charity handouts, looking for nonexistent jobs, sleeping in flop-houses or freight cars, or freezing in the cold winter nights.

The same conditions prevailed in the countryside. Hundreds of thousands of farmers were homeless and starving. America's sons and daughters wandered as wastrels in the midst of the abundance which they had themselves created. From this indescribable reality arose new and expressive depression songs, such as *Wandering*. The melody is related to a traditional Irish tune. The lyrics are in part inherited from earlier labor and "hard times" songs.

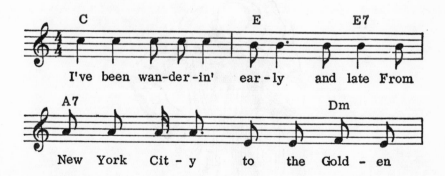

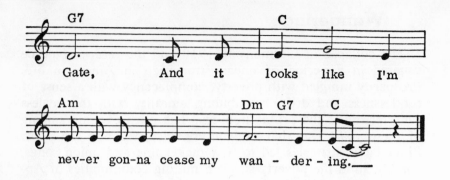

Gate, And it looks like I'm

nev-er gon-na cease my wan - der - ing.___

There's fish in the ocean, there's eels in the sea,
But a red-headed woman made a fool out of me,
And it looks like I'm never going to cease my wandering.

I've been working in the army, I've been working on a farm,
And all I've got to show is the muscle in my arm,
And it looks like I'm never going to cease my wandering.

Ashes to ashes and dust to dust,
If the Republicans don't get you, the Democrats must,
And it looks like I'm never going to cease my wandering.

O, I've been wandering far and wide,
I come with the wind, I drift with the tide,
And it looks like I'm never going to cease my wandering.

# Raggedy

In the first years of the depression, the people's only protection from starvation was the charity of their neighbors, family, or friends. In all of the cities of America long lines formed outside of churches and town halls, lines of patient, humble, angry people, waiting for a bowl of soup, a hunk of bread. But whatever pittance local charity could afford was not enough to keep adults from starving nor to quiet children crying from hunger. At Christmas, 1931, a young couple was found starving in a supposedly empty cottage near Anwana Lake in Sullivan County, New York. The *Times* reported that "three days without food, the wife, who is 23 years old, was hardly able to walk." And that same winter, at Youngstown, Ohio, a paper bore the headline FATHER OF TEN DROWNS SELF. Charles Wayne, a steel worker two years without employment, threw himself into the swirling Mahoning River, abandoning forever the destitute family he could no longer help. Reports such as these were frequent at this time; and one of the pioneer achievements for which the New Deal will longest be remembered was the passage of the Social Security Act in 1935, which introduced for the first time the concept of Federal responsibility to cope with the hazards of unemployment and old age.

"Raggedy," a song arising out of the suffering of these years, vividly and bleakly expressed the predicament of a nation.

Rag - gedy, rag - gedy are we, Just as
rag - gedy, rag - gedy can be, Well we
don't get noth- ing for our la - bor, So

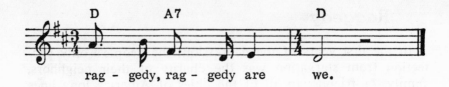

rag - gedy, rag - gedy are we.

Hungry, hungry are we,
Just as hungry, hungry can be,
Well we don't get nothing for our labor,
So hungry, hungry are we.

Homeless, homeless are we,
Just as homeless, homeless can be,
Well we don't get nothing for our labor,
So homeless, homeless are we.

Landless, landless are we,
Just as landless, landless can be,
Well we don't get nothing for our labor,
So landless, landless are we.

Pitiful, so pitiful are we,
Just as pitiful, pitiful can be,
Well we don't get nothing for our labor,
So pitiful, pitiful are we.

Raggedy, raggedy are we,
Just as raggedy, raggedy can be,
Well we don't get nothing for our labor,
So raggedy, raggedy are we.

# The Mouse's Courting Song

Everywhere, shantytowns for the homeless sprang up, made of cardboard, newspaper, old boards, orange crates—anything that came to hand. They called them Hoovervilles. Men and women lived in these garbage dumps, and children were born there. Many children didn't go to school at all; some didn't have shoes, and many knew days when there was no food. Some stayed in bed because they had no clothes. But they sang and played and romped, as kids will, in the dingy streets and dusty alleys, around the shacks of Hooverville.

"The Mouse's Courting Song," collected from the singing of neighborhood children in Pittsburgh in the early 1940's, is an American version of "The Frog and the Mouse," which in one form or another has been a favorite with American children for three centuries. In the original British song, which dates from the sixteenth century,

> A frog he would a wooing go,
>   Heigh ho, said Rowley;
> A frog he would a wooing go, whether his mother
>   would let him or no,
> With a rowley powley,
> Gammon and spinnage, heigh ho, said Rowley.

We include this song here, not only as a sample of children's singing during the New Deal period, but also because it beautifully illustrates the process of continuity and development in our song tradition, to the present time.

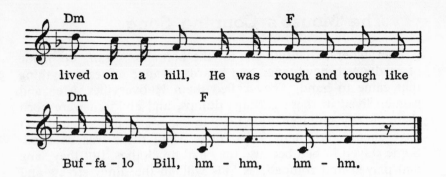

lived on a hill, He was rough and tough like
Buf-fa-lo Bill, hm - hm, hm - hm.

One day he decided to take a ride, hm-hm,
One day he decided to take a ride
With two six-shooters by his side, hm-hm.

Then Mickey rode till he came to a house,
And in this house was Minnie Mouse.

He strutted right up to the kitchen door,
And bowed and scraped his head on the floor.

O Minnie, Minnie, will you marry me?
Away down yonder in the orchard tree!

Without my Uncle Rat's consent,
I would not marry the Pres-eye-dent!

Her Uncle Rat gave his consent,
The Weasel wrote the publishment.

Oh, what you gonna have for the wedding feast?
Black-eyed peas and hogshead cheese.

The first one came was Uncle Rat,
Head as long as a baseball bat.

Second one came was Mr. Snake,
He wrapped himself 'round the marble cake.

The next one came was a little moth,
To spread on the tablecloth.

The next one came was a big black bug,
Carrying 'round a little brown jug.

The next one came was a bumblebee,
With a broken wing and a crooked knee.

The next one came was a nimble flea,
Saying Minnie, Minnie Mouse, will you dance with me?

The next one came was Mr. Cow,
He wanted to dance but he didn't know how.

Last one came was Mr. Cat,
He ruffled and tuffled and ate Uncle Rat.

And that was the end of the wedding feast,
Black-eyed peas and hogshead cheese.

Reprinted by permission of the Johns Hopkins Press from Jacob A. Evanson, "Folksongs of an Industrial City," in *Pennsylvania Songs and Legends,* edited by George Korson, the Johns Hopkins Press, Baltimore, 1949. Copyright by George Korson.

# Which Side Are You On?

At the end of 1932, in the very depths of the depression, the American people turned away from Herbert Hoover and the Republican Party. In November, Roosevelt was elected President. Franklin Delano Roosevelt was an experienced politician who had made a comeback into active life from a crippling disease in the early twenties. There was a warmth and directness about the man that won the hearts of the people; and Roosevelt promised action.

One of the achievements for which the New Deal will longest be remembered was the organization of American labor. In 1933, notwithstanding a century of struggle for the right to organize, most American workers still lacked trade unions; conditions of work were hard, bitter, and often dangerous. Under the National Industrial Recovery Act of May, 1933— section 7-A subsequently expanded into the Wagner Act of 1935—workers received the right to bargain collectively with their employers through unions of their own choice.

This law opened the floodgates to the organization of millions of unorganized workers. A new spirit of labor militancy spread across the land; dozens of new songs were born on the picket lines.

"Which Side Are You On?" was written by Florence Reece and set to a traditional ballad tune. It arose out of the struggle of miners in Harlan County, Kentucky to organize a union in 1931, and out of the bloody collisions between miners and gun-toting coal company deputies. In the great organizing movement of the following years, few songs were sung more than this one.

Come all of you good work - ers, Good

news to you I'll tell Of how the good old

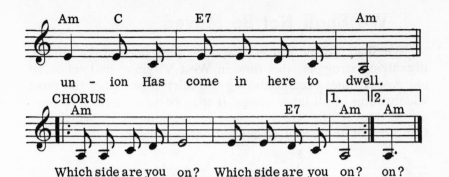

un - ion Has come in here to dwell.

CHORUS

Which side are you on? Which side are you on? on?

My daddy was a miner,
And I'm a miner's son,
And I'll stick with the union
Till every battle's won.
*Chorus*

They say in Harlan County
There are no neutrals there;
You'll either be a union man,
Or a thug for J. H. Blair.
*Chorus*

Oh workers, can you stand it?
Oh tell me how you can,
Will you be a lousy scab,
Or will you be a man?
*Chorus*

Don't scab for the bosses,
Don't listen to their lies,
Us poor folks haven't got a chance
Unless we organize.
*Chorus*

# We Shall Not Be Moved

"We Shall Not Be Moved," another song born of the miners' organizing struggles, this time in West Virginia, and set to an old gospel tune, became during the thirties probably the most widely sung of all labor songs. It may be said literally to have presided over the great organizing movement in which the Congress of Industrial Organizations was born.

The un - ion is be - hind us, we shall not be moved, The un - ion is be - hind us, we shall not be moved, Just like a tree, that's stand - ing by the wa - ter, We shall not be moved.

CHORUS

We shall not, we shall not be moved,

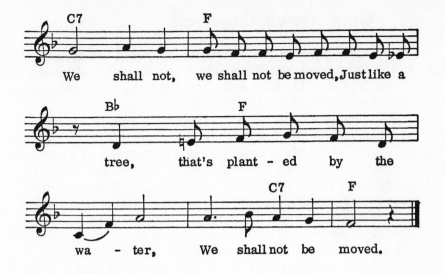

We shall not, we shall not be moved, Just like a
tree, that's plant - ed by the
wa - ter, We shall not be moved.

We're fighting for our freedom, we shall not be moved,
We're fighting for our freedom, we shall not be moved
Just like a tree, that's planted by the water,
We shall not be moved.
*Chorus*

We're fighting for our children, we shall not be moved,
We're fighting for our children, we shall not be moved
Just like a tree, that's standing by the water,
We shall not be moved.
*Chorus*

We'll build a mighty Union, we shall not be moved,
We'll build a mighty Union, we shall not be moved
Just like a tree, that's standing by the water,
We shall not be moved.
*Chorus*

# Goin' Down the Road

The early years of the New Deal witnessed the appearance of the Dust Bowl, which converted vast expanses of the High Plains into a wilderness and completed the ruin of tens of thousands of farmers who lived and worked there.

The great dust storms which hit the plains in these years and blotted out the harvests were a result of the ploughing up of the grasslands and the enormous extension of cultivated acreage that resulted from the huge demand for bread and clothing in the first World War. The farmers' problems of mortgaged land, surplus capacity, declining prices, and chronic indebtedness came to a climax in the depression years; the terrible droughts of 1932–1936 and the swirling dust completed the catastrophe. Ruined tenants from the Dust Bowl hit the trail and moved West to California in search of any jobs they could find. "Goin' Down the Road," an old sharecroppers song, expressed both the courage and the despair of people coping with a new calamity. It was taken up, too, by city and farm workers everywhere who were seeking to organize unions to protect them from eviction and to secure fair wages. *I won't be treated this-a way* became almost an official motto of the New Deal and an eloquent expression of the popular mood underlying it.

treat-ed this-a way._____

2. I'm goin' where the dust storms never blow,
   I'm goin' where the dust storms never blow,
   I'm goin' where the dust storms never blow, Lord, Lord,
   And I ain't gonna be treated thisaway.

3. I'm lookin' for a job with honest pay,
   I'm lookin' for á job with honest pay,
   I'm lookin' for a job with honest pay, Lord, Lord,
   And I ain't gonna be treated thisaway.

4. Two dollar shoes hurt my feet,
   Two dollar shoes hurt my feet,
   Two dollar shoes hurt my feet, Lord, Lord,
   And I ain't gonna be treated thisaway.

5. But ten dollar shoes fit 'em neat,
   But ten dollar shoes fit 'em neat,
   But ten dollar shoes fit 'em neat, Lord, Lord,
   And I ain't gonna be treated thisaway.

6. I'm goin' where the water tastes like wine,
   I'm goin' where the water tastes like wine,
   I'm goin' where the water tastes like wine, Lord, Lord,
   And I ain't gonna be treated thisaway.

7. Forty cents an hour won't pay my rent,
   Forty cents an hour won't pay my rent,
   Forty cents an hour won't pay my rent, Lord, Lord,
   And I ain't gonna be treated thisaway.

8. I can't live on cornbread and beans,
   I can't live on cornbread and beans,
   I can't live on cornbread and beans, Lord, Lord,
   And I ain't gonna be treated thisaway.

9. I'm goin' down the road feelin' bad,
   I'm goin' down the road feelin' bad,
   I'm goin' down the road feelin' bad, Lord, Lord,
   And I ain't gonna be treated thisaway.

# Roll On, Columbia

Under the Roosevelt administration, a program of public works construction got under way. Public works, it was thought, might kill several birds with one stone: create jobs, reforest the countryside, check floods and soil erosion, and make abundant electrical power at low cost available to the farmer. The most grandiose of these projects was the building of the Federal dams—the great dams on the Tennessee River, Black Canyon on the Colorado, Grand Coulee on the Columbia River, Bonneville on Cascade Rapids in western Oregon.

"Roll On, Columbia" is one of many songs written by Woody Guthrie when he was in the Northwest and employed by the Bonneville Power Administration. Its graceful lyric is set to an old Scots tune "My Bonnie Lies Over the Ocean," but reworked in Woody's own inimitable style. Woody was an "Okie" who led the wandering existence typical of his generation, but what he saw and felt during the Twenties and Thirties he expressed in hundreds of songs, the best of which sum up the mood and meaning of the times. Woody is an American Burns: he has immersed himself in the traditional music of his people to produce lyrics of extraordinary intensity, imagination, and tenderness through which throb a boundless love of country and of people.

Green Doug-las firs where the wa-ters break through, Down the wild moun-tains and val-leys she flew, Ca-na-dian North-west to the o-cean so blue, So roll on, Co-lum-bia, roll on._____

**CHORUS**

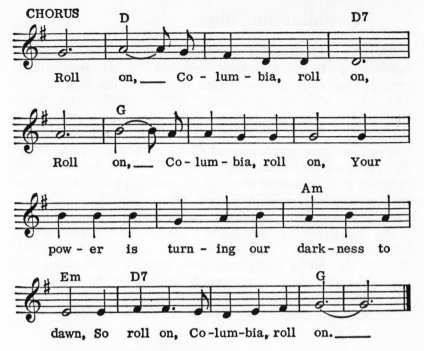

Roll on, ___ Co - lum - bia, roll on,

Roll on, ___ Co - lum - bia, roll on, Your

pow - er is turn - ing our dark - ness to

dawn, So roll on, Co - lum - bia, roll on. ___

Many great rivers add power to you
The Yakima Snake and the Clicketac too,
Sandy Willamette and Hood river too
So roll on, Columbia, roll on
*Chorus*

At Bonneville now there are ships in the locks
The waters have risen and cleared all the rocks,
Shiploads of plenty will steam past the docks,
So roll on, Columbia, roll on.
*Chorus*

And on up the river is Grand Coulee dam,
The mightiest thing ever built by a man,
To run the great factories and water the land,
So roll on, Columbia, roll on.
*Chorus*

These mighty men labored by day and by night,
Matching their strength 'gainst the river's wild flight,
Through rapids and falls they won the hard fight,
So roll on, Columbia, roll on.
*Chorus*

# Discrimination Blues

The New Deal had its accomplishments, and it had its failures too. It cut unemployment, but did not eliminate it: even at the height of Roosevelt's success, at the beginning of 1937, there were still more than 5 million people out of work. Worst of all, the Negro throughout the nation remained a second-class citizen, first fired last hired, segregated in rat-ridden Jim Crow ghettoes, excluded by white pride and prejudice from the mainstream of American life. In the South, this separation of the races was written into law; it was enforced by courts, police, jails, and most terrible of all, "extralegal" sanctions—beatings, mutilation, and murder.

Big Bill Broonzy, one of the great "country blues" singers and composers, wrote "Discrimination Blues" during World War II. This biting song dramatizes America's unfinished business. The melody is borrowed from the Southern "country blues" tradition: it is similar to that used by Blind Willie Johnson in his gospel song, "Jesus is Coming Soon."

This lit-tle song that I'm sing-ing a-bout__ Peo-ple, you all know it's true, ____ If you're black and got-ta work for a liv-ing Now this is what they'll

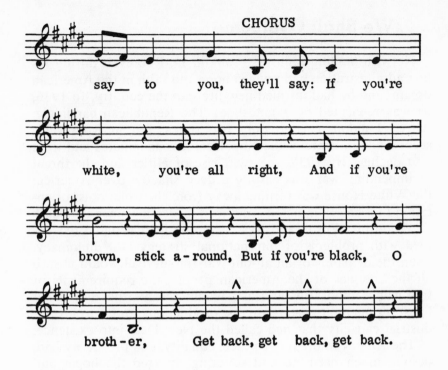

**CHORUS**

say__ to you, they'll say: If you're white, you're all right, And if you're brown, stick a-round, But if you're black, O broth-er, Get back, get back, get back.

2. I was in a place las' night,
   They was all havin' fun,
   They was all buyin' beer and wine,
   But they would not sell me none.
*Chorus*

3. I went to an employment office
   Took a number and got in line,
   They called out everybody's number,
   But they never did call mine.
*Chorus*

4. Me and a man was working side by side,
   This is what it meant,
   They was payin' him a dollar an hour,
   And they was payin' me fifty cent.
*Chorus*

# We Shall Overcome

Notwithstanding failures, Franklin D. Roosevelt during his first administration had revived hope and faith in the American dream, and he had instilled new life into the country. In 1936, he was re-elected by a landslide: The Republican candidate, Alfred Landon, carried only two states. But in Roosevelt's second administration, the New Deal lost its impetus and went into decline. By 1938, the swift rise of Hitler and the threat of impending war was casting a deep shadow over America; the White House was turning away from the isolationist orientation that had dominated American leadership since the death of Woodrow Wilson and was becoming increasingly preoccupied with problems of international strategy and diplomacy. Soon the demands of an all-out war for survival would absorb all the energies of the American people; the requirements of this war, temporarily at least, would resolve the dire problems of unemployment, excess production, and surplus industrial capacity that had called the New Deal into existence.

The American dream of peace, equality, and prosperity had, despite much hardship and suffering, spurred the hopes and deeds of millions during the New Deal years. At the very opening of the period, the coal miners of West Virginia had given the American people a new song to sing and had set it to the tune of an old spiritual. Better than any other, this song sums up the passionate hopes and aspirations of these years. People who cherish freedom and brotherhood are still singing it today.

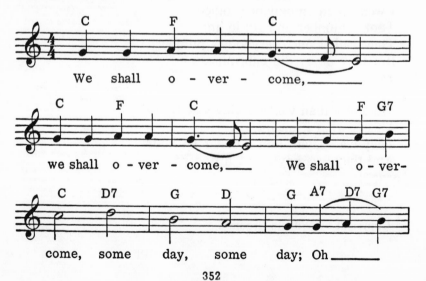

deep in my heart I know that I do be-

lieve We shall o-ver-come some day.____

We shall organize, we shall organize,
We shall organize some day, some day;
Oh, deep in my heart, I know that I do believe
We shall organize some day.

We shall end Jim Crow, we shall end Jim Crow,
We shall end Jim Crow some day, some day;
Oh, deep in my heart, I know that I do believe
We shall end Jim Crow some day.

We shall walk in peace, we shall walk in peace,
We shall walk in peace some day, some day;
Oh, deep in my heart, I know that I do believe
We shall walk in peace some day.

We shall build a new world, we shall build a new world,
We shall build a new world some day, some day;
Oh, deep in my heart, I know that I do believe
We shall build a new world some day.

We'll walk hand in hand, we'll walk hand in hand,
We'll walk hand in hand some day, some day;
Oh, deep in my heart, I know that I do believe
We'll walk hand in hand some day.

We shall overcome, we shall overcome,
We shall overcome some day, some day;
Oh, deep in my heart, I know that I do believe
We shall overcome some day.

# Die Moorsoldaten (Peat-Bog Soldiers)

Hitler became Chancellor of Germany in January, 1933, and immediately concentration camps sprang up—"like mushrooms," as William Shirer wrote—where the enemies of the regime were beaten, tortured, and put to death. The thousands of inmates of these first camps were Germans, and this underscores the fact that the first fighters against Hitler and the tyranny of fascism were Germans—Catholics, Jews, Social Democrats, Protestants, and Communists. These people were rounded up and sent off to suffer and die, because they had dared to oppose the National Socialist Party in either word or deed.

"Die Moorsoldaten" was one of the songs which this concentration camp experience produced. The prisoners sang it as they marched to and from their forced labor. When Hitler and Mussolini invaded Spain in 1936, anti-fascist soldiers took up the refrain, and "Die Moorsoldaten" became a marching song and a battle song. Ernst Busch made a famous recording of it in a Madrid studio, while the bombs fell and exploded in the street outside. By 1942, this song was known to millions in Europe; no other created at this time conveys so profoundly and so simply the meaning of the struggle against Hitler.

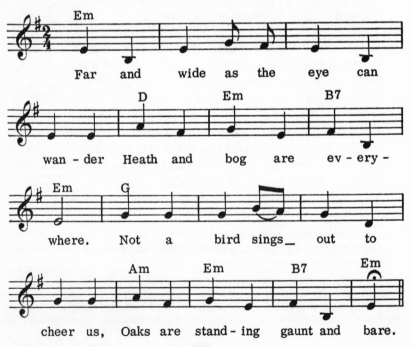

Far and wide as the eye can wan-der Heath and bog are ev-ery-where. Not a bird sings out to cheer us, Oaks are stand-ing gaunt and bare.

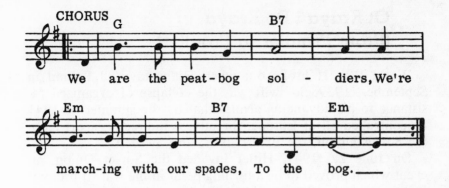

We are the peat-bog sol - diers, We're
march-ing with our spades, To the bog.___

Up and down the guards are pacing,
No one, no one can go through.
Flight would mean a sure death facing;
Guns and barbed wire greet our view.

*Chorus*

But for us there is no complaining,
Winter will in time be past;
One day we shall cry rejoicing,
Homeland dear, you're mine at last.

*Chorus*    Then will the peat-bog soldiers
     March no more with their spades
     To the bog.

\* \* \*

Wohin auch das Auge blicket
Moor und Heide ringsherum.
Vogelsang uns nicht erquicket,
Eichen stehen kahl und krumm.

*Chorus*    Wir sind die Moorsoldaten
     Und ziehen mit dem Spaten
     Ins Moor.

Auf und nieder gehen die Posten,
Keiner, keiner, kann hindurch.
Flucht wird nur das Leben kosten,
Fielfach ist umzäunt die Burg.

*Chorus*

Doch fur uns gibt es kein Klagen,
Ewig kann's nicht Winter sein.
Einmal werden froh wir sagen,
"Heimat, du bist wieder mein."

*Chorus*    Dann ziehen die Moorsoldaten
     Nicht mehr mit dem Spaten
     Ins Moor.

355

# Ot Kraya i Do Kraya
## (From Frontier to Frontier)

World War II broke out when Hitler invaded Poland in September, 1939. So swift was the collapse of organized resistance to his advancing armies that by the summer of 1941 he controlled all of Europe, directly or indirectly, apart from the Soviet Union, the British Isles, and Sweden.

On June 22, 1941, Hitler invaded the Soviet Union, an event which proved to be a turning point in the war. It brought Britain and the Soviets, hitherto distrustful of each other, into direct alliance. When the Japanese attacked the United States at Pearl Harbor on December 7, in fulfillment of their commitments to the Germans, the United States found themselves at war with Germany on the side of the British and the Soviets. Thus, the Allied nations coalition of anti-fascist powers, formally announced on January 1, 1942, came into existence.

Association of the United States with the Union of Soviet Socialist Republics in common conflict with Hitler brought about a thawing out of the somewhat frosty relationship that had prevailed between the two powers since Roosevelt had accorded diplomatic recognition to the Soviets in 1933. Massive industrial and military aid was sent to Russia; Russians visited the United States, made impassioned appeals for the opening of a Second Front in Europe, and were cordially received. Russian songs became popular both on the home front and in the army. "Ot Kraya i Do Kraya" was a Soviet marching song. Americans became familiar with it through a recording of the Red Army Chorus.

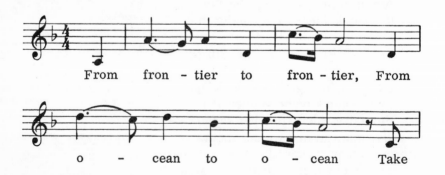

From    fron - tier    to    fron - tier,    From

o  -  cean    to    o - cean    Take

up your ri-fles to fight for your coun-try, And
to de-fend your soil. Be read-y for
dan-ger, Be read-y for sor-row. Be
read-y to fight to the end. end.

For country and for freedom,
For a better world to come,
We march again to war, we know the reason why,
We know the reason why:
For country and for freedom,
For a better world to come,
We are ready to fight to the end.

\*     \*     \*

Ot kraya i do kraya,
Ot morya i do morya,
Beret vintovku narod trudovoi,
Narod boevoi.
Gotov'i na gore,
Gotov'i na muki,
Gotov'i na smertn'i boi.

Za zemlyu, za volyu,
Za luchshuyu dolyu,
Idem opyat' no front, no znaya za chto,
M'i znaem za chto.
Za zemlyu, za volyu,
Za luchshuyu dolyu,
Gotov'i na smertn'i boi.

Used by permission of Edward B. Marks Music Corporation. Translated from the Russian by John Anthony Scott.

## D-Day Dodgers

In June 1943, the Allies invaded Sicily and in September crossed to Southern Italy. A long and heartbreaking winter campaign ensued as the troops moved slowly up the peninsula. The terrain, rocky and mountainous, was made to order for defensive fighting, and the Germans under Kesselring made the most of it. The attacking forces, advancing in rain, mud, and snow, suffered many casualties before they occupied Rome in June 1944.

At this point, the American-born Lady Astor, a member of Parliament, took it upon herself to criticize the conduct of the Italian campaign, and advised that British troops be pulled out of Italy and used in the invasion of Normandy. In this connection, she used the somewhat tactless phrase "D-Day Dodgers."

Lady Astor's remarks were of course reported in Italy and became the occasion for a crushing retort. The lyric was set to the tune of "Lili Marlene," one of the most widely sung and parodied songs of the war. Originally a German ditty, "Lili Marlene" was "captured" from German P.W.'s and promptly added to the British and American repertoire. "D-Day Dodgers" reproduced here, is more than a soldier's answer to Lady Astor; it is the fighting man's final comment upon the senseless cruelty and heartbreak of war itself.

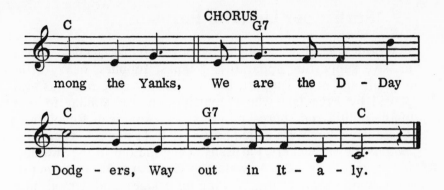

mong the Yanks, We are the D - Day

Dodg - ers, Way out in It - a - ly.

We landed in Salerno, a holiday with pay,
The Gerries brought out the panzer to greet us on our way,
Showed us the sights and gave us tea,
We all sang songs, the beer was free,

*Chorus* To welcome D-Day Dodgers
       To sunny Italy.

Naples and Cassino were taken in our stride,
We didn't go to fight there, we went just for the ride,
Anzio and Sangro were just names,
We only went to look for dames,

*Chorus* The artful D-Day Dodgers,
       Out in Italy.

Dear Lady Astor, you think you're mighty hot,
Standing on the platform talking tommy rot;
You're England's sweetheart and her pride,
We think your mouth's too bleeding wide,

*Chorus* We are the D-Day Dodgers,
       In sunny Italy.

Look around the mountains, in the mud and rain,
You'll find the scattered crosses, there's some that have
       no name.
Heartbreak and toil and suffering gone,
The boys beneath them slumber on,

*Chorus* They are the D-Day Dodgers,
       Who stay in Italy.

# Partizaner Lid (The Partisan)

World War II was fought by huge regular armies with a massive supporting apparatus of tanks, supplies, heavy artillery, air and naval support. But an indispensable role was also played by irregulars whose contribution was similar to that of the militia and sharpshooters of the American Revolution. These irregulars were called by a variety of names—guerrillas, *maquis,* bushwhackers, partisans. They hid out in the swamps, forests, and hills, keeping watch on German troop movements, ambushing supply trains, blowing up bridges, and demolishing communications. When the Allied invasion of Normandy took place in June, 1944, these people were instrumental in delaying the arrival of *panzer* reinforcements that might otherwise have pushed the British and American troops into the sea before a bridgehead was established. On the Eastern front, these partisans operated in German-occupied Russia and Poland, where Nazi communications were especially vulnerable owing to their extension over hundreds of miles of non-German territory.

Jewish people in Poland took part in this type of warfare. They had good reason to sell their lives dearly; in September, 1939, as soon as German troops were in Warsaw, Himmler's assistant, Reinhard Heydrich, began to plan the extermination of Poland's Jewish population. In June 1940, the infamous extermination center of Oswiecim was set up. Many stirring partisan songs came out of the war. "Partizaner Lid," one of the loveliest of these, is dedicated to Poland's Jewish fighters.

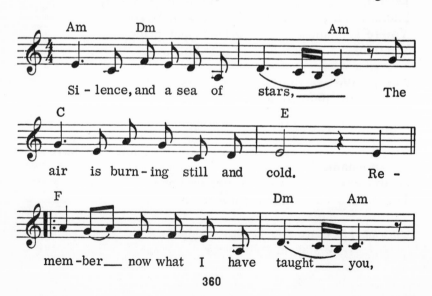

Si - lence, and a sea of stars,____ The air is burn - ing still and cold. Re - mem - ber__ now what I have taught__ you,

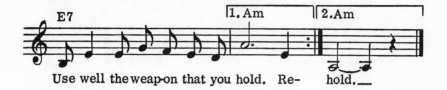

Use well the weap-on that you hold. Re- hold.—

A girl, in winter coat and cap
Firmly grasps her hand grenade;
A girl, with soft and silken face,
Is going on her first raid.

Carefully she aims, and fires,
And her bullet finds its foe.
A carrier, crammed with weapons,
Crashes in the frozen snow.

Dawn, she steals from the forest,
Snow is gleaming in her hair;
She sings of youth and hope and freedom
In a struggle all must share.

          *     *     *

Shtil, die nacht iz oysgeshternt,
Un der frost hot shtark gebrent.
Tsi gedenkstu vi ich hob dich gelernt
Haltn a shpayer in di hent?

A moyd, a peltsl un a beret,
Un halt in hant fest a nagan.
A moyd mit a sametenem ponim,
Hit op dem soyne's karavan.

Getsilt, geshosn un getrofn!
Hot ir kleyninker pistoyl.
An oto, a fulinkn mit vofn
Farhaltn hot zi mit eyn koyl!

Fartog, fun vald aroysgekrochn,
Mit shney girlandn oyf di hor.
Gemutikt fun kleyninkn nitsochn
Far undzer nayem, frayen dor!

Reprinted by permission of Schocken Books Inc. from *A Treasury of Jewish Folk Songs,* by Ruth Rubin, Copyright © 1950 by Schocken Books Inc., New York. Translation from the Yiddish by John Anthony Scott.

# VIII
# SINCE
# THE
# WAR

THE YEARS FOLLOWING World War II to the present constitute a new and separate chapter in the history of American
folk song. There has been an intense and widespread revival of
interest in the traditional song heritage; new songs, some of
them rivaling the finest creations of the past, have been born
out of the agonies and struggles of our modern age.

Full treatment of the contemporary folk song movement
would clearly require a book in itself. The most that can be
done here is to give some general impressions as to what is
going on, and to indicate the relationship between current
song and that of the past.

A great deal of our traditional song had its roots in the life
and experience of an America that was predominantly rural.
All this has changed. Folk song in twentieth century United
States has migrated to the metropolis; it has taken root in
the cities. In the period following World War II, it has become emphatically urban. College campus "hoots," North End
or Greenwich Village coffee houses, folk festivals, nation-wide
TV and jukebox coverage, all testify to this fact. Folk song
has become an important feature in the contemporary American scene.

The new outburst of song has been sustained and made possible by the anonymous work of devoted collectors and musicians who, since the closing years of the nineteenth century, have set themselves the task of conserving our national song heritage; thereby, they have ensured that this heritage might ultimately be made available to a potentially enormous audience. Between 1882 and 1898, Francis J. Child published his great collection of *English and Scottish Popular Ballads*. In 1888, there came into being the American Folklore Society, an association of folklore scholars whose purpose was to encourage the collection and preservation of the unwritten and unpublished literary and musical heritage; in the same year, the Society began publication of the *Journal of American Folklore*. In the first years of the new century, state and local folklore societies sprang up to direct, encourage, and finance the collection and conservation of song materials.

In 1910, John Lomax published his path-breaking *Cowboys Songs*. In 1915, the English musician Cecil J. Sharp visited the United States to prepare his *English Folk Songs from the Southern Appalachians,* a pioneer work in awakening American scholars to the incredible extent and variety of the musical resources to be found in the North American countryside. Subsequent years witnessed a rapid accumulation of materials. Elisabeth Greenleaf Bristol and Grace Yarrow Mansfield visited Newfoundland during the twenties to transcribe the words and music of nearly two hundred traditional songs; Dorothy Scarborough published *On the Trail of Negro Folk Songs* in 1925; Frank C. Brown, who had organized the North Carolina Folklore Society in 1913, was instrumental in amassing a vast collection of songs during the next quarter of a century; Phillips Barry, Helen Hartness Flanders, Eloise Hubbard Linscott and W. Roy Mackenzie collected the songs of New England and Nova Scotia; these are but a few of the collectors whose names might be mentioned.

During the thirties, with the development of the phonograph, the collecting and transcription of songs was made more rapid and exact. During the New Deal, an especially important contribution was made by the Archive of American Folk Song which was established at the Library of Congress in 1928 and which became, under the direction of John A. Lomax, Alan Lomax, and Ben Botkin, a national center for the preservation of material recorded on disc and tape.

Then came World War II, and a new generation appeared on the scene. It grew up in the aftermath of war amid the strident persecution of the McCarthy period, in an atmosphere poisoned by hatred, hysteria, and insecurity, in a time when life itself was threatened by the unleashing of nuclear power. Many young people looked at the world with angry eyes; they experienced a sense of passionate alienation from the vapid commercialism of our urban culture, the ugliness and machine-made conformity of urban life. They strove to find roots in the past, a meaning in the present, a sure vision for the future.

This generation has found a part of what it sought in America's songs. Some of these young people, when they were very little, were nurtured on the songs of Woody Guthrie, particularly his *Dust Bowl Ballads* and *Songs to Grow On;* some of them listened to the records of the Almanac Singers, that fabulous band of troubadours who, during the early years of World War II, gathered in Greenwich Village, created the institution of the hootenanny, sang, wrote, and recorded songs; they pored over the *People's Song Book* published in 1947 which made a great many folk songs, particularly songs of labor and of the New Deal, easily and cheaply available; they listened to traditional songs on the records of Burl Ives or studied them in the pages of the *Fireside Book of Folk Songs* (1947). They acquired their taste for blues from the early recordings of Josh White; like the rest of the country, they learned the spirituals from the incomparable singing of Marian Anderson and Paul Robeson.

In the darkest years of the Cold War, wandering balladeers kept this singing tradition alive and patiently educated the tastes of their youthful audience. The tradition of the wandering minstrel is an old one. We need go no further back than to the great blues singers like Blind Lemon Jefferson in the early 1900's, to Carl Sandburg in the 1920's, to Cisco Houston and Woody Guthrie in the 1930's. And in the 1940's Pete Seeger emerged as one of the most gifted of them all. He struggled successfully against McCarthyite persecution and blacklisting that sought to stifle his voice and ruin his career. His message and the force of his example has reached untold numbers of young people. His renown as an American folk-singer has become worldwide.

The modern singing movement began to bloom in 1953 with the ending of the Korean War and the partial reduction of acute cold war tension. With the organization of the Weavers (Pete Seeger, Ronnie Gilbert, Lee Hays, and Fred Hellerman) and the famous Carnegie Hall concert of Christmas Eve, 1955, the folk revival was fairly under way. There was a brilliance, an integrity, and an enthusiasm, in the Weavers' singing, which few others could match; a flock of younger performers—the Kingston Trio, Peter, Paul and Mary, the Chad Mitchell Trio, etc.—followed along the path that the Weavers had blazed. By 1960, folk song may have been crudely commercialized. But the market for music, records, and instruments had become enormous. And, in the school systems of New York and New England, another wandering minstrel, Bill Bonyun, singing over the years to hundreds of thousands of children, continued the patient, anonymous work of cultivating the love of song and the integrity of feeling that makes it real.

TV and the juke-box have played a limited but nonetheless significant role in the post-war popularization of the folk song heritage. How significant, may be illustrated by a personal anecdote.

It was 1942, and I was in New York City, just before my departure for overseas duty. I went to a bar in Harlem to listen to the legendary Huddy Leadbetter play his twelve-string guitar. He played all evening, sang in the dim, half-filled room, and finished by singing a lullaby. The beautiful melody came very slowly with an overpowering mood of weariness and sadness. I never forgot this song that I had heard only once, but I never met anyone else who knew it—until it hit the juke-box in 1950. It was a souped-up travesty of Leadbelly's song, but there was no mistaking it: *Good Night Irene*. Since then the list of folk songs that have become national favorites is an impressive one. *Tom Dula, This Land is Your Land, Michael Row the Boat Ashore, The House of the Rising Sun, Scarlet Ribbons, The Battle of New Orleans* are a few of the traditional songs that have been catapulted into fame and even into international prominence thanks to the commercial media.

In the post-war years, Americans have not only rediscovered their song heritage, but have utilized the traditional material for new purposes—to utter a new protest, to shape a new vision. The 1950's witnessed the burgeoning of a fresh lyrical and musical creativity as people began to demonstrate a new militancy in facing and tackling the issues of our time. As we have seen throughout this book, many topical songs have fulfilled, historically, a similar function: to celebrate a victory, to mourn a tragedy, to protest a wrong, to summon inspiration for a struggle or a test.

Songs of this order are being written and sung today. Many of them are freedom songs. The Supreme Court decision of May 17, 1954 declaring segregation unconstitutional was hailed throughout the nation, and most enthusiastically by the youth. They recognized, in the coming struggle to level the barriers of segregation everywhere, the central, most honorable challenge of contemporary American life. The movement that in the following decade hurled itself against the bastions of Jim Crow has been both a youth movement and a singing movement. Young people participating in sit-ins and walk-ins, on picket lines and marches, have faced great ordeals and have gained courage, unity, and inspiration from song. They have sung the traditional freedom songs and spirituals, they have composed new verses and set them to old tunes, and they have composed new songs altogether. Pete Seeger's *If I Had a Hammer* and Bob Dylan's *Blowin' in the Wind*, to cite two instances, have become known and loved by millions; they are examples of new songs born of the freedom movement that have already achieved the stature of folk songs.

Not all of the new songs have been freedom songs. The writers have found inspiration in many and various aspects of the contemporary scene: in the menace of atomic war, poverty and brutality in an affluent society, alienation, the commercialization of sport, capital punishment, and many more. By the early sixties, this modern broadside tradition had begun to make a significant contribution to the literature of social criticism. The writers have found an audience in the coffee houses, at the "hoots," campus sings, and other folk festivals, and through the sale of records. *Broadside* and *Sing Out*, in addition, provide channels of expression and communication.

A number of these new songs have already achieved wide popularity: notably *What Have They Done to the Rain* and *Little Boxes* (Malvina Reynolds); *A Hard Rain's a-Gonna Fall* (Bob Dylan); *Plastic Jesus* (Ernie Marrs); *Where Have All the Flowers Gone?* (Pete Seeger); and *As Long as the Grass Shall Grow* (Peter LaFarge). A few of these post-war freedom songs and broadsides are reproduced below.

Our national song is a body of music of enormous depth and variety. It mirrors the life and soul of our people, gives expression to their inmost feelings and aspirations. In each generation, it summons men and women to cherish the heritage from the past, to become more fully aware of the ties that bind them to each other and to all mankind, to exalt the dignity of human life, to protest cruelty, exploitation, and oppression. Folk song is an instrument of spiritual life and of social struggle. With its help, the prophet's vision of a new Heaven and a new earth will more surely and more speedily unfold.

# Plane Wreck at Los Gatos

California fruit and vegetable growers have long used immigrant labor to harvest their crops; in some years since 1900, more than one-fifth of a million such migratory workers have been employed there. Until the depression years of the thirties, Mexican fieldhands, *braceros,* made a special appeal to the California growers. They could be brought in at very low wages and fired or sent back to Mexico when the growing season was over. These noncitizens lived in tent communities, shanty towns, and migrant camps. They have been among the most shamefully exploited and pathetically poor in all the American community. In the nineteen thirties, unemployment was high among U. S. farm workers, and the Mexicans were dispensed with; but World War II and succeeding years witnessed a new manpower shortage and a consequent repetition of the traditional pattern. In January 1948, a group of Mexican deportees died in a plane crash near Coalinga; and Woody Guthrie recorded the tragedy in this broadside. His protest at the inhuman use of human beings is marked by the quiet but angry statement of the lyric and the deep tenderness of the refrain.

The crops are all in and the peach-es are rot-ting,___ The or-ang-es are piled in their cre-o-sote dumps;___ They're fly-ing them back to the

Mex-i-co bor-der.___ To pay all their
wag-es to Wade back a-gain.___

**REFRAIN**

Good-bye to my Juan, good-bye Ro-sa-li-ta;___
___ Ad-i-os muy a-mi-go, Je-sus and Ma-
ri-a,___ You won't have a name when you
ride the big aer-o-plane,___ And all they will
call you will be___ de-port-ees.

My father's own father he waded that river,
They took all the money he made in his life;
My brothers and sisters come working the fruit trees
And they rode the truck till they took down and died.

*Refrain*

Well, some are illegal and some are not wanted,
Our work contract's out and we have to move on;
Six hundred miles to that Mexico border,
They chase us like outlaws, like rustlers, like thieves.
*Refrain*

We died on your hills and we died on your deserts,
We died in your valleys and died on your plains;
We died neath your trees and we died in your bushes,
Both sides of that river we died just the same.
*Refrain*

The sky plane caught fire over Los Gatos Canyon,
Like a fireball of lightning it shook all our hills.
Who are all these friends all scattered like dry leaves?
The radio says they are just deportees.
*Refrain*

Is this the best way we can grow our big orchards?
Is this the best way we can grow our good fruit?
To fall like dry leaves to rot on my top soil
And be known by no name except deportees?
*Refrain*

Lyric by Woody Guthrie; Music by Martin Hoffman. © Copyright
1961 Ludlow Music Inc., New York, N. Y. Used by permission.

# In Contempt

The years 1947–1953 witnessed a massive reaction against the personalities and policies of the New Deal. Radicals, artists, intellectuals, liberals, and teachers who had been supporters of Roosevelt or who had taken part in his administration were stigmatized as "agents of a foreign power." Spearheaded by Senator Joseph McCarthy of Wisconsin, a determined effort was made to isolate, discredit, and remove such people from positions of leadership and influence in American life. Congressional committees began to investigate people for their beliefs and associations; many, innocent of any crime, were jailed for contempt of Congress when they refused to submit to this kind of questioning.

*Sing Out* began publication in May 1950, at the height of the inquisition. In the following years, it would print many new topical songs, and not a few of these would be devoted to the theme of human freedom. The first number of *Sing Out* had upon its cover the words and music of Pete Seeger and Lee Hays' *Hammer Song,* a freedom ballad that has become one of the most widely known and loved songs of our time. *In Contempt* first appeared in the October 1950 issue.

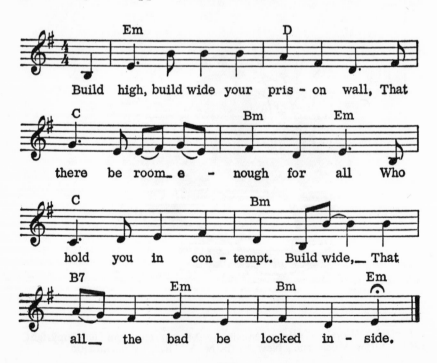

Build high, build wide your pris - on wall, That there be room e - nough for all Who hold you in con - tempt. Build wide,— That all— the bad be locked in - side.

Though you have seized the valiant few
Whose glory casts a shade on you,
How can you now go home with ease,
Jangling your heavy dungeon keys?

The birds who still insist on song,
The sunlit stream still running strong,
The flowers still blazing red and blue,
All, all are in contempt of you.

The parents dreaming still of peace,
The playful children, the wild geese
Who still must fly, the mountains too,
All, all are in contempt of you.

When you have seized both moon and sun
And jailed the poems one by one,
And trapped each trouble-making breeze,
Then you can throw away your keys.

Words by Aaron Kramer; music by Betty Sanders; copyright 1950
by SING OUT! Inc., as printed in *Sing Out!* The National Folksong
Magazine; used by permission.

# Bull Connor's Jail

In May 1963, the young people of Birmingham, Alabama, staged their famous march in protest against segregation in that city. Not only teenagers but tiny children dressed in their Sunday best were confronted by police dogs and fire hoses, and herded by the hundreds into the filthy city jails. The naked brutality exhibited on this occasion by Bull Connor, Birmingham's tough director of "public security" led immediately to a national protest—the historic March on Washington of August 28. Guy and Candie Carawan were among those jailed. With the help of Ernie Marrs they rewrote *Down in the Valley* to suit the occasion. It was published in *Broadside* #26 (May 1963), and reissued in *Songs for the March on Washington,* August 28.

Down in Al - a - bam - a, In the
land of Jim Crow, There is a place where
Lots of folks go. Bir-ming-ham jail -
house, Bir-ming-ham jail, Wait-ing for
free - dom In Bull Con-nor's jail.

Three thousand prisoners,
    More coming in
Even little children
    Are singing this song.
*Chorus*

Bull Connor tells us
    "Don't raise a squawk
You need a permit
    Even to walk."
*Chorus*

Went to the church house
    To sing and pray,
Started downtown and
    They hauled us away.
*Chorus*

Pushed by policemen,
    Herded like hogs
Some got the fire hose
    And some got the dogs.
*Chorus*

Crammed in like sardines
    In Bull Connor's can,
Some can lay down,
    But others must stand.
*Chorus*

Iron bars around me
    Cold walls so strong
They hold my body,
    The world hears my song.
*Chorus*

# Keep On a-Walkin'

This song, to the tune of an old spiritual, was born out of the demonstrations that took place in Albany, Georgia, in July 1962. It has since become one of the most popular of all the modern freedom songs. First published by *Broadside* in August 1962, it was sung by thousands at the March on Washington of August 1963, and was reissued in *Songs for the March on Washington,* August 28, 1963.

Ain't gonna let   no - bod - y,   Law - dy,
turn me 'round,   turn me 'round, turn me 'round,
Ain't gon-na   let   no - bod - y,   Law - dy,
turn me 'round;   Keep on   a - walk - in', (yea!)
Keep   on   a - talk - in',   (yea!)
March-in'   on   to   Free-dom   land.

Ain't gonna let segregation, Lawdy, turn me 'round, turn me
'round, turn me 'round,
Ain't gonna let segregation, Lawdy, turn me 'round,
Keep on a-walkin', (yea!)
Keep on a-talkin', (yea!)
Marchin' on to Freedom land.

Ain't gonna let no jailhouse, Lawdy, turn me 'round, turn me
'round, turn me 'round,
Ain't gonna let no jailhouse, Lawdy, turn me 'round,
Keep on a-walkin', (yea!)
Keep on a-talkin', (yea!)
Marchin' on to Freedom land.

Ain't gonna let no nervous Nelly, Lawdy, turn me 'round,
turn me 'round, turn me 'round,
Ain't gonna let no nervous Nelly, Lawdy, turn me 'round,
Keep on a-walkin', (yea!)
Keep on a-talkin', (yea!)
Marchin' on to Freedom land.

Ain't gonna let Chief Pritchett turn me 'round, turn me 'round,
turn me 'round,
Ain't gonna let Chief Pritchett turn me 'round,
Keep on a-walkin', (yea!)
Keep on a-talkin', (yea!)
Marchin' on to Freedom land.

Ain't gonna let no shotgun turn me 'round, turn me 'round,
turn me 'round,
Ain't gonna let no shotgun turn me 'round,
Keep on a-walkin', (yea!)
Keep on a-talkin', (yea!)
Marchin' on to Freedom land.

Ain't gonna let no Uncle Tom, Lawdy, turn me 'round, turn
me 'round, turn me 'round.
Ain't gonna let no Uncle Tom, Lawdy, turn me 'round,
Keep on a-walkin', (yea!)
Keep on a-talkin', (yea!)
Marchin' on to Freedom land.

Ain't gonna let nobody, etc.

# One Man's Hands

This song is the result of a collaboration between Dr. Alex Comfort and Pete Seeger. It has a specific and urgent meaning for our own times and also embodies a permanent human truth.

One man's hands can't break a pris-on down, ___ Two men's hands can't break a pris-on down, ___ But if two and two and fif-ty make a mil-lion, We'll see that day come 'round, We'll see that day come 'round.

One man's voice can't shout to make them hear,
Two men's voices can't shout to make them hear,
But if two and two and fifty make a million,
    We'll see that day come 'round,
    We'll see that day come 'round.

One man's feet can't walk around the land,
Two men's feet can't walk around the land
But if two and two and fifty make a million,
    We'll see that day come 'round,
    We'll see that day come 'round.

One man's eyes can't see the way ahead,
Two men's eyes can't see the way ahead,
But if two and two and fifty make a million,
　　We'll see that day come 'round,
　　We'll see that day come 'round.

One man's strength can't ban the atom bomb,
Two men's strength can't ban the atom bomb,
But if two and two and fifty make a million,
　　We'll see that day come 'round,
　　We'll see that day come 'round.

One man's strength can't break the color bar,
Two men's strength can't break the color bar,
But if two and two and fifty make a million,
　　We'll see that day come 'round,
　　We'll see that day come 'round.

One man's strength can't make the Union roll,
Two men's strength can't make the Union roll,
But if two and two and fifty make a million,
　　We'll see that day come 'round,
　　We'll see that day come 'round.

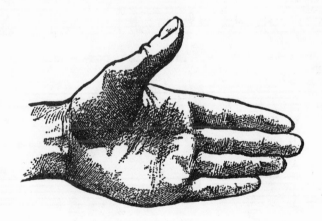

# Little Boxes

Malvina Reynolds is one of the more prolific contemporary song writers. When *Broadside* made its first appearance in February 1962, she became a regular contributor to its pages. She wrote union songs, ballads about brass hats (*Leave My Van Allen Belt Alone* and *The Little Generals*) and satirical verses about The House Committee on un-American Activities. *Little Boxes* appeared in *Broadside* #20, February 1963. "Much to our surprise," wrote editor Sis Cunningham the following July, *"Little Boxes is the most popular of all the songs we've printed so far."* Another of Malvina Reynolds' songs, *What Have They Done to the Rain?* has become widely known through the singing of Joan Baez.

Lit - tle box - es on the hill - side, lit - tle box - es made of tick - y tack - y, Lit - tle box - es on the hill - side, lit - tle box - es all the same. There's a green one and a pink one and a blue one and a yel - low one,_ And they're

all made out of tick-y tack-y and they all look just the same. And the boys go in-to busi-ness And they mar-ry and raise a fam-i-ly In box-es made of tick-y tack-y And they all look just the same.

Little boxes on the hillside, little boxes made of
    ticky tacky,
Little boxes on the hillside, little boxes all the same.
There's a green one and a pink one and a blue one and
    a yellow one,
And they're all made out of ticky tacky and they all
    look just the same.

And the people in the houses all went to the university
Where they were put in boxes and they came out all
    the same;
And there's doctors, and there's lawyers and there's
    business executives
And they're all made out of ticky tacky and they all
    look just the same.

And they all play on the golf course and drink their
     martini dry
And they all have pretty children and the children go
     to school
And the children go to summer camp and then to the
     university
Where they are all put in boxes and they come out
     all the same.

*Coda* (*retard like a music box running down*)

# Sources

*Note:* Performances of specific songs appearing in this book are listed separately under "records," below.

## GENERAL

Charles Haywood, *A Bibliography of North American Folklore and Folksong* (New York: Dover Publications, 1961), is a valuable guide to published materials and records. Gilbert Chase, *America's Music: from the Pilgrims to the Present* (New York: McGraw Hill, 1955), provides a general musical reference. The best single introduction to our historical ballads and songs is a little book by Russell Ames, *The Story of American Folk Song* (New York: Grosset and Dunlap, 1955). Ames deals with the history of our song and does not provide music; music and lyrics together for many songs are available in a number of low-priced paperbacks. We recommend: *The Burl Ives Song Book* (New York: Ballantine Books, 1953); *Song Fest* (ed. Dick and Beth Best. New York: Crown Publishers, 1961); *The Ditty Bag* (ed. Janet E. Tobbitt, and available at Girl Scout centers); *Songs of All Time* (College Box 2000, Berea, Kentucky: Council of the Southern Mountains, Inc., 1957); the *Dell Book of Great American Folk Songs* (New York: Dell Publishing Co., 1963); a *New Treasury of Folk Songs* (ed. Tom Glazer. New York: Bantam Books, 1961); and *Living Documents in American History* (ed. John Anthony Scott. New York: Washington Square Press, 1964). Much valuable material, in addition, is reproduced from time to time in the following folk song magazines: *Sing Out* (121 W. 47th Street, New York, N. Y.) and *Broadside* (Box 193, Cathedral Station, New York 25, N. Y.)

A number of collections in hard cover and with piano accompaniments serve as an admirable introduction to the whole field of national music. The following, in our opinion, are the ones to buy first: *The Fireside Book of Folk Songs* (ed. Margaret Boni. New York: Simon and Schuster, 1947); *The American Songbag* (ed. Carl Sandburg. New York: Harcourt Brace and Co., 1927); *Best Loved American Folk Songs* (ed. John A. and Alan Lomax. New York: Grosset and Dunlap, 1947); and *American Folk Songs for Children* (ed. Ruth Crawford Seeger. New York: Doubleday and Co., 1948). All of these works have valuable notes and commentary.

For the study of our national song, of course, records are indispensable. One of our principal resources for field recordings is the great Archive of American Folk Song of the Library of Congress; part of this is directly available to the public through a series of special Library of Congress records. The list includes traditional ballads, shanties, spirituals, work songs, blues, miners' songs, cowboy ballads, and many more; the catalogue may be obtained from the Music Division of the Library of Congress, Washington 25, D. C.

# COLONIAL PERIOD

SONGS AND BALLADS OF BRITISH ORIGIN  The best introduction to these songs is a little book edited by R. Vaughan Williams and A. C. Lloyd, *The Penguin Book of English Folk Songs* (London, England, and Baltimore, Md.: Penguin Books, 1959); another valuable source is *Folk Songs of England, Ireland, Scotland, and Wales,* selected and edited by William Cole with piano and guitar arrangements by Norman Monath (New York: Doubleday and Co., 1961); and *English Folk Songs* collected and arranged by Cecil J. Sharp (London, England: Novello and Co. Ltd., centenary edition, 1959). The single most valuable contribution in this field brings together the fruits of the researches of dozens of scholars and musicians over the past fifty years. It is Bertrand Bronson, *The Traditional Tunes of the Child Ballads* (New Jersey: Princeton University Press, 1959—). Two volumes of this great study have appeared to date. A modern edition of Francis James Child, *The English and Scottish Popular Ballads* is also available in five volumes (New York: Pageant Book Co., 1957). The work of the great Scots collector, Gavin Greig, is invaluable: *Folk Song of the North East* (Hatboro, Pennsylvania: Folklore Associates, 1963).

A great many of the old ballads sung both by "folk" and professionals have been recorded, particularly on this side of the Atlantic, and not a little of this singing is commercially available. A brilliant introduction to these songs is Ewan MacColl and Peggy Seeger, *Matching Songs of the British Isles and America* (Riverside Folklore Series). MacColl, the greatest ballad singer of our generation, is available on a number of records (especially Washington, Tradition, and Offbeat labels). Among American singers, we might single out the contributions of Jean Ritchie and Cynthia Gooding (both on Elektra), and the superb rendering of Virginia variants by Andrew Rowan Summers (Folkways). Many field recordings are available from the Library of Congress, and, for Britain, the Caedmon series, *The Folksongs of Great Britain* edited and collected by Alan Lomax and Peter Kennedy.

COLONIAL SONGS AND BALLADS  Here, I relied heavily on the great folklore collections made on a state or regional basis by individual collectors or state folklore societies. These are wonderful stores of material; a few of the most valuable that are still available and in print include: Eloise Hubbard Linscott, *Folk Songs of Old New England* (2nd. ed. Hamden, Conn.: The Shoe String Press, 1962); Cecil Sharp, *English Folk Songs from the Southern Appalachians* (New York: Oxford University Press, 1960); Mary O. Eddy, *Ballads and Songs from Ohio;* John Harrington Cox, *Folk Songs of the South;* W. Roy Mackenzie, *Ballads and Sea Songs* from Nova Scotia (all reissued 1963-1964 by Folklore Associates, Hatboro, Pennsylvania); H. M. Belden, *Ballads and Songs Collected by the Missouri Folklore Society* (Columbia, Missouri: Missouri Folk-Lore Society, 1955); the Frank C. Brown Collection of North Carolina Folklore, volumes II to V (Durham, N. C.:

Duke University Press, 1952-1962); Elisabeth B. Greenleaf, *Ballads and Sea Songs of Newfoundland* (Cambridge, Mass.: Harvard University Press, 1933. Available in Xerox edition from University Microfilms, Ann Arbor, Michigan); and Helen Creighton, *Maritime Folk Songs* (East Lansing: Michigan State University Press, 1962).

Colonial songs are scattered through the repertoire of many recorded singers. But some have specialized in this field, and we recommend in particular Jean Ritchie, Bill Bonyun, Burl Ives, (Tradition, Heirloom, and Decca labels respectively); and Frank Profitt and Margaret MacArthur (Folkways)

## THE AMERICAN REVOLUTION

The prime sources here are the great broadside collections. I relied in particular on the Isaiah Thomas Collection in the keeping of the American Antiquarian Society at Worcester, Mass. Two books by Frank Moore, a great pioneer collector of historical song, are invaluable, but they have long been out of print: *A Diary of the American Revolution, 1775-1781* and *Songs of the American Revolution*. For the British background of the broadside tradition, see Leslie Shepard, *The Broadside Ballad* (London, England: Herbert Jenkins, 1962, available from Folklore Associates, Hatboro, Pennsylvania). No study is available of American broadside balladry in the eighteenth century, but G. Malcolm Laws Jr., *American Balladry from British Broadsides* (Philadelphia: The American Folklore Society, 1957) has some helpful comments. As for records, the best introduction to the subject available is the Heirloom documentary, *The American Revolution through its Songs and Ballads*. The military music of the times may be studied in *Fife and Drum Music of the American Revolution,* available from Colonial Williamsburg.

## THE EARLY MODERN PERIOD

For this period, I relied primarily on state and regional collections of the type listed above, supplemented by broadsides and songsters. A definitive edition of *The Songs of Robert Burns,* edited by James C. Dick, is available from Folklore Associates, Hatboro, Pennsylvania. The great Scots songwriter may also be studied from the incomparable recordings of Ewan MacColl (Folkways); and the military music is covered by Colonial Williamsburg's *War of 1812.* For the rest, this period of our history, musically speaking, still awaits its investigators, writers, and interpreters. For sources on Irish music, see under THE SEA AND IMMIGRATION below.

## JACKSONIAN AMERICA

SEA AND IMMIGRATION  The definitive study of British shanties is Stan Hugill, *Shanties From the Seven Seas* (New York: E. P.

Dutton and Co., 1961). For American singing, see Joanna Colcord, *Songs of American Sailormen* (New York: Oak Publications, 1964); Frederick P. Harlow, *Shanteying Aboard American Ships* (Barre, Mass.: Barre Gazette, 1962); and William Doerflinger, *Shantymen and Shantyboys* (New York: Macmillan, 1951). Gale Huntington, *Songs the Whalemen Sang* (Barre, Mass.: Barre Publishers, 1964) gives a picture of the whalerman's songs as recorded in journals, logs, and manuscript song collections. Richard Henry Dana's *Two Years Before the Mast,* (various editions) is indispensable for the understanding of sea song during this period. *The Story of Yankee Whaling* (New York: American Heritage, 1959), is a first-rate pictorial introduction to the whaling industry that makes readily available the nautical wisdom of Edouard A. Stackpole, Curator of Mystic Seaport. There are a number of superb records of shantying and whalermen's songs by Bill Bonyun (Heirloom) and Ewan MacColl (Tradition and Washington).

Irish song, with Gaelic originals, serviceable translations, music, and notes may be found in Donal O'Sullivan, *Songs of the Irish* (New York: Crown Publishers, 1960); and in Colm O Lochlainn, *Irish Street Ballads* (New York: Corinth paperback, 1960). For the American student, the best introduction to Irish singing is in the records of Tommy Makem and the Clancy Brothers (Tradition), and the Fieldston student documentary, *Irish Immigration through its Songs and Ballads* (Heirloom).

THE WESTWARD MOVEMENT  Here the principal resource was the various state and regional collections cited above, to which should be added William A. Owens, *Texas Folk Songs* (Dallas: Texas Folklore Society, 1950); Charles J. Finger, *Frontier Ballads* (New York: Doubleday, 1927); Norman Cazden, *The Abelard Folk Song Book* (New York: Abelard-Schuman, 1957); Theodore C. Blegen and Martin B. Ruud, *Norwegian Emigrant Songs and Ballads* (Minneapolis: University of Minnesota Press, 1936); Alan Lomax, *The Folk Songs of North America* (New York: Doubleday, 1960); Phillips Barry, *The Maine Woods Songster* (Cambridge, Mass.: Power Printing Co., 1939); and two books by Harold W. Thompson, *A Pioneer Songster: texts from the Stevens-Douglass Manuscripts of Western New York 1841-1856* (Ithaca: Cornell University Press, 1958); and *Body, Boots, and Britches: folk-tales, ballads and speech from country New York* (New York: Dover paperback, 1962).

SLAVERY DAYS  Harold Courlander, *Negro Folk Music USA* (New York: Columbia University Press, 1963) is a fine introduction to the whole field of American Negro music. Basic sources for songs originating with slavery, and primarily the spirituals, are: William Francis Allen, Charles Pickard Ware, and Lucy McKim Garrison, *Slave Songs of the United States* (New York, 1867. Reissued by Peter Smith, Gloucester, Mass., 1951); Henry Edward Krehbiel, *Afro-American Folk Songs* (New York, 1913, reissued by the Frederick Ungar Publishing Co., New York, 1962); Dorothy

Scarborough, *On the Trail of Negro Folk Songs* (Hatboro, Pennsylvania: Folklore Associates, 1963); Lydia Parrish, *Slave Songs of the Georgia Sea Islands* (New York: Creative Age Press, 1942); and George Pullen Jackson, *White and Negro Spirituals: their life span and kinship* (Locust Valley, N. Y.: J. J. Augustin, n. d.). Two contemporary observers whose writings are valuable sources for Negro singing are Frances Ann Kemble, *Journal of a Residence on a Georgian Plantation in 1838-9* (ed. John Anthony Scott. New York: Alfred A. Knopf, 1961), and Thomas Wentworth Higginson, *Army Life in a Black Regiment* (East Lansing, Michigan: Michigan State University Press, 1960). The spirituals, both Negro and white, may be studied from the Library of Congress field recordings. Efforts to reconstruct the singing of slavery days and to record it for the benefit of modern students have hardly begun, but the work of Folkways in this field might be mentioned.

## THE CIVIL WAR

My main sources were Civil War songsters in the American Antiquarian Society and other collections; a number of song books edited by Frank Moore, who did pioneering work in this field as remarkable as that which he did for the American Revolution; and the broadsides and sheet music of the Harris Collection of the University of Rhode Island. Many of the better known Civil War songs will be found in Irwin Silber, *The Songs of the Civil War* (New York: Columbia University Press, 1960), with piano arrangements and chording by Jerry Silverman. There are a dozen or more records of Civil War music and song available, but this field is still largely untapped.

## BETWEEN THE CIVIL WAR AND THE FIRST WORLD WAR

Labor, railroad, and Western songs for this period are abundantly available in: Edith Fowke and Joe Glaser, *Songs of Work and Freedom* (New York: Dolphin Magnum paperback, 1960); John A. and Alan Lomax, *American Ballads and Folk Songs* (New York: Macmillan, 1957); Alan Lomax, *Best Loved American Folk Songs* and *Folk Songs of North America,* cited above; John Greenway, *American Folksongs of Protest* (New York: Perpetua paperback, 1960); and in the various works of George Korson (Philadelphia: University of Pennsylvania Press). For Yiddish songs, I relied principally on Ruth Rubin, *A Treasury of Jewish Folksong* (New York: Schocken Books Inc., 1950), and Nathan Ausubel, *A Treasury of Jewish Folklore* (New York: Crown Publishers, 1948). The best introduction to French-American singing is Edith Fulton Fowke and Richard Johnston, *Folk Songs of Quebec* (Waterloo, Ontario: Waterloo Music Co., Ltd., 1957). For the songs of the Negro People in the post-war South, all the works by the Lomaxes cited above are indispensable, as are Courlander's *Negro Folk Music USA* and Lydia Parrish's *Slave Songs of the Georgia Sea Islands,* though unfortunately the latter work is out of print. The history of the blues is beginning to receive attention from writers, and two valuable works are Samuel B. Charters, *The Country Blues* (New York: Rinehart, 1959), and Paul Oliver, *The Meaning of the Blues* (New York: Collier paperback, 1963).

Much of the material dealt with in this chapter may be studied from Library of Congress field recordings. For cowboy songs, Merrick Jarrett, *Songs of the Old West* (Washington), deserves special mention, for it makes available a number of the songs originally published in John A. Lomax's pioneer *Cowboy Songs and Other Frontier Ballads* in 1910. Pete Seeger and John Greenway both give special attention to industrial ballads and songs (Folkways and Riverside labels, respectively). Yiddish songs receive specialised attention from Ruth Rubin (Washington) and Morton Freeman (Tikvah).

Negro work songs, combining elements of calls, rhythms, and melodies inherited from slavery days, are available on a number of Folkways recordings; a classic introduction to this type of song is *Negro Prison Songs from the Mississippi State Penitentiary* collected and edited by Alan Lomax (Tradition). Country blues were first recorded in the late twenties; a revival of interest in this singing has made available a large number of records by the great singers of these songs. Among them might be mentioned Mississippi John Hurt (Piedmont); Lightnin' Hopkins (Vee-Jay, Tradition, Prestige, Arhoolie); John Lee Hooker and Blind Lemon Jefferson (Riverside); Big Bill Broonzy, Leadbelly, Furry Lewis, Blind Willie Johnson, and sleepy John Estes (Folkways); and *Roots of the Blues* (Atlantic).

## BETWEEN TWO WORLD WARS

For World Wars I and II songs see E. A. Dolph, *Sound off: Soldiers' Songs from the Revolution to World War II* (New York: Farrar and Rinehart, 1942); John Jacob Niles *Singing Soldiers* (New York: Scribner, 1927), and Edgar A. Palmer, *G.I. Songs* (New York: Sheridan House, 1944). Songs of this period (including war songs) are scattered through many collections. The most easily available are *Songs of Work and Freedom,* cited above; Waldemar Hille, *The People's Song Book* (New York: Oak Publications, n.d.); Moses Asch, *American Folk Song—Woody Guthrie,* and *California to the New York Island* (same publisher); Carl Sandburg, *American Songbag* (cited above); and John A. and Alan Lomax, *American Ballads and Folk Songs* (New York: Macmillan, 1934).

Woody Guthrie singing his own songs is available on a number of Folkways records. Cisco Houston and Pete Seeger sing New Deal Songs (Folkways and Vanguard). Two records helpful in different ways for a study of the period are The New Lost City Ramblers' *Songs from the Depression* (Folkways), and the Fieldston documentary, *The Depression and New Deal through Songs and Ballads* (Heirloom). Soldiers' Songs from the two World Wars have been recorded by the Four Sergeants (ABC Paramount) and Oscar Brand.

## CONCLUSION

For the background of folk song collecting, recording and publishing, see D. K. Wilgus, *Anglo-American Folksong Scholarship* (New Brunswick, N. J.: Rutgers University Press, 1959). For contemporary songs the pages of *Sing Out!* and *Broadside* are indispensable. There is a collection of freedom songs put together by Guy and Candie Carawan, *We Shall Overcome* (New York: Oak Publications, n.d.).

Two records of broadside ballads have been published under the title *Broadside Ballads* vols. I and II. Pete Seeger's *We Shall Overcome* is a brilliant concert performance devoted to contemporary songs (Columbia). Note also his *Broadsides* (Folkways). Freedom songs are available on a number of records, primarily those of the Freedom Singers (Mercury and others); but few of the concert and studio performances have the same quality as when sung and recorded on the streets. See also the Fieldston documentary, the *Negro People through their Songs and Ballads* (Heirloom).

Bob Dylan has a number of records out on the Columbia label, including *The Times They Are a-Changing, The Freewheelin' Bob Dylan,* and *Bringing It All Back Home.* Peter LaFarge sings about the Indians on *As Long As The Grass Shall Grow* (Folkways). Phil Ochs sings on *All the News That's Fit to Sing* and *I Ain't Marchin' Any More* (Elektra). Tom Paxton sings on *Ramblin' Boy* (Elektra). Contemporary ballads are also scattered throughout the repertoire of various other singers, for example Dave Van Ronk (Prestige), Joan Baez (Vanguard), Peter Paul and Mary (Warner Bros.), and Judy Collins (Elektra).

# Recordings

Below will be found, under the appropriate chapter heading and song title, a listing of available recordings of a number of the songs included in this book.

## THE COLONIAL PERIOD

*The British Heritage*

Bawbee Allen

Ewan MacColl
*The English and Scottish Popular Ballads*
Riverside LP 12-624

I Will Give My Love an Apple

John Langstaff
*American and British Folksongs and Ballads*
Tradition 1009
Cynthia Gooding
*The Queen of Hearts*
Elektra 131

The Bonny Boy

Grainne Ni Eigeartaigh
*Irish Folk Songs*
Spoken Arts 206
for other variants: Ewan MacColl,
*English and Scottish Popular Ballads,*
Riverside LP 12-629; and Joan Baez, Vanguard 9094.

The Bonnie Lass o' Fyvie

Ewan MacColl
*Scots Folk Songs*
Riverside LP 12-609

The Keys of Canterbury

Jean Ritchie and Oscar Brand
*Courtin's a Pleasure*
Elektra 122
COLONIAL SONGS AND BALLADS

Siubhail a Gradh

Deirdre O'Callaghan
*Folk Songs from Erin*
Westminster 12025

Johnny Has Gone for a Soldier

Burl Ives
*America's Musical Heritage*
vol. 2 Franklin Watts Inc.
(variant, with bowdlerized Gaelic refrain)

| | |
|---|---|
| | Jane Wilson |
| | *The Making of a Nation* |
| | Life: The Sounds of History, vol. 2. |
| Sweet William | Peggy Seeger |
| | *Matching Songs of the British Isles and America* |
| | Riverside LP 12-637 (also on this record, a fine Scots variant sung by Ewan MacColl) |
| The Old Man Who Lived in the Woods | Bill Bonyun |
| | *Yankee Legend* |
| | Heirloom 500 |
| The Young Man Who Couldn't Hoe Corn | same |
| Jenny Jenkins | same |
| Katie Cruel | same |

## THE AMERICAN REVOLUTION

All the songs reproduced in this chapter will be found on:

Bill and Gene Bonyun, and John Anthony Scott
*The American Revolution through Its Songs and Ballads*
Heirloom 502

## THE EARLY NATIONAL PERIOD

| | |
|---|---|
| Caitilín Ní Uallacháin | Joseph Ransohoff |
| | *Irish Immigration through Its Songs and Ballads* |
| | Heirloom Ed. 2 |
| Green Grow the Rushes O | Ewan MacColl |
| | *The Songs of Robert Burns* |
| | Folkway Record 8758 |
| Jefferson and Liberty | Ed McCurdy |
| | *American History in Ballad and Song* |
| | Folkways Record 5801 |
| The Constitution and the Guerrière | Burl Ives |
| | *America's Musical Heritage,* Vol. 2 |
| | Franklin Watts Inc. |
| The Hunters of Kentucky | same. Also (abbreviated version): |

|  | *The Growing Years*<br>Life: The Making of a Nation, vol. 3 |
| John Anderson My Jo | Burns' version of "Johnny Bull My Jo,-John" is sung by<br>Betty Sanders<br>*Songs of Robert Burns*<br>Riverside LP 12-823 |
| The Bonny Bunch of Roses O | Fine variants of the song reproduced here are sung by:<br>Ewan MacColl<br>*Scots Streets Songs*<br>Riverside LP 12-612<br>Seamus Ennis<br>*The Bonny Bunch of Roses*<br>Tradition LP 1013 |

## JACKSONIAN AMERICA

*Sea and Immigration*

| Haul on the Bowline | Paul Clayton<br>*Fo'c'sle Songs and Shanties*<br>Folkways Record FA 2429 |
| | John Binnington<br>*Roll and Go*<br>Heirloom 504 |
| Blood-red Roses | A. C. Lloyd and Ewan McColl<br>*Whaling Ballads*<br>Washington LP 724 |
| Leave Her, Johnny, Leave Her | Paul Clayton<br>*Fo'c'sle Songs and Shanties* |
| The Golden Vanity | Ewan MacColl and Peggy Seeger<br>*Matching Songs of the British Isles and America*<br>Riverside LP 12-637 |
| Off to Sea Once More | Bill Bonyun<br>*Songs of Yankee Whaling*<br>American Heritage (available from Heirloom) |
| The Greenland Whale Fishery | same |
| The Banks of Newfoundland | Ewan MacColl<br>*Blow Boys Blow*<br>Tradition LP 1026 |

| | |
|---|---|
| The Praties They Grow Small | *Irish Immigration through Its Songs and Ballads*<br>Heirloom Ed. 2 |
| | Mary O'Hara<br>*Songs of Ireland*<br>Tradition LP 1024 |
| The Farmer's Curst Wife | Richard Sinaiko<br>*Irish Immigration through Its Songs and Ballads*<br>Heirloom Ed. 2 |
| The Castle of Dromore | Deirdre O'Callaghan (Gaelic)<br>*Folk Songs from Erin*<br>Westminster 12025 |
| | Liam Clancy (English)<br>Tradition 1042 |
| The Pesky Sarpent | Lynn Gold<br>*The New World*<br>Life: The Making of a Nation, vol. 1 |

*The Westward Movement*

| | |
|---|---|
| Hush, Little Baby | Burl Ives<br>*America's Musical Heritage,*<br>Vol. 4, Franklin Watts Inc. |
| Let's Go a-Huntin' | Alan Lomax<br>*Texas Folksongs*<br>Tradition LP 1029 |
| | Bill Bonyun<br>*Let's Go a-Hunting*<br>Heirloom EP 501 |
| The Single Girl | Jean Ritchie<br>*The Sweep Westward*<br>Life: Sounds of History, vol. 4 |
| The Lumberman's Alphabet | Gus Schaffer<br>*Songs of the Michigan Lumberjacks*<br>Library of Congress, Music Division AAFS L56 |
| The Jam on Gerry's Rock | Bill McBride<br>same |
| Sioux Indians | Alec Moore<br>*The Ballad Hunter,* Part 1<br>Library of Congress, Music Division, AAFS L49 |

| | |
|---|---|
| The Fools of Forty-Nine | Pat Foster<br>*Gold Rush Songs*<br>Riverside LP 12-654 |
| Santy Anno | Odetta<br>*Ballads and Blues*<br>Tradition 1010 |
| The Dying Californian | Pat Foster<br>*Gold Rush Songs*<br>Riverside LP 12-654 |

### Slavery Days

| | |
|---|---|
| Roll, Jordan, Roll | Carol Brice<br>*The Union Sundered*<br>Life: The Sounds of History,<br>vol. 5 |
| Sail, O Believer | Linda Schreyer<br>*The Negro People through their<br>Songs and Ballads*<br>Heirloom Ed. 3 |
| Poor Rosy | Radha Bhattacharji *et al.*<br>same |
| Hushabye | Alan Lomax<br>*Texas Folk Songs*<br>Tradition LP 1029 |
| | Joan Socolow<br>*The Negro People through their<br>Songs and Ballads*<br>Heirloom Ed. 3 |
| Lay This Body Down | Hilary Baum *et al.*<br>same |
| The Rose of Alabama | Frank Warner<br>*Songs of the Civil War*<br>Prestige International 13012 |

## THE CIVIL WAR

| | |
|---|---|
| Song of the Southern<br>  Volunteers | LaVonne Beebe<br>*The Civil War through its<br>Songs and Ballads*<br>Heirloom 503 |
| Flag of the Free | Ed Wilson<br>same |
| The Homespun Dress | Jean Ritchie<br>*The Union Sundered*<br>Life: Sounds of History, vol. 5 |

392

| | |
|---|---|
| On to Richmond | Frank Warner<br>*The Civil War through its*<br>*    Songs and Ballads*<br>Heirloom 503 |
| General Lee's Wooing | Ed Wilson<br>same |
| Many Thousand Gone | *The Negro People through their*<br>*    Songs and Ballads*<br>Heirloom Ed. 3 |
| Oh, Freedom | same; also<br>Pete Seeger<br>*Carnegie Hall, June 5, 1963*<br>Columbia 2101 |
| Roll, Alabama, Roll | Frank Warner<br>*The Civil War through its*<br>*    Songs and Ballads*<br>Heirloom 503 |
| Sherman's March to the Sea | Bill Bonyun<br>same |

# BETWEEN THE CIVIL WAR AND THE FIRST WORLD WAR

*Farmers and Workers*

| | |
|---|---|
| I Ride an Old Paint | Burl Ives<br>*America's Musical Heritage,*<br>*    vol. 6, Franklin Watts Inc.*<br><br>Woody Guthrie<br>*Sod Buster Ballads*<br>Commodore FL 30,002 |
| Goodbye, Old Paint | *The Ballad Hunter,* Part I<br>Library of Congress, Music<br>    Division AAFS L49 |
| Brennan on the Moor | same<br>*The Clancy Brothers and Tom-*<br>*    my Makem,*<br>Tradition LP 1042 |
| The Farmer Is the Man | Pete Seeger<br>*American Industrial Ballads*<br>Folkways 5251 |
| Peter Emberley | Marie Hare<br>Folk-Legacy Records, Hunting-<br>    ton, Vermont, FSC-9 |
| The Colorado Trail | Cisco Houston<br>*Cisco Special*<br>Vanguard |

| | |
|---|---|
| The Colorado Trail | Sue Pomeranze and Ellin Kardiner |
| | *The Story of the Cowboy Through His Songs and Ballads* |
| | Heirloom Ed. 5. |

*Immigrants*

| | |
|---|---|
| Ot Azoy Neyt a Shnayder | Ruth Rubin |
| | *Yiddish Folk Songs* |
| | Prestige International 13019 |
| Mayn Yingele | Ruth Rubin |
| | same |
| Papir Iz Doch Vays | Ruth Rubin |
| | *Yiddish Love Songs* |
| | Washington LP 726 |
| | Mort Freeman |
| | Tikva Records 49 |

*The Negro People*

| | |
|---|---|
| Pick a Bale o' Cotton | Leadbelly |
| | Take This Hammer |
| | Folkways FP 4 |
| No More Cane on This Brazos | Alan Lomax |
| | *Texas Folk Songs* |
| | Tradition LP 1029 |
| Another Man Done Gone | Vera Hall |
| | Library of Congress, Music Division Archive of American Folk Song 78 r.p.m. |
| | Odetta |
| | *Ballads and Blues* |
| | Tradition LP 1010 |
| Godamighty Drag | Alan Lomax |
| | *Texas Folk Songs* |
| | Tradition LP 1029 |
| No More, My Lord | *The Ballad Hunter,* Part VIII |
| | Library of Congress, Music Division AAFS L51 |
| | *Negro Prison Songs:* Mississippi State Penitentiary |
| | Tradition LP 1020 |
| Settin' Side That Road | *A Sampler of Louisiana Folk Songs* |
| | Louisiana Folklore Society A-1 |

| | |
|---|---|
| The Ballad of the Boll Weevil | Vera Hall<br>*Sounds of the South*<br>Atlantic 1346 |
| | *The Ballad Hunter,* Part VI<br>Library of Congress, Music<br>    Division AAFS L51 |
| Ragged and Dirty Blues | William Brown<br>*Negro Blues and Hollers from<br>    the Archive of Folk Song*<br>Library of Congress, Music<br>    Division AFS L59 |
| | Blind Lemon Jefferson<br>Riverside Jazz Archives 12-136 |
| | John W. Scott<br>*The Negro People through their<br>    Songs and Ballads*<br>Heirloom Ed. 3 |
| Yonder Come Day | Bessie Jones and Group<br>*Georgia Sea Islands* vol. II<br>Prestige International 25002 |
| Raggedy | Pete Seeger<br>*American History in Ballad and<br>    Song*—V: or, *American<br>    Industrial Ballads*<br>Folkways FH 5801 E, or<br>    FH 5251 |
| Which Side Are You On? | *Weavers' Almanac*<br>Vanguard RS 9100 |
| Goin' Down the Road | Burl Ives<br>*America's Musical Heritage,*<br>    Album 6, Franklin Watts Inc. |
| | Elizabeth Cotton<br>*Negro Folk Songs and Tunes*<br>Folkways FG 3526 |
| | Big Bill Broonzy<br>*Last Session:* Part I<br>    (under title: *I Ain't Gon' Be<br>    Treated This Away*)<br>Verve V3001 |
| Discrimination Blues | Big Bill Broonzy<br>*Big Bill Broonzy Memorial*<br>Mercury MG 20822 |
| | Denis Berger and Chorus<br>*The Negro People in America*<br>Heirloom Ed. 3 |

| | |
|---|---|
| We Shall Overcome | Pete Seeger<br>*We Shall Overcome*<br>Columbia CL 2101 |
| Wandering<br>We Shall Not Be Moved<br>Dark as a Dungeon<br>Roll On, Columbia | These four songs will be found<br>  on *The Depression and the*<br>  *New Deal through Songs and*<br>  *Ballads*<br>Heirloom Ed. 1. |
| Die Moorsoldaten | Ernst Busch and Chorus<br>*Songs of the Spanish Civil War*<br>Folkways FH 5436; or<br>*Songs of the Lincoln Brigade*<br>Stinson LP 52 |
| D-Day Dodgers | Ewan MacColl<br>*British Army Songs*<br>Washington 711 |
| Partizaner Lid | Ruth Rubin<br>*Yiddish Love Songs*<br>Washington 726<br><br>Mort Freeman<br>*Jewish Folk Songs*<br>Tikva Records T 49 |

## SINCE THE WAR

| | |
|---|---|
| Plane Wreck at Los Gatos | Cisco Houston<br>*Songs of Woody Guthrie*<br>Vanguard 9089 |
| Keep on a-Walkin' | Freedom Singers<br>  (under title: Ain't Gonna Let<br>  Segregation Turn Us Around)<br>*Broadside Ballads* Vol. 1<br>Broadside Records 301 |
| Little Boxes | Pete Seeger<br>*We Shall Overcome*<br>Columbia CL 2101 |
| One Man's Hands | Jackie Washington<br>*Newport Folk Festival 1963*,<br>  vol. 2, Vanguard 9149 |

# Index of Titles and First Lines

NOTE: Titles of songs are in *italics*. When a song title and first line are exactly the same, only the title is given. Titles followed by an asterisk have no accompaniment.

# General Index

Napoleon I, Emperor, 92, 102-107, 113, 121
National Industrial Recovery Act, 342
National Socialist Party, 354
"National song," definition of, 3-4
Negroes
  after Civil War, 301-302
  discrimination against, 350-351, 365-366, 372-375
  emancipation of, 233, 236, 238, 255-256
  in slavery, 125, 190-194
  songs of, 194-215, 217, 238-242, 303-323
New Deal, 325, 337, 342, 352, 363
  reaction against, 370
*New England Diadem*, 183
Newfoundland, 36, 105, 363
New Jersey *Gazette*, 77, 88
Normandy, allied invasion of, 358, 360
Nova Scotia, 9

O'Hare, Felix, 276
Old Sturbridge Village, 48, 50
Oregon Trail, 179

Pakenham, Maj. Gen. Sir Edward, 113-114
Paris, Treaty of (1763), 54
Parker, Sir Peter, 64-65
Parrish, Lydia, 321
Paulding, John, 85
Peace movement (1815), 121
Pentatonic scale, 30, 169
*People's Song Book*, 364
Peter, Paul, and Mary, 365
Pilgrim, 126
Populist movement, 267
Port Royal, capture of, 194, 199
Privateers, 81
Prometheus, 138
Protestant religion, 54
Puritans, Psalms of, 28
*Put's Original California Songster*, 183

Quebec, siege of, 36

Reichstadt, Duke of, 105
Revivalist movement, 191-192
Reynolds, Malvina, 378
Riis, Jacob, *How the Other Half Lives*, 285
Robeson, Paul, 364
"Robin Adair," 223
Rockefeller, John D., 279
*Roebuck*, 77
"Roll the Cotton Down," 245
Roosevelt, Franklin D., 356
  elected, 325
  *See also* New Deal
Rosenfeld, Morris, 285
"Rosin the Beau," 248
Rubin, Ruth, *A Treasury of Jewish Folk Songs*, 293n

Sandburg, Carl, *American Songbag*, 260, 262, 364
Santa Ana, General, 183
Saratoga campaign, 75
Sarsfield, Patrick, 94

Scarborough, Dorothy, *On the Trail of Negro Folk Songs*, 193, 208n, 211-213
*Scarborough*, 81
Schaffer, Gus, 172
*Scots Musical Museum*, 118
Scott, John W., 319
Sea Island Singers, 321
Seeger, Peggy, 50
Seeger, Pete, 366, 370, 376
*Serapis*, 81
Seven Days' Fight, 231
*Shannon*, 111-112
Shanties (work songs), 127-129, 131-137
Sharp, Cecil J., *English Folk Songs from the Southern Appalachians*, 31n, 363
Sherman's March to the Sea, 248-250
Ships
  *Alabama*, 245-247
  *Alert*, 126
  *Bonhomme Richard*, 81-83
  *Bristol*, 64
  *Chesapeake*, 111-112
  *Constitution*, 108-110
  *Couronne*, 245
  *Cumberland*, 229
  *Guerrière*, 108-110
  *Kearsarge*, 245
  *Pilgrim*, 126
  *Roebuck*, 77
  *Scarborough*, 81
  *Serapis*, 81
  *Shannon*, 111-112
  *Vulture*, 84-85
Shirer, William, 354
Slavery, 125, 190-194
  songs of, 194-215
*Songs for the March on Washington*, 372, 374
Soviet Union, 356
Spirituals, 191-203
Steele, Silas S., 214
Stewart, A. L., 161
St. Helena, 105
Stock Market Crash, 324-325
Sullivan's Island, 64

Tikxas, Louis, 279
Townsend, A. E., 243
Townshend, Acts of, 1767, 56
Trenton, Battle of, 72-74
Tucker, George, 193, 206
Tucker, Glenn, *Poltroons and Patriots*, 114n

Union Pacific Railroad, 257
Union of Soviet Socialist Republics, 356
United Mine Workers, 276, 279
University of Rhode Island, Harris Collection, 36, 69
University of Virginia Collection of Folk Music, 183
Urquhart estates, 16

Valley Forge, 77
Versailles Treaty, 325
*Vulture*, 84-85

War of 1812, 108-117
  objectives of, 92
War Hawks, 108